ABOUT TIME

THE UNAUTHORIZED GUIDE TO
DOCTOR WHO

1970–1974

SEASONS 7 TO 11

LAWRENCE MILES & TAT WOOD

C000090429

Also available from Mad Norwegian Press...

FACTION PARADOX NOVELS
Stand-alone novel series based on characters and concepts
created by Lawrence Miles
Faction Paradox: The Book of the War [#0] by Lawrence Miles, et. al.
Faction Paradox: This Town Will Never Let Us Go [#1] by Lawrence Miles
Faction Paradox: Of the City of the Saved... [#2] by Philip Purser-Hallard
Faction Paradox: Warlords of Utopia [#3] by Lance Parkin (upcoming)
Faction Paradox: Warring States [#4] by Mags L. Halliday (upcoming)

THE ABOUT TIME SERIES
by Lawrence Miles and Tat Wood

About Time 1: The Unauthorized Guide to Doctor Who (Seasons 1 to 3)
About Time 2: The Unauthorized Guide to Doctor Who (Seasons 4 to 6)
About Time 3: The Unauthorized Guide to Doctor Who (Seasons 7 to 11)
About Time 4: The Unauthorized Guide to Doctor Who (Seasons 12 to 17)
About Time 5: The Unauthorized Guide to Doctor Who (Seasons 18 to 21)
About Time 6: The Unauthorized Guide to Doctor Who (Seasons 22 to 26, the TV Movie)

OTHER MAD NORWEGIAN SCI-FI REFERENCE GUIDES
Dusted: The Unauthorized Guide to Buffy the Vampire Slayer
by Lawrence Miles, Lars Pearson and Christa Dickson

Redeemed: The Unauthorized Guide to Angel (upcoming)
by Lars Pearson and Christa Dickson (edited by Lawrence Miles)

*A History of the Universe [revised]: The Unauthorized Timeline
to the Doctor Who Universe* (upcoming) by Lance Parkin

I, Who: The Unauthorized Guides to Doctor Who Novels and Audios
three-volume series by Lars Pearson (volume four upcoming)

OTHER NOVELS
Dead Romance by Lawrence Miles, contains rare back-up stories

All rights reserved. No part of this book may be reproduced or transmitted in any
form or by any means, electronic or mechanical, including photography, recording or any information storage and retrieval system, without express written permission from the publisher.

Copyright © 2004 Mad Norwegian Press (www.madnorwegian.com)

Cover art by Steve Johnson.
Jacket & interior design by Metaphorce Designs (www.metaphorcedesigns.com)

ISBN: 0-9725959-2-9
Printed in Illinois. First Edition: October 2004.

mad norwegian press | new orleans

table of contents

how does this book work ?

About Time prides itself on being the most comprehensive, wide-ranging and at times almost *shockingly* detailed handbook to *Doctor Who* that you might ever conceivably need, so great pains have been taken to make sure there's a place for everything and everything's in its place. Here are the "rules"…

Every *Doctor Who* story gets its own entry, and every entry is divided up into four major sections. The first, which includes the headings **Which One is This?**, **Firsts and Lasts** and **X Things to Notice**, is designed to provide an overview of the story for newcomers to the series (and we trust there'll be more of you, after 2005) or relatively "lightweight" fans who aren't too clued-up on a particular era of the programme's history. We might like to *pretend* that all *Doctor Who* viewers know all parts of the series equally well, but there are an awful lot of people who - for example - know the '70s episodes by heart and don't have a clue about the '60s. This section also acts as an overall Spotters' Guide to the series, pointing out most of the memorable bits.

After that comes the **Continuity** section, which is where you'll find all the pedantic detail. Here there are notes on the Doctor (personality, props and cryptic mentions of his past), the supporting cast, the TARDIS and any major Time Lords who might happen to wander into the story. Following these are the **Non-Humans** and **Planet Notes** sections, which can best be described as "high geekery"… we're old enough to remember the *Doctor Who Monster Book*, but not too old to want a more grown-up version of our own, so expect full-length monster profiles. Next comes **History**, which includes all available data about the time in which the story's supposed to be set.

Of crucial importance: note that throughout the **Continuity** section, *everything* you read is "true" - i.e. based on what's said or seen on-screen - except for sentences in square brackets [like this], where we cross-reference the data to other stories and make some suggestions as to how all of this is supposed to fit together. You can trust us absolutely on the non-bracketed material, but the bracketed sentences are often just speculation.

The only exception to this rule is the **Additional Sources** heading, which features any off-screen information from novelisations, writer interviews, etc that might shed light on the way the story's supposed to work. (Another thing to notice here: anything written in single inverted commas - 'like this' - is a word-for-word quote from the script, whereas anything in double-quote marks "like this" isn't.)

The third major section is **Analysis**. It opens with **Where Does This Come From?**, and this may need explaining. For years there's been a tendency in fandom to assume that *Doctor Who* was an "escapist" series which very rarely tackled anything particularly topical, but with hindsight this is bunk. Throughout its history, the programme reflected, reacted to and sometimes openly *discussed* the trends and talking-points of the era, although it isn't always immediately obvious to the modern eye. (Everybody knows that "The Sunmakers" was supposed to be satirical, but how many people got the subtext of "Destiny of the Daleks"?). It's our job here to put each story into the context of the time in which it was made, to explain *why* the production team thought it might have been a good idea.

Up next is **Things That Don't Make Sense**, basically a run-down of the glitches and logical flaws in the story, some of them merely curious and some entirely ridiculous. Unlike a lot of TV guidebooks, here we don't dwell on minor details like shaky camera angles and actors treading on each others' cues - at least unless they're *chronically* noticeable - since these are trivial even by our standards. We're much more concerned with whacking great story loopholes or particularly grotesque breaches of the laws of physics.

Analysis ends with **Critique**; though no consensus will ever be found on *any* story, we've not only tried to provide a balanced (or at least not-too-irrational) view but also attempted to judge each story by its own standards, *not just* the standards of the post-CGI generation.

The last of the four sections is **The Facts**, which covers ordinary, straightforward details like cast lists, viewing figures and - where applicable - the episodes of the story which are currently missing from the BBC archives. We've also provided a run-down of the story's cliffhangers, since a lot of

---

This product is not authorized by the BBC. Doctor Who and TARDIS are trademarks of the BBC.

Doctor Who fans grew up thinking of the cliffhangers as the programme's defining points. This gives you a much better sense of a story's structure than a long and involved plot breakdown (which we're fairly sure would interest nobody at this stage, barring perhaps those stories presently missing from the BBC archives).

The Lore is an addendum to the Facts section, which covers the off-screen anecdotes and factettes attached to the story. The word "Lore" seems fitting, since long-term fans will already know much of this material, but it needs to be included here (a) for new initiates and (b) because this *is* supposed to be a one-stop guide to the history of *Doctor Who*.

A lot of "issues" relating to the series are so big that they need forums all to themselves, which is why most story entries are followed by mini-essays. Here we've tried to answer all the questions that seem to demand answers, although the logic of these essays changes from case to case. Some of them are actually trying to find *definitive* answers, unravelling what's said in the TV stories and making sense of what the programme-makers had in mind. Some have more to do with the real world than the *Doctor Who* universe, and aim to explain why certain things about the series were so important at the time. Some are purely speculative, some delve into scientific theory and some are just whims, but they're *good* whims and they all seem to have a place here. Occasionally we've included footnotes on the names and events we've cited, for those who aren't old enough or British enough to follow all the references.

We should also mention the idea of "canon" here. Anybody who knows *Doctor Who* well, who's been exposed to the TV series, the novels, the comic-strips, the audio adventures and the trading-cards you used to get with Sky Ray ice-lollies, will know that there's always been some doubt about how much of *Doctor Who* counts as "real", as if the TV stories are in some way less made-up than the books or the short stories. We'll discuss this in shattering detail later on, but for now it's enough to say that *About Time* has its own specific rules about what's canonical and what isn't. In this book, we accept everything that's shown in the TV series to be the "truth" about the *Doctor Who* universe (although obviously we have to gloss over the parts where the actors fluff their lines). Those non-TV stories which have made a serious attempt to become part of the canon, from Virgin Publishing's New Adventures to the recent audio adventures from Big Finish, aren't considered to be 100% "true" but do count as supporting evidence. Here they're treated as what historians call "secondary sources", not definitive enough to make us change our whole view of the way the *Doctor Who* universe works but helpful pointers if we're trying to solve any particularly fiddly continuity problems.

It's worth remembering that unlike (say) the stories written for the old *Dalek* annuals, the early Virgin novels were an honest attempt to carry on the *Doctor Who* tradition in the absence of the TV series, so it seems fair to use them to fill the gaps in the programme's folklore even if they're not exactly - so to speak - "fact".

You'll also notice that we've decided to launch this six-volume set with Volume III, covering the early '70s, rather than starting from the programme's roots in 1963. The reason's simple. The '70s programme is far better-known than the '60s version, partly because so few fans actually remember the '60s (and if they did, then they weren't really there, etc) and partly because so much of the early series is missing from the archive. The '70s is the best-known and best-recognised era of *Doctor Who*, so we've started there in order to give everyone a sense of something familiar, before we start dissecting episodes that nobody's seen since 1965.

There's a kind of logic here, just as there's a kind of logic to everything in this book. There's so much to Doctor Who, so much material to cover and so many ways to approach it, that there's a risk of our methods irritating our audience even if all the information's in the right places. So we need to be consistent, and we have been. As a result, we're confident that this is as solid a reference guide / critical study / monster book as you'll ever find. In the end, we hope you'll agree that the only realistic criticism is: "Haven't you told us *too* much here?"

And once we're finished, we can watch the *new* series and start the game all over again.

7.1: "Spearhead from Space"

(Serial AAA. Four Episodes, 3rd January - 24th January 1970.)

Which One is This? The Third Doctor stumbles out of the TARDIS and straight into his new job as UNIT's scientific advisor, just in time to find shop-window dummies coming to life on Britain's high streets. The phrase "behind the sofa" was just *made* for this.

Season 7 Cast/Crew

- Jon Pertwee (the Doctor)
- Caroline John (Liz Shaw)
- Nicholas Courtney
  (Brigadier Lethbridge-Stewart)
- John Levene (Sergeant Benton)

- Barry Letts (Producer)
- Terrance Dicks (Script Editor)

Firsts and Lasts The first 1970s story, the debut of Jon Pertwee as the Third Doctor and the beginning of the Doctor's exile on Earth, "Spearhead from Space" sees the start of what can only be called "the UNIT era" and marks the greatest single shift in the series' history. But more than anything else, what *really* changes things is that it's also the first *Doctor Who* story shot in full colour. And the difference is more than cosmetic, as arrival of colour changes all the audience's expectations of the programme and how it's supposed to work. Whereas the black-and-white stories suggested worlds full of moody, claustrophobic, dream-like spaces, the shift into colour turns the *Doctor Who* universe into something bright, brash and *action-packed*.

Although the Pertwee-era stories are usually compared to the BBC's earlier *Quatermass* serials (mainly because of the Earth-bound setting, and it's true, the first scene of "Spearhead from Space" is an obvious lift from the original 1953 *Quatermass Experiment*), in terms of style this steps away from *Quatermass*, not towards it. From this point on *Doctor Who* follows the lead of the full-colour action serials of the late '60s, and the Doctor consequently makes the jump from "eccentric wanderer" to "adventure hero". Even the programme's format change, from a series about a man who travels through space and time to one about a man who defends Earth from aliens, fits the action serial format. There's a sudden love of gadgetry, so the Third Doctor spontaneously picks up a Bond-style homing-beacon wristwatch, and the tradition of the Doctor having a single female companion also begins here. Capping it all off, there's the new luminous day-glo opening sequence, which says "welcome to the '70s" like nothing else on Earth.

To make the shift seem even greater, "Spearhead from Space" is the only *Doctor Who* story ever shot completely on film (with one camera) instead of video (with three). Video, with its "everything in the studio" look, suggests that *Doctor Who* is more like a recorded stage-play than a movie. Film, with its added depth and glossiness, has a way of making you think that Roger Moore or Tony Curtis are going to turn up at any moment.

On a more prosaic level, this story also sees the first appearance of both Liz Shaw and the Autons. Turning up surprisingly late in the series' history, this is the first time we're told the Doctor has two hearts.

Four Things to Notice
About "Spearhead from Space"...

1. The moment when the shop-window dummies come to life, and begin the mass-slaughter of bystanders in English suburbia, is one of the most famously scary scenarios in the entire *Doctor Who* run. Everybody who grew up in the '60s or '70s remembers seeing this, although curiously not everybody remembers *where* they saw it. (Among non-fans, it's often mis-remembered as an episode of *The Avengers*, which just shows how far *Doctor Who* was straying into action serial territory).

2. Jon Pertwee's shameless gurning when he's strangled by the rubber Nestene tentacle, as if he's already realised what a strange way this is to make a living. This is also, uniquely, the story in which the Doctor gets a nude shower scene.

3. The endearingly over-wrought "'50s B-movie" opening sequence, in which a nervous tracking station operative sees the Nestene energy

This product is not authorized by the BBC. Doctor Who and TARDIS are trademarks of the BBC.

When are the UNIT Stories set?

Since the aim of this present volume is to provide definitive (or at least fairly convincing) answers to all questions relating to *Doctor Who*, we might as well go straight for one of the big ones.

In the whole of *Doctor Who* fandom, there's no single question as controversial as this. The reason's simple. To answer it, you have to make a choice between the intentions of the production team in the late '60s and the actual statements made by the series in the early '80s, a choice which comes with a built-in generation gap.

Nobody doubts that when writers Derrick Sherwin and Kit Pedler first conceived UNIT (for 1968's "The Invasion"), the plan was for new Earthbound stories to take place in the near-future rather than in the present. The *Radio Times* write-ups and BBC continuity announcements for "The Invasion" state the story takes place in 1975 (although it's important to remember that the actual story never states this, so it's therefore not technically "true"). The Target novelisation of "Invasion of the Dinosaurs" - re-titled, with the usual Target panache, *The Dinosaur Invasion* - baldly states that it's 1977, meaning that the Doctor's had a remarkably busy two years.

But 1977 is also the date for the wholly canonical "Mawdryn Undead" (20.3), made in 1983, in which the Brigadier has been retired from UNIT for at least a year. This is a fact. There's no ambiguity, no room for manoeuvre. When Sarah Jane claims that she comes from '1980' in "Pyramids of Mars" (13.3), she might be approximating. After all, if someone from 1998 went back to the early 1900s, they'd be well within their rights to make things simple and tell any passers-by they'd just come from 2000.

But in "Mawdryn Undead" the date is used, clearly and explicitly, over and over and over again. The story's even set against the backdrop of the Queen's Silver Jubilee, and this finally ties the UNIT episodes to a proper calendar. (It's not hard to see how the '80s production team ended up doing this. By the time "Mawdryn Undead" was made, the UNIT stories were seen as a distinctly early-'70s phenomenon. The fact that they were originally meant to be a little more futuristic was no longer remotely relevant. The '80s programme-makers just assumed the stories were always supposed to be contemporary.)

So, we have a timetable. The first UNIT-age story - 5.5, "The Web of Fear" - takes place in 1967, the same year it was written, which is evidently what its writers had in mind anyway. "The Invasion" takes place four years later, in 1971, and the stories from "Spearhead from Space" to "Terror of the Zygons" take us from 1971 to 1976. A real pedant might point out that there are still pre-metric price-tags in the shops in "Spearhead", suggesting 1970 or early 1971 at the latest, meaning that the Brigadier was rounding up when he described "The Invasion" as taking place four years after "The Web of Fear". But that's as much leeway as you've got.

And yet sometimes even the most exacting and obsessive *Doctor Who* fans are unwilling to swallow this early-'70s version of UNIT. Why? Perhaps because so many of them grew up thinking of the UNIT era as representing a shiny new near-future Britain that with hindsight, they can't think of it any other way, even though the near-future in question is now several decades in the past.

Certainly, it's telling that there don't seem to be many "late-'70s UNIT" supporters among fans born after 1970. In the foreword to his novel *The Face of the Enemy*, David A. McIntee refutes the "Mawdryn Undead" dating and claims that it doesn't count because the Doctor was in the middle of a warp ellipse at the time (well, that explains everything). Lance Parkin's *History of the Universe* is a book so obsessed with detail that one throwaway line in "Nightmare of Eden" is enough to make the author change the entire chronology of the twenty-first century. Even so it positively refuses to definitively date the UNIT stories, despite the blatant "Mawdryn" evidence and despite the fact that it treats the New Adventures as canonical (the UNIT-related novel *No Future* doesn't make any sense at all unless you stick with the early-'70s dating). Charmingly, Parkin's appendix to the book claims that 'there's no right answer', even though the programme explicitly provides one.

It's not that there's no answer, it's that there'll always be the need for an argument. Some fans will ignore even the biggest and most obvious facts - if we can use the word "facts" here - simply to back up their own "golden age" view of the programme's history, a tendency we might describe as positively infantile if we weren't just as bad ourselves. It is, if you will, like the *Doctor Who* version of creationism.

We should ask a simple question here, and leave it at that. Given what we know about the *Doctor Who* universe, is there any real reason that the UNIT stories *shouldn't* be set in the early '70s? Is there any real reason that the "hard" evidence should be ignored, just to make a point about the intentions of the production team in the late '60s?

continued on page 9...

ABOUT TIME 1970-1974

units land on Earth and tells his superior: 'I suppose they must have been meteorites... *mustn't they?*'

4. The Doctor's beautifully off-hand response, on being told that he arrived during a meteorite shower, sets the tone for the era: 'Did I really? How terribly exciting.'

The Continuity

The Doctor The Doctor collapses as soon as he reaches Earth [immediately after his change of body?], and for the first few hours his behaviour's erratic, with selective amnesia. It's established that he has two hearts, and his blood - when analysed - doesn't seem human [q.v. the TV Movie, 27.0, in which his blood doesn't appear to be real blood of any kind]. He can apparently put himself in a self-induced coma, during which an EEG scan shows no brain activity. When he arrives on Earth he's dressed in clothes that look a lot like the Second Doctor's, even though the jacket nearly fits him and the Second Doctor was obviously less broad in the shoulder.

The Third Doctor's personality is fully-formed within hours of his emerging from the TARDIS, presenting himself as an over-extravagant scientist / adventurer and calling the Brigadier 'my dear fellow' as soon as he regains consciousness. He uses the pseudonym "Dr. John Smith" for the first time [but see 5.7, "The Wheel in Space"], and is obviously a competent driver.

[Here, as in later regeneration stories, there's the implication that the first things the Doctor sees and hears once he starts to recover shape his new personality. The Third Doctor establishes his "dandy" look when he steals some clothing from a hospital visitor, and he's so enamoured by the car he "borrows" that he eventually gets his own in the shape of Bessie (7.2, "Doctor Who and the Silurians"). Indeed, this seems to make the Third Doctor so inclined towards vehicles in general, since neither of his previous incarnations seemed to care for them.]

He has a serpent-like mermaid tattoo on his right forearm. [Seen once more in "The Silurians", then never again. *The Discontinuity Guide* misidentifies the tattoo as a dragon and suggests it's a Time Lord criminal brand, something that's backed up in the New Adventures but nowhere on-screen.]

• *Ethics.* The Third Doctor is happy to lie, steal

and manipulate Liz Shaw in order to get the TARDIS key from the Brigadier. Right from the start he makes his freedom in the TARDIS of prime importance, so much so that he tries to leave Earth even when there's a potential alien threat on the planet. He's still not entirely "heroic" at this point.

• *Inventory.* The Doctor wears a wrist-watch which homes in on the TARDIS. [Never seen before or since. The Second Doctor apparently didn't own this, perhaps evidence that a series of unseen adventures *did* occur between Seasons Six and Seven, as some people claim. See 6.7, "The War Games".]

• *Background.* The Doctor claims he can communicate in the language of the planet Delphon, which involves much showing-off with the eyebrows. Here he describes himself as a doctor of 'practically everything'.

The Supporting Cast

• *Liz Shaw.* Here introduced as a wry, intelligent, rather relaxed woman in her twenties, self-confident without being aggressive and having no time for UNIT's cloak-and-dagger methods. [She is, in fact, much closer to being a true "feminist" companion than any of the later ones who actually try to be.] Still, she doesn't seem to object to the Doctor commandeering her as an assistant.

Liz has degrees in medicine, physics and 'a dozen other subjects', plus a research programme at Cambridge. She's also an expert in meteorites. UNIT originally hires Liz to be a form of scientific adviser, much like the Doctor himself, but it's not a job she particularly wants.

• *UNIT.* The Brigadier believes it's UNIT's mandate to investigate the 'unexplained' rather than just alien activity. The official line seems to be that Earth is more likely to be attacked now that humanity's sending out space probes and drawing attention to itself. [In fact, of all the alien crises during the UNIT era, only "Spearhead from Space", "The Ambassadors of Death" (7.3), and "The Android Invasion" (13.4) could feasibly have been caused by space missions].

Liz is told, without having to sign any official paperwork, that two alien attacks have occurred on Earth since UNIT was formed. [UNIT wasn't technically in existence during "The Web of Fear" (5.5), but was during "The Invasion" (6.3). The Brigadier probably simplifies for Liz's benefit, since he says the Doctor was involved in both.

 This product is not authorized by the BBC. Doctor Who and TARDIS are trademarks of the BBC.

When are the UNIT Stories set?

...continued from page 7

Is there anything in the televised UNIT stories which makes it impossible, or even difficult, to accept that those stories might be set as early as 1970?

Other than Sarah Jane's off-hand comment, the answer would seem to be "no". Though the space-age Britain we see in Season Seven is clearly ahead of the "real" Britain in the early '70s, it's massively ahead of Britain in the *late* '70s as well, so no history of the UNIT era is going to gel with known history. And despite many fan-writers' best efforts, it really isn't worth trying to exactly match political events in the UNIT world to our own. Yes, the Prime Minister is female in 1975's "Terror of the Zygons", but it's silly to assume that she's Margaret Thatcher when the previous Prime Minister in 1973's "The Green Death" clearly isn't James Callaghan. Paul Cornell's suggestion in *No Future*, that it's actually Labour MP Shirley Williams, is at least a lot more entertaining. Since the PM in "The Green Death" is called "Jeremy", and seems inspired by that other great B-list '70s politician Jeremy Thorpe, this makes a kind of sense (and see **Who's Running the Country?** under 10.5, "The Green Death").

More importantly, it must be remembered that *Doctor Who* is rooted in the *Quatermass* tradition of SF. In *Quatermass*, Britain has a world-beating space programme as early as the 1950s, and if the guarded reference to *Quatermass* in "Remembrance of the Daleks" (25.1) is anything to go by then the *Doctor Who* version of UK history follows the same pattern. This explains the state of the country in the Pertwee era in much the same way that the intervention of the Cybermen explains the advanced transistor technology in "The Invasion".

In fact you could reasonably argue that only "The Invasion" was deliberately written as a near-future story, and that by 1971 the writers were already starting to forget they weren't supposed to set stories in the present day. Other than the British space programme, and the blatantly absurd technology which seems an inevitable part of any family SF series (q.v. the Mad Professor with Pet Monster in 12.1, "Robot", or the colour video-screens in all the public buildings), there's little to suggest the writers thought of themselves as churning out anything but contemporary adventure stories.

Season Seven is no more "futuristic" than any of the ITC action serials of the time.

In "The Invasion" we see a world where there'll soon be a computer in every home, but in "Terror of the Autons" it's rare for people to sit close enough to a transistor radio for the signal to activate the killer plastic flowers. And when Barry Letts wrote his UNIT-era novel *The Ghosts of N-Space* in 1996, he chose to set it in 1975 rather than 1980. Since this was the man who had his hands on the steering-wheel throughout the UNIT era, who are we to argue? Even if *Ghosts* isn't 100% canonical, it tells you a lot about the attitudes of the people who were there at the time.

The UNIT stories are, on the whole, quite at home in the years 1970-76. There's simply no reason to move them, again. Fan-writers have now reached the stage where they'll not only attempt to rationalise UNIT history, but attempt to explain why it *needs* to be rationalised. The novels *Unnatural History* and *Interference* have both suggested an in-jokey "temporal slippage" which causes the dates of the UNIT era to slide around in time, but the truth is that these explanations are only necessary as long as older fans insist there's some need for explanations. And frankly, the "early '70s" version of things just doesn't have enough flaws to demand another re-writing.

For a more detailed chronology, see **What's the UNIT Timeline?** under "The Daemons" (8.5).

Then again, he immediately makes the connection between the Doctor and the mysteriously-appearing police box even though he's never seen the TARDIS before, so there's arguably a "missing" UNIT story that's never seen or alluded to ever again. Oddly, the offending line seems to have been re-dubbed by Jon Pertwee. The Brigadier is shot from behind, the pitch of "his" voice goes up and he lisps slightly. Perhaps the production team was correcting something which, technically speaking, wasn't a mistake.]

UNIT has its own tracking station. The Brigadier takes orders from Major-General Scobie, who's regular military rather than UNIT, and he can usually call on support platoons as well as his headquarters staff. The Brigadier has no qualms about facing the press, so UNIT is a well-known organisation by this stage.

• *The Brigadier.* When trying to convince Liz Shaw that there's a possible threat from outer space, it's Brigadier Lethbridge-Stewart who's the open-minded one [a contrast to his behaviour in later stories]. He finds it remarkably easy to accept that the new Doctor is *the* Doctor.

ABOUT TIME 1970-1974

The TARDIS The TARDIS arrives on Earth in the same area as the Nestene meteorites [either another remarkable coincidence, or the Time Lords deliberately set the Doctor down close to the first Earth-bound crisis of the era]. The Doctor describes the TARDIS as 'dimensionally transcendental'.

The Ship is currently incapable of dematerialising, as the Time Lords have changed the dematerialisation code [q.v. 8.1, "Terror of the Autons"]. The TARDIS key only works for the Doctor, not the Brigadier, as has a metabolism detector [something evidently turned off by 11.3, "Death to the Daleks", when the Doctor can lend the key to anyone he likes].

The Non-Humans

• *The Nestenes*. A collective consciousness, moving from world to world as energy and creating a suitable physical shell for itself on arrival, the Nestene intelligence acts as a single "brain" even though Channing - its mouthpiece - refers to himself as 'the Nestenes'. It first comes to Earth in 'five or six' hollow plastic meteorites. Six months later, around fifty more enter the atmosphere through a funnel of thin superheated air, including an all-important 'swarm leader'. The energy units then send out a signal, enabling the Autons to detect them for collection [presumably the energy from the original five or six meteorites controlled the minds of the humans who found them, in order to set up the Auton construction process].

The meteorite energy is stored inside an environment tank, where it takes shape as a tentacled, octopoid monstrosity, ideal for Earth but not the Nestenes' natural form. The Nestenes seem to believe all energy is a form of life, and they have 'no individual identity'.

Nestenes can control human beings' thoughts, apparently through telepathy. Channing claims they've been colonising other planets for a thousand million years. There are others apart from those assembling on Earth.

• *Autons*. Plastic creations of the Nestenes, the implication being that the Nestene intelligence can animate anything made from the alien plastic. An Auton mannequin is superhumanly strong and immune to gunfire, while the right hand swings open to reveal a weapon which makes a rocket-like "whoosh" when fired. This weapon normally just kills, but can alternatively completely vaporise a body.

Auton facsimiles are perfect replicas of human beings, even retaining the original's memories, although there's a waxy sheen to the skin. When a facsimile is destroyed, its face reverts to a blank plastic mask while the original human being regains consciousness. [The facsimile-making process must induce a trance-state, for some reason. Nestenes are telepathic, so does the facsimile permanently "tap into" the subject's mind?]

Autons can track individual human beings by their brain-patterns, albeit over a limited range. It's safe to assume that the Autons, not being wholly autonomous, shut down when the Nestene consciousness is destroyed.

Planet Notes The Institute of Space Studies in Baltimore believes that Earth's section of the galaxy contains over five-hundred planets capable of supporting life [The usual figure, based on astronomer Frank Drake's formula, is 530,000 for the whole galaxy. In the 1960s Drake worked on Project OZMA, listening for signals from space. Presumably the UNIT stories take place in a world free from Senate budget cuts; see also 18.7, "Logopolis". The estimate has increased since then, as a closer examination of our own planet has broadened the criteria for supporting life.]

According to the Doctor, the people of the planet Delphon communicate using their eyebrows.

History

• *Dating*. [Probably 1970, or at the latest early 1971. See **When are the UNIT Stories Set?**. Since there's little real evidence to suggest the UNIT stories occur in the late '70s, and since all the Third Doctor's Earth-based stories seem to be set in the "immediate future" rather than the "near future", it's reasonable to suppose that "Spearhead from Space" takes place either in the year it was made or soon afterwards. "Planet of the Spiders" (11.5) claims the Third Doctor arrived on Earth 'months' after "The Invasion". The clothes in the shop window are still priced in pounds, shillings and pence rather than decimal currency, and Britain went decimal in February 1971. In the production-line scene, we hear a record that was in the charts during the week of broadcast: "Oh, Well" by Fleetwood Mac.]

The Analysis

Where Does This Come From? The people of the late '60s and early '70s were terrified of inanimate objects turning out to be alien invaders. Or at least that's the claim made by Gerry Anderson, whose late '60s serial *Captain Scarlet* (in which the Earth is threatened by Mysterons, aliens who can create perfect "intelligent" duplicates of any object or human being) was ostensibly a reaction to Cold War spy paranoia.

This was an era in which English gentlemen could turn out to be secret communists, and sugarlumps could turn out to be bugging devices. And there's an awful lot of *Captain Scarlet* in "Spearhead in Space", even if the scene in which Major-General Scobie comes face-to-face with his own double is lifted straight out of the Bond movie *Thunderball*, a film driven by exactly the same kind of angst. It's there in '50s movies like *Invasion of the Body-Snatchers* and *I Married a Monster from Outer Space*, to name but two post-McCarthy flicks to equate this sort of alien possession with subversion of a more routine kind, but in the '60s miniaturisation and plastic surgery made the whole thing seem so much more hi-tech.

Except that... "Spearhead" isn't really about the Cold War at all. Even if the world hadn't been reading newspaper headlines about evil Eastern European sugarlumps and radio-transmitters the size of bluebottles, the fear of mass-production comes across most clearly here.

And why not? Britain has traditionally - if inaccurately - liked to think of itself as a country full of homely, amateur craftsmen, of inventors in garden sheds rather than industrialists. The "plastic age" was always bound to upset the nation, and it's hard to imagine a *Doctor Who* writer in 1970 coming up with a story about (say) aliens who could inhabit wood. The plastics company in "Spearhead" used to be a modest, homespun sort of business, but as soon as the Nestene industrialists arrived and introduced their methods it instantly became evil, setting old friends against each other. (See, also, how a modern transistor-age radio signal activates the Autons; q.v. 6.3, "The Invasion".) As one of a set of stories in which horrible aliens disguise their plans behind cheap consumer goods, it's fairly obvious what was on people's minds.

It's also interesting to note that the Brigadier takes the time to re-introduce UNIT to the view-ers, as if he's talking to a new audience, and rather than the full-on military outfit of "The Invasion", the organisation has become a general bureau of sorting-out-strange-events. Much like *The Avengers*, or *The Challengers*, or *Department S*, or... you get the idea.

Things That Don't Make Sense Liz Shaw, stealing the TARDIS key from the Brigadier's office, doesn't even react to the fact that the Brigadier's interviewing a man who's babbling about being attacked by plastic monsters with ray-guns in their arms [she's *very* cynical about all of this]. Moments later the Brigadier (rightly) expects the Doctor to try to leave in the TARDIS as soon as possible, even though it's completely out of character for the Doctor he knows; the Second Doctor never had any visible urge to leave in the middle of a crisis. And moments after *that*, Liz is ready to acknowledge that the Doctor was trying to escape, even though she still doesn't believe in aliens and certainly doesn't believe in a time-travelling police box.

Having created a plastic facsimile of Major-General Scobie, the Nestenes then "waxify" the original and put him on display at Madame Tussaud's, for no apparent reason other than to give people a chance to notice. And despite being in Essex, the area around Ashbridge Cottage Hospital seems populated by the Welsh to an odd extent.

Critique Such a massive change in the series' style that it's not surprising there are glitches. Much of '60s *Doctor Who* came from the ancient-and-noble BBC tradition of televised theatre, but theatre's a slower medium than action-packed TV. "Spearhead from Space" aims to be a modern high-tempo adventure, while still structuring itself like an old-fashioned four-part story - most TV action stories are only fifty minutes long, remember - and it consequently goes on too long, with most of the major incidents crammed into the first and last episodes. This story's crying out to be an hour, not an hour and a half.

But then, almost *all* '70s television made is too long, and "Spearhead" contains so much that's striking, memorable or just alarming for small children that it sums up an entire era of television, even if the all-film shooting makes it seem a little odd from a *Doctor Who* point of view. (There are times when it looks curiously like a British public information film, so when the Brigadier's lecturing

11

Liz Shaw about aliens you almost expect him to turn and tell the audience what they can do to reduce the risk of invasion in their own homes.) The overt use of hand-held cameras and dolly tracking is in itself years ahead of anything else on British TV at the time, so today it seems oddly contemporary.

The Facts

Written by Robert Holmes. Directed by Derek Martinus. Viewing figures: 8.4 million, 8.1 million, 8.3 million, 8.1 million.

Supporting Cast Hugh Burden (Channing), Neil Wilson (Seeley), Talfryn Thomas (Mullins), John Breslin (Captain Munro), Antony Webb (Dr. Henderson), Helen Dorward (Nurse), George Lee (Corporal Forbes), Tessa Shaw (UNIT Officer), Alan Mitchell (Wagstaffe), Hamilton Dyce (Major General Scobie), Henry McCarthy (Dr. Beavis), John Woodnutt (Hibbert), Derek Smee (Ransome).

Working Titles "Facsimile".

Cliffhangers UNIT soldiers shoot the Doctor as he runs through the woods towards the guarded TARDIS; one of the mannequins at the plastics factory comes to life, and menaces the former employee who's snooping around there; Major-General Scobie opens his front door, to come face-to-face with his Auton replica.

The Lore

• While the film-work and consequent flaws in sound recording were forced on the production team by the scene-shifters' union, the hurried writing of the story - to accommodate cast and locations intended for a different story altogether - was the fault of writers Mervyn Haisman and Henry Lincoln (for more on this see 6.1, "The Dominators"). The Yeti (5.2, "The Abominable Snowman" and 5.5, "The Web of Fear") were originally slated as the returning monsters to launch the new Doctor, hence their appearance in Season Seven's publicity shots alongside Silurains and the spacesuited Ambassadors of Death. As the Yeti are inanimate objects activated by "souls" in spheres, it's at least possible that the Nestene energy-unit props pre-date everything else in the story.

Likewise, the climactic scenes of "Spearhead" were shot in the same factory which doubled for International Electromatics in "The Invasion" just a year earlier.

• Outgoing producer Derrick Sherwin, looking as if he hasn't slept for a month, plays the dumbfounded doorkeeper with whom the Doctor argues in episode two.

• Robert Holmes had written a sizeable amount of this script before, in the screenplay for the 1965 British SF movie *Invasion*. (The hospital setting is a perfect match, especially when one alien tries to escape and two others posing as nurses pursue him.) The same missile footage used in "The Invasion" (6.3) also crops up in *Invasion*, a film apparently made on less than the budget of a four-part *Doctor Who* story.

• Jon Pertwee's friend Tenniel Evans suggested it might be worth applying for the role of the Doctor, and Pertwee returned the favour for "Carnival of Monsters" (10.2), in which Evans played Major Daly. Pertwee had hitherto been a comedy actor, specialising in funny voices for radio shows such as *Waterlogged Spa* and *The Navy Lark*, his film roles including several doddery old men in the *Carry On* series. *Carry On Screaming* has him playing Scotland Yard's scientific advisor, the Doc, who's killed by a regenerating ape-man with uncertain anthropological origins (q.v. 7.4, "Inferno").

7.2: "Doctor Who and the Silurians"

(Serial BBB. Seven Episodes, 31st January - 14th March 1970.)

Which One is This? There are three-eyed reptile-men hibernating in the caves under a nuclear reactor in Derbyshire, and now they've been woken up, they want their planet back. Can the Doctor make peace between them and the humans? Well... guess.

Firsts and Lasts The start of the "classic" look for '70s *Doctor Who*, not only because it's the first story to use full-colour video but also because it sees the first use of CSO; *the* defining special-effect of '70s television, a process which delighted a generation by ensuring that all giant monsters had little yellow lines around them. (In fact most other

 This product is not authorized by the BBC. Doctor Who and TARDIS are trademarks of the BBC.

television programmes put blue lines around their monsters, but after "Day of the Daleks" *Doctor Who* avoided the blue part of the spectrum in case it accidentally made the TARDIS vanish.) Crucially, it's the first story produced by Barry Letts, who steers the series for the rest of the Pertwee run.

Here we see the first appearance of the Doctor's car, Bessie, of the Silurians themselves and of fully-fledged dinosaurs. This is also the only *Doctor Who* story to have "Doctor Who and..." in its title, something that was always a feature of the early Target novelisations, although in this case there's no particular reason for it to be there.

Plus, this is the first *Doctor Who* story which doesn't mention the TARDIS, and the first since "The Romans" not to involve it (unless you count 3.2, "Mission to the Unknown").

Seven Things to Notice About "The Silurians"...

1. The first of Season Seven's monumental seven-part stories, "The Silurians" walks the line between fast-paced '70s action TV and old-fashioned slow-paced SF thriller, so in many ways this is *Doctor Who* at its most Quatermassy. Alert viewers might want to tick off the *Quatermass* leftovers as they appear, including the ancient hi-tech civilisation, the prehistoric race-memories, the British scientific institute in crisis, the alien disease, the psychic force that makes people go mad, and the post-war paranoia of an invisible threat right in the middle of London.

2. That said, as a seven-part story "Doctor Who and the Silurians" is renowned for being a little *long* in parts. This is particularly obvious in episode six, which includes nearly two minutes' worth of the Doctor sitting in his laboratory and looking at microscope slides.

3. One of the series' great understatements, made by the Doctor as he inspects one of the Silurians' victims: 'She was found in the barn, paralysed with fear... she may have seen something.' (And an honourable mention goes to: 'Hello, are you a Silurian?')

4. Jon Pertwee gets the chance to gurn horribly again, when he's knocked out by the Silurians' eye-weapons at the end of episode six. And he also sports a t-shirt and jeans in episode seven, the only time the Doctor dresses casual in this way. It really doesn't suit him.

5. The final scene - in which the Brigadier does what England expects and apparently wipes out the entire Silurian race, while the Doctor can only look on, appalled - is one of the series' key moments. As a story in which the Doctor attempts to act as peacemaker between the human and the alien, "The Silurians" says a lot more about the series' ethics than any straightforward invasion-from-outer-space story.

6. The Doctor stops the nuclear reactor going critical by 'fusing the control of the neutron flow', the first time the Third Doctor uses this sort of shameless technobabble to save the day.

7. The amusingly-named Dr. Quinn (Fulton Mackay) seems to be on happy-pills as he describes the constant threat of meltdown, the emotional disturbances at the facility and savage deaths of two of his close friends, grinning from ear to ear throughout. And as Liz hears the Doctor suggest they try 'every drug known to man', you have to wonder what goes on at the taxpayers' expense down in these caves...

The Continuity

The Doctor The Doctor's feud with UNIT is obviously underway even before the Brigadier blows up the Silurians. He's happy to refer to the Silurian civilisation as 'alien' even though it's apparently native to Earth, and claims that his life 'covers several thousand years'. [He's not several thousand years old. See **How Old is the Doctor?** under 16.5, "The Power of Kroll". It's notable that he claims his life *covers* several thousand years, though, possibly referring to the span of history he's witnessed.]

• *Ethics.* The Doctor values Silurian lives as highly as human ones, and has no problem with the idea of helping the two species live together even though he must realise that a human / Silurian world would contradict known history. [The Third Doctor's less concerned with changes to the timeline than the First; see 1.6, "The Aztecs". His frustration with the Time Lords, and with UNIT, may have given him a sense of "to hell with it". Or has his memory been compromised?]

• *Inventory.* He's still carrying his sonic screwdriver.

• *Background.* He hasn't been potholing 'in some time'. He's seen dinosaurs before, in the flesh, but doesn't know enough about Earth's pre-history to recognise the Silurians. Yet he seems aware that the moon is a relatively new arrival in the solar system. [Not something human research acknowledges. For more on the solar system's pre-history, see 15.3, "Image of the Fendahl".]

• *Bessie*. The vehicle traditionally referred to as "the Doctor's yellow roadster", he's evidently only acquired "her" recently and is already making modifications. The licence-plate reads WHO 1. [Has this been officially registered? If he chose the number himself, then it's the first sign that he's trying to generate a deliberate air of mystery around himself, as befits a more showman-like Doctor. See also 3.10, "The War Machines". Bessie herself appears to be a 1905 Winton Flyer, actually an American model.]

The Supporting Cast

• *Liz Shaw*. By now she's accepted that the Doctor isn't human, and she's formally a UNIT member rather than just a consultant. Her grasp of medicine is good enough for her to suggest treatments the Doctor hasn't thought of.

• *UNIT*. There's nothing about the Doctor in the files at Central Intelligence Records, and the Brigadier sees him as a personal responsibility. UNIT is called in to investigate scientific and personnel problems at the Wenley Moor nuclear research centre, which seems a little outside its usual mandate [suggesting that the British government uses the organisation to troubleshoot important national projects]. The Brigadier needs ministerial approval to get reinforcements from the regular army.

• *The Brigadier*. Much more cynical than during previous crises, refusing to take the Doctor's word that there's a prehistoric monster in the caves even after everything he's seen [he's under a lot of pressure from the powers-that-be here]. He waits for the Doctor to leave before detonating the explosives which either kill the Silurians or, at the very least, seal the caves; it's only the Doctor's supposition that genocide is taking place. [The existence of the Silurians isn't in the Brigadier's report to Masters, the Permanent Under-Secretary, so despite Liz Shaw's belief that the government is scared, it's possible that the politicians don't even find out about the Silurians until later on.] Whatever the truth, the Brigadier does his "duty" here without compunction.

The Non-Humans

• *The Silurians*. Upright-walking sentient reptiles, with clawed hands, triceratops-like crests and third eyes in their foreheads. Silurians can apparently see through these extra eyes, but they appear artificial. At will, the third eyes can cause pain, unconsciousness or death in living beings. More impressively, they can burn through walls and seal up the holes with a solid ash-like substance afterwards, or even act as remote-controls for Silurian technology.

Silurians don't wear clothes, but have curious "ruffs" of reptilian skin around their necks [their ancestors possibly had defensive frills, like Australian frill-necked lizards]. Silurians are stronger and tougher than humans, and being cold-blooded [as dinosaurs were thought to be in 1970, though it's much-disputed now] they're comfortable in great heat.

The Silurians originally occupied Earth millions of years ago, before humanity's development. Dr. Quinn, who makes the first contact with them, believes they were native to the Silurian era - roughly 430,000,000 years ago - yet has a globe among his effects which depicts the world as it was 200,000,000 years ago. Either date is clearly wrong. [As the Doctor establishes in 9.3, "The Sea Devils". There was no life anywhere on land during the Silurian era, and 200,000,000 BC is still some way short of the "large reptile" period. See **What's the Origin of the Silurians?**] Both the Doctor and Dr. Quinn (along with his assistant Miss Dawson) seem to come up with the name "Silurians" independently of each other.

The Silurians are familiar with apes, but not with humans until now. Their leader states that millions of years ago they detected a 'small planet' approaching the Earth, and calculated that it would draw off the atmosphere. They built a shelter in the Wenley Moor caves [plus other shelters in other places, judging by later events] and went into hibernation, waiting for life to return, but the approaching planet was drawn into Earth's orbit and became the moon. The hibernation mechanism was faulty, and didn't begin to revive them until the nuclear research station was built above them.

Silurian technology is much more advanced than human technology, with mechanical hibernation chambers ["hibernation" rather than "suspended animation", suggesting that Silurians hibernate naturally but need machinery to do it for such long periods]. They can speak and understand English [built-in technology, much like the eye]. The Silurians in the caves have their own personal agendas instead of a racial masterplan, frequently threatening to kill each other [these must be quite high-ranking Silurians if

What's the Origin of the Silurians?

Despite *two* separate attempts to establish their time of origin, there's still some dispute about the era in which the Silurians (and therefore the first sentient life on Earth) evolved. However, most of the people who dispute it are either ignoring what's actually said on-screen or are just confused about Earth's pre-history.

"Doctor Who and the Silurians" implies - naturally enough - that the Silurians were the children of the Silurian era (c. 430,000,000 years BC), although curiously there's a globe among Dr. Quinn's effects which depicts the world as it was 200,000,000 years ago. Neither of these dates can be accurate, as they both miss the age of the reptiles by some considerable distance. By his own admission, Malcolm Hulke was a writer who knew next to nothing about science.

In "The Sea Devils" (9.3) the Doctor clears things up, or so anyone might have thought, by stating that the person who called them Silurians (i.e. Dr. Quinn) didn't have a clue and that they should properly be called Eocenes. Leaving aside the question of where the 200,000,000 BC globe came from, this makes perfect sense. The Silurians encountered apes before they went into hibernation, and since the first modern primates would have existed in the Eocene period (beginning 54,000,000 BC), everything's all right so far.

However, fan-lore frequently claims that the Silurians should actually be called *Cretaceans*, and that they hail from the Cretaceous era, the era which ended with the mass-extinction of the dinosaurs 65,000,000 years ago. It's a belief which seems to stem solely from the fact that the Silurians have a pet tyrannosaurus, but it's led to the even more bizarre theory that the Doctor was wrong about the Silurians hibernating in order to avoid the oncoming moon, and that in fact they were hiding from the freighter full of Adric-and-anti-matter which kills off the dinosaurs in "Earthshock" (19.6).

This, though, is clearly nonsense. The ship in "Earthshock" hits the planet mere minutes after materialising in the late Cretaceous, yet the Silurians had enough advance warning of *their* catastrophe to neatly mothball their whole culture. (This theory has nonetheless appeared in print, in Jean-Marc Lofficier's *Terrestrial Index*, 1991. Then again, Lofficier has a problem with Silurian stories. His *Doctor Who Programme Guide* claims that the Young Silurian released a disease to "wipe out the Universe".) Weirdly, in 1983 Barry Letts wrote an article for *Doctor Who – A Celebration* in which he quoted the line about the Eocenes from "The Sea Devils" but mis-remembered it as "Cretaceans", which might have been the biggest single source of the confusion. And Letts' article got the pre-historic dating wrong *again*, mixing up the Silurian with the Jurassic.

In fact, the idea that the Silurians own a pet tyrannosaurus comes not from the TV series but from the Target novelisation *Doctor Who and the Cave-Monsters*. The TV story only refers to the Silurians' guard-dog as 'some kind of dinosaur'. It clearly isn't a tyrannosaurus, since its skeleton is out of proportion even by BBC effects standards, and the Doctor can't identify it despite his experience with known dinosaur species. *The Discontinuity Guide* suggests the Eocene-period Silurians technologically cloned Cretaceous-era dinosaurs in the style of *Jurassic Park* - a concept which takes in four whole eras at once, impressively - but scientifically speaking this wouldn't really be necessary. To explain:

Although the extinction of the dinosaurs can still keep palaeontologists arguing for hours, the most widely-known and widely-accepted theory holds that sixty-five million years ago a large object smacked into the Earth in the vicinity of Mexico, releasing a vast amount of kinetic energy. (The *Doctor Who* version insists that the object was a freighter full of Cybermen rather than a meteor, but the principle's the same.) This impact, though obviously lethal to billions of animals in the area, certainly didn't wipe out all the dinosaurs in the course of one day. Instead it dislodged trillions of tons of matter at ground level, causing massive ecological / atmospheric damage and blotting out much of the planet's sunlight. Without light, plants die; without plants, large herbivores die; without large herbivores, large carnivores die. This is why small mammals, which need less food and are better at squeezing into the cracks to get at it, did so well out of the catastrophe and eventually evolved into things like us.

Let's assume, however, that by this point the Silurians already existed on Earth; perhaps not as a fully-fledged technological civilisation, but at least as a semi-sentient species. If the Silurians were at least partly sentient when the freighter hit the planet, they could easily have survived, for the simple reason that they would have had the ability to use tools. Unlike non-sentient animals, a tool-building species knows how to exploit limited food supplies (a carnosaur can't crack open a brontosaur skull to get at the tasty brains inside,

continued on page 17...

15

they've got access to a weapon as powerful as the molecular disperser].

When one of the men who encounters the Silurians' pet dinosaur loses his mind, he draws Paleolithic-style pictures on the wall, including the outline of a Silurian even though he's apparently never seen one. The Doctor believes this is a 'race memory'. [The man draws mammals on the wall as well as reptile-men, suggesting a time when Silurians and large mammals co-existed. If seeing the Silurians' dinosaur triggered this state, then some kind of dinosaur life must have been around as well.]

Humans facing the Silurians for the first time tend to suffer absolute atavistic terror, with headaches and feelings of oppression common among susceptible people working closest to the caves. [This is never fully explained. It may be part of the same race memory process, with the humans subconsciously sensing the Silurians' presence, or a side-effect of the buried Silurian technology. Probably the latter, as it gets worse whenever the Silurians drain the station's power.]

Apes once raided the Silurians' crops, and the Silurians used a bacterium [engineered] to kill them off. The bacterium is highly contagious and kills humans within hours. They also have a microwave-based molecular disperser, which they intend to use to destroy the 'protective belt' around the Earth [see **Things That Don't Make Sense**].

The Silurians think of Earth as their planet, but here it's never explicitly stated that they evolved on Earth. The Doctor's reference to them as "alien" arguably indicates that they colonised the world [although later writers don't take this view; see 4.2, "The Tenth Planet", for a possible sidelight on this].

• *Dinosaurs.* The Silurians at Wenley Moor apparently only have one dinosaur to act as a guard dog, clearly related to large carnivores like the tyrannosaurus although its arms and teeth are noticeably different. [The Doctor identifies a tyrannosaurus on sight in 11.2, "Invasion of the Dinosaurs", but says the Silurians' creature is like nothing he's seen before.]

History

• *Dating.* [Early 1971.] Again, Britain is still using pre-decimal currency, and the police drive Mk. II Jaguars with bells [as opposed to the "Panda" cars which replaced them in our world c.

1971, as seen in 11.5, "Planet of the Spiders"].

The UK has an advanced nuclear research project by this stage, attempting to find a safe, reliable form of energy [obviously this project is shut down, which may explain the government's great interest in new forms of power in 7.4, "Inferno"]. In London there's a Ministry of Science so well-known that taxi drivers don't have to ask for its address [as befits a Britain with its own space programme].

Additional Sources The Target novelisation of the story, *Doctor Who and the Cave-Monsters* (1974), is one of the most fondly-remembered of the early novels and fleshes out much of the background to the plot.

All three of the "important" reptiles get names (Okdel for the Old Silurian, Morka - a name later used in Jim Mortimore's novel *Blood Heat* - for the Young Silurian, K'to for the scientist). There's a prologue set millions of years in the past, which sees the species enter hibernation and establishes their shelter as one of many across the world. There's more of a "morality play" feel to the human characters, with Quinn dying because he's basically a bad man (he's planning to wipe out the Silurians once he's learned their secrets, something not at all true of the TV version). Major Baker believes communists, bankers and trade unionists are laying siege to Britain, and we're told that he had to resign from the army after shooting a surrendering IRA sniper. The Doctor and Liz discuss Jung (in a children's book!) during their conversation about race memory. It's established that the Silurian who kills Quinn is the Young Silurian himself, and the Brigadier only seals up the caves in the final chapter instead of killing the occupants.

But most notably the word "Silurians" is never used anywhere in the text of the novel, only on the back cover, since by 1974 Hulke had already figured out that his palaeontology was off-beam. The book prefers to call them "reptile people".

In addition, the novelisation has a cover illustration which neatly sums up most of the great childhood obsessions of the 1970s: *Doctor Who*, an alien monster, a dinosaur and - for some reason - a volcano erupting. Although it loses marks for the back cover blurb, which describes a "40 ft. high Tyrannosaurus Rex, the biggest, most savage *mammal* which ever trod the earth!".

What's the Origin of the Silurians?

...continued from page 15

for example, and a triceratops can't lever a boulder onto its side to get at the plant tissue underneath).

Not only that, but these early Silurians could have deliberately bred surviving dinosaurs for food or other purposes. An animal won't go hungry if a smarter form of life rears it. By the time the Silurian civilisation reached its peak in the Eocene era, around eleven million years later, their dinosaurs would have become as domesticated as dogs... and sure enough, the dinosaur we see in "Doctor Who and the Silurians" bears about as much relation to a tyrannosaurus as a domestic dog does to a prehistoric wolf.

So it was during the Eocene period that the moon swung into Earth's orbit, convincing the then-technological Silurians to put themselves into hibernation and avoid *another* eco-catastrophe. Except, of course, that the moon never did the damage they expected. (The novel *Eternity Weeps* confirms this version of events, also revealing that the moon was actually an artificial construction steered into orbit by aliens, but that's a different and much more confusing story. The Big Finish audio adventure "Bloodtide" nearly-but-not-quite contradicts this, by suggesting that the catastrophe predicted by the Silurians *did* take place, though this could mean environmental damage caused by the moon's gravity rather than a full-on collision with it.) Any domesticated dinosaurs which didn't fit into the Silurians' chiller-cabinets wouldn't have lasted long in the wild.

The description of the Silurians as "Eocenes" is an accurate one, then. Though it's likely that the Silurians began to develop as a sentient species during the Creaceous, they had their golden age during the Eocene era, and finally went into hibernation until the twentieth century. Unless you still want to believe that they went underground just to avoid Adric, and had their crops raided by time-travelling apes from several million years in the future.

It might also be worth mentioning that since this story was broadcast, Dr. Dale Russell of the Canadian National Institute of Natural Sciences has gained considerable publicity for his idea that the dinosaur stenonychosaurus - a scavenger with a hefty brain capacity - could have evolved into something anthropomorphic. His hypothetical "lizard man" has no third eye, but the Silurians' extra orbs do appear artificial, and some adaptation of the pineal gland would be useful for reptiles in any case. Russell's humanoid dinosaurs even have the right number of fingers for our purposes. (But see **What's Wrong with the Centre of the Earth?** under 4.2, "Inferno", for more wanton prehistoric speculation.)

The Analysis

Where Does This Come From? The connections to *Quatermass* are obvious (especially *Quatermass and the Pit* this time, which also deals with the alien influence on Earth's pre-history), but the truth is that "Doctor Who and the Silurians" is a distinctly '70s-flavoured story. This was the era which gave us ley-line hunting, *Chariots of the Gods* author Erich von Daniken (who theorised that aliens previously visited some ancient Earth civilizations, accounting for a number of tales about divine beings) and Israeli psychic Uri Gellar, who used his "psychic abilities" to bend spoons and who used to claim that his powers came from extra-terrestrials before it got too embarrassing.

This was also the era in which evolution became part of popular culture rather than just a scientific theory - "The Silurians" turned up just two years after Kubrick's *2001* - and every other writer had his or her own theory about the relationship between Atlantis and the Missing Link.

Whereas *Quatermass and the Pit* was a grim, sombre statement about human primitivism, complete with a "proper" political message, "The Silurians" presents a much more pop-ish and t-shirt-wearing kind of ancient horror. There were plenty of children's TV shows like this over the following years, all fitted out with ancient civilisations, Neolithic stone circles and buried psychic powers, and "The Silurians" is a good lead-in.

Then there's the Silurian disease. Bacterial weapons were another great favourite of '60s and '70s TV (after the nuts-and-bolts flying-saucer sci-fi of the '50s, it was almost as if the public's sudden interest in evolution and biology gave writers a whole new arsenal of weapons which didn't require fiddly laser-beam explosions). The trend eventually reached its own kind of godhood with Terry Nation's *Survivors*.

It's tempting to claim that this reflects a Cold War terror of germ warfare, but... it probably doesn't. The bacterium sub-plot is just another hold-over from *Quatermass*, a way of bringing something nasty-but-feasible into the heart of modern Britain. The lab-work scenes in episode six, the dissolves in particular, echo British plague-dramas like *80,000 Suspects* or biopics of the great scientists and their breakthroughs. Or, indeed, Hartnell curing the Sensorites of their "plague" in the very first year of *Doctor Who*.

What's striking, though, is that overall it's impossible to imagine a story like this being made only a year earlier. "The Silurians" just wouldn't have worked in 1969, and once again the real difference is the use of colour. Stories shape themselves to their medium. A scriptwriter working for a black-and-white series will automatically stray towards sterile, monochrome space stations and gleaming white robot-monsters. Season Seven demanded a more colourful kind of world - even if most of the audience still had black-and-white sets - and "The Silurians" provides it. The shiny corridors of stories like 6.5, "The Seeds of Death" suddenly gave way to fleshy, coral-coloured underground empires, while the aliens' usual flat, grey computer-banks are replaced by almost *organic*-looking technology.

It's ironic that the original colour prints of "The Silurians" have been lost, and that much of fandom only knew the monochrome prints before it was re-coloured in 1993... but it's fitting that this was the first story to use CSO, AKA "Chromakey", the most garish special effects system of the age. Somehow it seems part of the story's whole nature.

Of course, the literary roots of "The Silurians" go back a lot further than the '50s. As with "Inferno", the main influence is Arthur Conan-Doyle's second-best-known hero, Professor Challenger (in this case *The Lost World*, although it'd be churlish to ignore Lord Bulwer-Lytton's *The Coming Race*, a book about a subterranean troglodyte culture threatening to rise up and engulf us which - inter alia - gave us the word "Bovril"). The idea that places exist where time has stood still invites the primordial to visit us and shatter our illusions of control, c.f. *Godzilla*, *The Beast from 20,000 Fathoms*, and just about every other dinosaur movie ever made.

Things That Don't Make Sense Human beings suffer uncontrollable terror, even amnesia, when faced with the Silurians. At least until episode four, when the Silurians show themselves in full and characters keep forgetting to be scared. Liz Shaw, who recoils with primal horror the first time

she sees one, doesn't even flinch the second time. And when a hunting-party of Silurians finally overruns the base in the last episode, not one single member of staff has the expected nervous breakdown. It's said that only "certain" humans react badly, but we're never told why. Don't all humans have the same ancestry?

The protective "belt" around the Earth, which filters out a lot of the sun's radiation, is cited as the Van Allen Belt. Whereas in fact the Van Allen Belt is just a 4,000-mile-high layer of radiation, and the thing that filters radiation is supposed to be the ozone layer. [But only Liz explicitly mentions the Van Allen Belt, and she's under a lot of stress.]

How did Dr. Lawrence land up in charge of a project as big as Wenley Moor, given that the Permanent Under-Secretary knows him of old and always thought him a bit unstable? And a logic flaw that only becomes clear after "The Ambassadors of Death" (7.3): a few weeks later the honour of a successful "First Contact" with non-humans is enough for Sir James Quinlan to justify murders, conspiracies and sabotage, yet Whitehall sanctions whatever action the Brigadier takes expressly to stop it happening at Wenley Moor. Clearly, some aliens are more equal than others.

Critique Arguably the story which sums up the *Doctor Who* ethos better than any other, with charm, principles and hugely endearing monster costumes, "The Silurians" is perhaps *the* definitive four-part story. Unfortunately it's seven parts long, but if you can ignore the fact that around 3/7 of the screen-time is taken up with people sitting around in laboratories and rehashing the same arguments, it's still immensely likeable thirty-five years on.

It's odd, though, that a story which begins by introducing us to an enormous rampaging monster (i.e. the dinosaur) has a "final act" in which the monster does nothing worthwhile at all, leaving the Silurians to produce an unexpected doomsday weapon out of thin air at the last minute. Opinion is divided as to whether the electro-kazoo music is thoroughly awful, or just appropriately bizarre (because, to be fair, it does *sound* like a prehistoric civilisation playing with radiophonics).

The Facts

Written by Malcolm Hulke. Directed by Timothy Combe. Viewing figures: 8.8 million, 7.3 million, 7.5 million, 8.2 million, 7.5 million, 7.2 million, 7.5 million.

Supporting Cast Fulton Mackay (Dr. Quinn), Norman Jones (Major Baker), Peter Miles (Dr. Lawrence), Thomasine Heiner (Miss Dawson), Ian Cunningham (Dr. Meredith), Paul Darrow (Captain Hawkins), Peter Halliday (Silurian voices), Geoffrey Palmer (Masters), Richard Steele (Sergeant Hart), Dave Carter (Old Silurian), Nigel Johns (Young Silurian), Harry Swift (Private Robins), Pat Gorman (Silurian Scientist), Alan Mason (Corporal Nutting).

Working Titles "The Monsters". (Intended as a clever double-meaning. Probably.)

Cliffhangers The Doctor descends into the caves, and finds himself menaced by a dinosaur; alone in a barn, Liz Shaw finds something inhuman bearing down on her and breathing heavily; the Doctor (along with the audience) comes face-to-face with a Silurian for the first time in Dr. Quinn's cottage; in the Silurian base, the Young Silurian uses his third eye to try to kill the captive Doctor; Major Baker dies of the horribly disfiguring bacteria outside the hospital, and the Doctor announces that he's just the first victim; the Silurians burn their way into the lab where the Doctor's working on the cure for the disease, and use their eye-weapons to bring him down.

The Lore

• This story sees the first *Doctor Who* appearance of actor Peter Miles (as Dr. Lawrence), and he displays the same talent for playing neurotic, high-pitched villains that stands him in such good stead in both "Invasion of the Dinosaurs" (11.2) and "Genesis of the Daleks" (12.4), plus 17 years later in Big Finish's *Sarah Jane Smith* audio series. Here, however, he plays a scientist who doesn't believe in dinosaurs instead of a scientist who makes them appear from out of nowhere.

• Meanwhile the Brigadier's rapid turnover of Captains results in future *Blake's 7* star Paul Darrow (Captain Hawkins) getting juvenile lead status (as actors call it). It's not established whether Darrow's character is called "Jimmy" like

all the others.

• Only after a day of shooting a man in a dinosaur suit against a CSO backdrop did it occur to the production team that they could have used a puppet. This is why the dinosaur looks half-decent for once (c.f. "Invasion of the Dinosaurs").

• Bessie is based on a not-too-elderly Austin A4 chassis with a glass-fibre shell. Subsequent stories gave her an 'unexpected turn of speed' by undercranking the camera, but here she's merely transport. (The abortive Gerry Anderson project *Secret Service* features a remarkably similar vehicle, "Gabriel", which can be seen in most episodes of *UFO*.) Publicity for this story emphasised the car and the family-appeal, not the increasingly "adult" elements of the drama this year.

• Carey Blyton, composer of this story's soundtrack, rang director Timothy Coombe to play him the "shawm" sound he wanted for the Silurans. Contrary to what's stated elsewhere it was a genuine wind instrument, a mediaeval oboe, and not a synthesiser effect. It sounded even worse over the 'phone. Nevertheless, Blyton's music also gave a "distinctive" sound to "Death to the Daleks" (11.3) and "Revenge of the Cybermen" (12.5). Oh, and his aunt wrote *Noddy*.

• Also contrary to popular belief, the ticket-collector at the train station isn't script editor Terrance Dicks. Terrance is there in the crowd, though, as are many of the production team in a typical cost-cutting exercise. Marylebone Station will appear in the series once more, this time assailed by less-good prehistoric monsters (11.2, "Invasion of the Dinosaurs", again).

7.3: "The Ambassadors of Death"

(Serial CCC. Seven Episodes, 21st March - 2nd May 1970.)

Which One is This? British astronauts are swapped for radioactive aliens in spacesuits; UNIT gets an extended shoot-out in a warehouse, a la *The Ipcress File*; and the Doctor once again sides with the "monsters" instead of the politicians, in the space-based conspiracy thriller that's *not* about faking the moon-landings.

Firsts and Lasts The TARDIS console is removed from the Ship for the first time, allowing the Doctor to work on it in his UNIT HQ lab.

Sergeant Benton, veteran of "The Invasion" (6.3), returns to the programme to make his colour debut. (Here Benton's just an average UNIT member, not the all-purpose odd-job man for the Brigadier he becomes later. He only appears in two episodes of this story and doesn't even get to meet the Doctor.)

This is the first time that episodes end with the radiophonic "sting" leading into the end title music, something which becomes standard for the next two decades. When the Doctor's gassed in episode six, we also get our first sight of the "Pertwee Death Pose", supine with one knee aloft. There'll be many, many more...

Seven Things to Notice
About "The Ambassadors of Death"...

1. The moment which sums up the Third Doctor's entire relationship with the Earth authorities, when he makes his entrance into the space control centre and shouts down the lift-well behind him, to someone we never see or hear: 'My dear fellow, I simply don't happen to *have* a pass. [Pause.] Because I don't believe in them, that's why.'

2. The magic bread-van. You'll know it when you see it. A vehicle driven by sinister government conspirators, its ability to change its external appearance is technically a lot more feasible than almost everything else in *Doctor Who*, and yet it still looks *less* convincing than a man in a monster costume. The programme-makers wasted a lot of time on this "special effect" which might have been better spent checking that Liz Shaw's hair is the same length from scene to scene.

3. In a rare change to the programme's usual opening sequence, the story title doesn't appear on-screen all at once. Instead the words "The Ambassadors" arrive first, followed by the sudden and pleasantly over-dramatic addition of "OF DEATH", complete with sinister electronic sound-effect. This is also the only story to sandwich the recap of the previous episode's cliffhanger halfway through the opening credits, another attempt to make the series look more exciting and dynamic.

4. Note the light *Whiter-Shade-of-Pale*-style organ music during the spacecraft docking sequences, *Doctor Who*'s response to *2001: A Space Odyssey*. (Actually the space sequences here are actually rather good, apart from the nasty CSO rocket take-off.)

5. The sight of the spacesuit-clad "ambassa-

dors" walking towards the space centre, faceless and framed against the sun, is one of those scenes that nobody who saw the programme as a child has ever been able to comfortably forget.

6. This being a David Whitaker story, "radiation" behaves exactly like static electricity. Except that it's conducted by wood as well.

7. And see how the people who put up the signs on the location sets can't spell "variant"...

The Continuity

The Doctor Still brooding over the Brigadier's slaughter of the Silurians, although he's at least prepared to work with UNIT. It's implied that the Doctor still doesn't have all of his memories. [In "Spearhead from Space" he barely even seems able to remember his trial by the Time Lords. Season Seven generally seems to imply that large chunks of his mind are missing, although it's not yet suggested that he can't remember how the TARDIS works - the problem keeping him on Earth, according to later stories - and he works on the console as if the fault's purely technical.] He can withstand considerably more g-force than humans.

The Doctor is capable of making an object in his hand vanish without trace, then reappear again moments later. He calls this 'transmigration of object', and says there's a great deal of difference between that and 'pure science'. [This isn't time travel, nor can it be simple sleight-of-hand. The Doctor never demonstrates this ability again, ever.] Even the Third Doctor, fond as he is of machinery, doesn't trust computers.

• *Ethics*. On this occasion, he doesn't actively try to make peace between humans and aliens but considers his work done as soon as he's made sure they don't kill each other. [Getting off the planet is still his priority, and he only does what's necessary rather than seeing himself as a full-time peace-maker.]

• *Inventory*. There's a jeweller's eyeglass in his pocket.

• *Background*. He recognises the sound of the aliens' communication, but can't remember where from. [He's had prior experience of this species, which his amnesia is blotting out.]

• *Bessie*. A switch on the dashboard activates an anti-theft device, so anyone touching the car gets stuck to it by a force-field. Victims of this soon escape as the device isn't strong enough 'yet'.

This product is not authorized by the BBC. Doctor Who and TARDIS are trademarks of the BBC.

How Believable is the British Space Programme?

Since the space-bound version of Britain we see in "The Ambassadors of Death" is usually taken as pure fantasy, and since at time of writing various real-world governments are thinking about starting *another* space race, this might be a good point to set the record straight.

If you'd asked anyone in post-war Britain which nation would be first to the moon and when, most people would have said "us" and "about 1980". In the era of *Dan Dare*, the conquest of Everest and the Festival of Britain, UK aerospace companies were busily trying to beat the sound barrier and harness jet-power for commercial use. Both of these were immediate goals of the Hertfordshire-based de Havilland company. Its "Comet" airliner ushered in the Jet-Set and, until the death of dashing test-pilot (and son of the founder) Geoffrey de Havilland, Mach 1 - the speed of sound - was an attainable goal. America's Chuck Yaeger finally got there first in the Bell X1, in 1947... or at least, he was the first accredited for it. Some Spitfire pilots managed it by accident in tight dives, but few were conscious at the time.

The shift in emphasis from aircraft to rockets is less obvious than it seems now. Despite the 1946 attempts by UK scientists to get a captured German A4 going, post-War Britain didn't make rocketry one of its priorities. "Operation Backfire" was more concerned with getting America and Russia to cease the undignified scramble for parts and personnel. While ICBM programmes meant the development of missiles capable of the kind of thrust required for escape velocity, the process developed for the X1's successors - dropping a small rocket-plane from a high-altitude jet like a B52 - continued well into the 1970s for the Space Shuttle tests.

Something like this resulted in Neil Armstrong *almost* becoming the first astronaut in 1960, in the X15. In Britain, various aircraft companies had advanced test-bed models of such craft until 1962-63. English Electric's "Mustard" was, in effect, the Space Shuttle two decades early. A prototype was shown to visitors from Lockheed and Bell, who promptly went back to America and made their own. Arthur C. Clarke, a member of the British Interplanetary Society and one of the developers of the first plans, wrote *A Prelude To Space* in 1948 and described how this approach might get a British astronaut into orbit by 1965. In 1952 Clarke had received a visit from the Americans' secret weapon, Alexander Satin, Chief Engineer of the Office of Naval Research and (incidentally) nephew of the composer Rachmaninoff. America,

Satin realised, almost had the thrust but not the navigation. Clarke's paper on "Geostationary Satellites", from 1945, was all that was missing.

However, pure rocketry wasn't the British way, as the big money and prestige went into aircraft design. "Piggy-back" would have been the obvious route into space, using a bomber as launcher for a smaller ship. Bristol Siddely had developed an air-breathing engine, the Thor (as seen in the stock footage used in 6.3, "The Invasion"). With refinements it could well have propelled an aircraft to Mach 7, i.e. seven times the speed of sound, easily within reach of escape velocity had a ship been launched piggy-back. The most effective air-breathing engine is a ramjet, which uses the speed of the air intake to compress the air with the injected fuel, usually self-igniting. It's low-maintenance and fuel-efficient. Ramjet research in the US was left to one side, but British companies continued to investigate the problems of supersonic combustion and openly speculated on materials needed to withstand Mach 14. The size of the payload as a percentage of the launch mass goes up from 4%, the best any rocket ever managed, to 35%. Southampton University had something suitable by 1962.

Rocketry, though, was a more interesting "fringe" interest until 1956. When Britain suddenly decided to build its own launchers, in the shape of "Blue Streak" and later "Black Arrow", the principal site of the test-launches was Woomera in Australia. What the Americans had in industrial muscle, British technicians made up for in skilled detail work. If you were making rockets one at a time, then the Rolls Royce company's traditions - good enough for US companies to use its aero-engines - would have sufficed.

Certainly, the "Blue Streak" engines were phenomenally fuel-efficient, and well in advance of anything the Russians had at Baikonur or the Americans had at White Sands. Several fuel / oxidant combinations were tried, most of them ingenious self-igniting combos like nitric acid / aniline or hydrazine and hydrogen peroxide; the latter has all the properties of the fictional "M3 Variant" in "The Ambassadors of Death", but is somewhat safer. It's also comparatively cheap, especially set against the costs of the Rocketdyne F1 used in NASA's Saturn V.

But the fact that a project was streets ahead of anybody else's was insufficient reason to prop it up with taxpayers' money. Defence Secretary

continued on page 23...

21

The Supporting Cast

• *Liz Shaw.* Apparently has less reservations than the Doctor about UNIT's mass-murder of the Silurians, and she doesn't seem to want to rock the boat. She knows French.

• *The Brigadier.* As in the Silurian crisis, the Brigadier is wary of aliens and doesn't wholly disagree with General Carrington's assessment that they're a threat. He's prepared to use force, but only once he knows the facts, and has the power to hold people on security charges for 'a very long time'. He's not averse to appearing on TV, either.

• *Benton.* Promoted to Sergeant, he's able to run basic forensic checks and handle distraught scientists. [He has to be instantly likeable here so that his "doppelganger" in the next story seems downright evil.]

The TARDIS The TARDIS console has been removed from the Ship and set up in the lab at UNIT HQ, where the Doctor's trying to reactivate its time vector generator. ["Reactivate", not "repair". See **What's Wrong with the TARDIS?**, under 9.2, "The Curse of Peladon".] The reactivated generator is capable of projecting someone several seconds into the future, with a miniature version of the usual TARDIS wheezing, groaning noise. [It's fair to assume the console can make short hops in space as well, since it wouldn't have squeezed through the TARDIS doors otherwise; "The Mind Robber" (6.2) also seems to imply this. In "The Edge of Destruction" (1.3) it's suggested that the power of an entire star lies under the TARDIS time rotor, and it's doubtful that the displaced console has access to this energy. See also 7.4, "Inferno".]

The Non-Humans

• *The Aliens.* Never named, the aliens encountered by the Mars Probe mission aren't native Martians. General Carrington notes that they were 'on Mars' before humans, and believes them to come from a different galaxy. The aliens require exposure to radiation to survive, and their ambassadors emit radiation measured at over 2,100,000 rads. One touch from an alien - even through clothing - can kill or cause small explosions, and when one of them touches a metal beam the soldier at the other end of it instantly collapses [probably only stunned, since he seems to be back on duty several episodes later].

This death-touch appears to be a controlled, conscious act, as it doesn't happen every time they touch something [though they killed one of the Mars Probe 6 astronauts by accident, so among their own kind it might just be like a handshake]. The aliens aren't damaged by bullets, which are deflected by some kind of force-field around them, and they're not susceptible to g-force.

The alien on board the spacecraft, though never seen in full, is roughly humanoid but covered in a featureless silver substance which sparkles in a way that just screams "radioactive". On the other hand, the alien ambassadors on Earth are similar to human beings, though their skin is pale blue and their facial features are covered in hideous disfiguring lumps. [Fairly obviously, the alien on the ship is the same species but clothed, wearing a kind of shroud. Their skin may suggest that they evolved on an Earth-like planet, but then damaged themselves with radiation and eventually became dependent on it. Much like the original Daleks, really. Do they wear the shrouds out of some sort of ultural shame?]

The alien spacecraft is an ovoid mass of glowing matter which looks almost organic, half a mile in diameter and very manoeuvrable for its mass. Alien machinery can easily condition human minds, and they apparently possess some kind of limited teleportation technology. They're prepared to enter into diplomatic relations with Earth, but have very little patience, so they're prepared to destroy the entire planet if betrayed. [It's fair to assume they don't open talks with Earth after this encounter.] They "speak" through radio impulses.

History

• *Dating.* [Early 1971. It's not long after the events of "Doctor Who and the Silurians", as the Doctor's still brooding.] The British police cars are white now, but still pre-Panda.

By this point Britain has its own incredibly advanced space programme, Mars Probe 7 being the latest to put astronauts on the Martian surface. [The first manned flight to Mars would have occurred in the late '60s, which suggests the first manned flight to the moon took place a lot earlier than 1969. General Carrington was an astronaut on Mars Probe 6 and is now head of the new Space Security section, suggesting the last mission was perhaps around a year ago. But we're not told which of the Mars Probes was the first to actually put people on the planet's surface; the early mis-

How Believable is the British Space Programme?

...continued from page 21

Duncan Sandys' spending review killed off "Blue Streak" and "Mustard" in 1962. This, more than any technical matter, was why the space race became a two-horse one. However, the set-up presented in "The Ambassadors of Death" and "The Android Invasion" (13.4) posits a UK space department more like the BBC than NASA. If such a body had existed, and pooled various projects from university departments and aerospace companies instead of setting them to compete for a contract, only to cancel it when things got too expensive, then the trajectory envisaged for British aerospace in the 1951 Festival of Britain guidebook (with the moons of Saturn in our grasp by 2001) is more viable.

A semi-independent space quango, co-ordinating smaller projects with clear objectives, seems to have been all that was missing. As "Blue Streak" became embroiled in red tape, resulting in protracted discussions about who got to see which bit of the blueprint, the bills mounted and defence priorities over-rode those of prestige or employment. Yet, as Concorde showed, national pride and a set task can achieve wonders.

Specifically, the fictional Mars programme seems to have benefited from one of the other key discoveries in '70s Doctor Who: some kind of effective anti-radiation treatment. In addition, the problems of prolonged microgravity and the detrimental effect on bones and muscles must have been overcome. Soviet biologists devoted whole careers to this, so the apparent thawing of the Cold War in the Doctor Who universe must have yielded a peace dividend long before such things happened in our world.

As with "Inferno", the main implausibility of the scenario in "The Ambassadors of Death" is that it all takes place in the south of England. Aside from Woomera, the logical place for launch and landing would have been as close to the Equator as possible, perhaps British Colombia or Uganda. Many Foreign Office field stations in these locations were kept "on ice" after the 1940s, and would have been highly suitable.

---

sions could have been unmanned. In a world where the authorities have some inkling of the potential alien threat to Earth, it makes sense for more resources to be put into space exploration. See **How Believable is the British Space Programme?**] Video and computer technology are also surprisingly advanced, for either the early '70s or the late '70s.

Mars Probe 6 was the first mission to encounter the aliens, who inadvertently killed General Carrington's fellow astronaut [Carrington didn't tell the authorities about the aliens, but set his own agenda to destroy them as head of Space Security]. Mars Probe 7 took off from Mars nearly eight months ago, and is now only a few hours' rocket-travel from Earth. Recovery 7 and Recovery 8 take off here, although the latter wasn't scheduled to go into space for another three months. [If Recovery units are sent out to meet returning capsules which can't get back to Earth on their own, then there's at least one other mission going on at this point.]

The American space agency is also capable of preparing space missions at short notice. Carrington, as Space Security head, liases with a security council in Geneva. [But compare this with 6.3, "The Invasion", in which Britain doesn't seem to have any rocket capability at all.]

On the whole, the general public doesn't know about the existence of aliens despite the Yeti, Cyberman and Auton incidents. But since TV presenter John Wakefield makes a worldwide live broadcast about the alien UFO, interrupted by gunfire and the sound of Carrington shouting 'we're being invaded', a lot of people must be getting suspicious. [Possibly the authorities pass it off as an Orson-Welles-style hoax, assuming nobody blocked the transmission.] There's no indication that humans have found any trace of the Ice Warriors on Mars.

The SOS signal was done away with 'years ago'. [In the real world it was done away with in 1985.]

The Analysis

Where Does This Come From? Another action serial in Quatermass clothing, "The Ambassadors of Death" is Doctor Who at its most gun-heavy, set in a world of international espionage rather than pure fantasy (complete with occasional jazzy saxophone music, a la The Man from UNCLE or Breathless). More noticeable, though, is all the messing-around in space.

Doctor Who was never really a "space" programme, but as one of its heydays occurred during the moon-race it couldn't help being tempted

ABOUT TIME 1970-1974

sometimes. As ever, the British love of the amateur over the professional always comes through. Those pesky Americans and Russians think they're clever, but we've got an eccentric scientist who can stroll into any high-security space centre and pilot the latest piece of rocket technology to Mars without a single day's training. (It's worth pointing out that episode five, in which the Doctor attempts to rescue three astronauts stranded in orbit, was shown in the same week as the Apollo 13 crisis. If things hadn't gone well for the American astronauts then it's doubtful the last few episodes would have been broadcast at all.)

It's also one of the very few space-based *Doctor Who* stories to flirt with realism, at least making an attempt to get all the "bits" looking right. In the end, of course, the needs of TV drama stop it going the distance and it only takes a day or so for the Great British Mars Programme to prep a rocket for the Doctor.

In fact, many of the technical aspects on show here come from Project SETI as much as from Apollo. Started in 1960, SETI's purpose was (and is) to listen out for alien life and signal it using pictograms, q.v. the aliens' radio signals here. The accurate names of the radio-telescopes show that someone working on "The Ambassadors of Death" had done his homework on First Contact scenarios. This, and the factoid about the number of planets capable of supporting intelligent life, suggests that the production team had a much more well-read audience in mind than it did when making earlier stories like "The Seeds of Death" (with its rather haphazard, children's-TV approach to Yuri Gagarin and Leonardo da Vinci).

It's also worth mentioning General Carrington, the Enoch Powell[1] of space exploration. As a villain he's primarily a way of putting the Doctor's "gentleman of time and space" persona up against a paranoid, xenophobic warmonger, but really it's impossible to look at things in context and not see some link with the politics of the era. In 1970, the UK press was paranoid about immigration from Pakistan, the first West-Indian-British generation growing up alongside the children of Middle England, and "repatriation" becoming part of the popular language. Simultaneously, *Doctor Who* presents us with a villain who's terrified of his planet being infected by people who actually turn out to be quite civilised. Like Enoch, just two years earlier in 1968, he foresees rivers of blood. And even if Carrington tries to justify what he

does in purely military terms, the fact that he perceives the menace as a creeping, insidious horror - not a new Armada - says plenty. (Compare this with Malcolm Hulke's debut on the series, 4.8, "The Faceless Ones".)

Things That Don't Make Sense Even given that space exploration in the *Doctor Who* universe is vastly in advance of the real world; and even given the presence of the mysteriously powerful "M3 variant" rocket-fuel, the rockets of the 1970s are so fast that a mission from Earth can somehow go into a terminal orbit of the sun within fifteen minutes. (Compare with 4.6, "The Moonbase".) Actually, what's strangest about this is the complete disregard for launch-windows, given the Doctor and Cornish choose a launch-time to suit their own agenda, not the orbital period of Mars Probe 7.

According to the map that Sergeant Benton uses, the launch-site is right next to Heathrow Airport. In fact he points to Windsor Castle, near enough. And speaking of Benton... who actually kills Professor Lennox? It isn't Carrington - whom the Professor would recognise - and nor can it be the thug Reegan, who's displaying an unlikely knowledge of rocket-science elsewhere at the time. This means, amusingly, that Benton appears to be the chief suspect. (Possibly an earlier draft of the script had the Brigadier's right-hand man turn out to be a traitor, before the decision was made to re-introduce Benton to the series?)

In episode six even Carrington refers to the people in spacesuits as 'aliens', even though he's been trying to keep up the pretence that they're the astronauts. No-one picks him up on this. And considering that it's designed to kill both the Doctor and Dr. Taltalian, the time-bomb in the space centre's computer room really is a shockingly weak piece of ordnance. It doesn't even destroy the table it's sitting on.

Critique An obvious attempt to pitch *Doctor Who* at an older audience, with a plot that flirts with at least two different genres (shady government thriller vs. radioactive things from outer space), only resorting to a more child-like and '60s-style kind of fantasy TV when it wants to gloss over the fiddly details of space travel. It's smart, complex and even atmospheric, but like the rest of Season Seven it's also just too long. Much as it tries to use its extra weight to suggest something bigger and broader than a standard four-parter, there are signs of shameless padding in the middle, especially when Liz Shaw escapes from her kidnappers and then gets recaptured ten minutes later.

It's also another scientific-installation-in-crisis story, coming right on the heels of "Doctor Who and the Silurians", although this time the Doctor's attempts to stop an inter-species war actually get somewhere. The story's conclusion, with General Carrington revealed as a desperate, terrified man who genuinely thinks he's got a duty to save the world, is unusually humanistic even by modern TV standards. The script (rightly) feels that it doesn't have to kill him to leave the audience with a sense of justice, and the Doctor even seems to feel sympathy as he's led away. Nevertheless, as with the rest of its season, there's a lasting impression of "stunt of the week" here.

The Facts

Written by David Whitaker (and Malcolm Hulke, uncredited, then drastically re-written by Trevor Ray). Directed by Michael Ferguson. Viewing figures: 7.1 million, 7.6 million, 8.0 million, 9.3 million, 7.1 million, 6.9 million, 5.4 million.

Only episode one survives in full colour, though the 2002 BBC video release also features recovered and re-coloured clips from the remaining episodes.

Supporting Cast Ronald Allen (Ralph Cornish), Robert Cawdron (Taltalian), John Abineri (General Carrington), Ric Felgate (Van Lyden), Michael Wisher (John Wakefield), Dallas Cavell (Quinlan), James Haswell (Corporal Champion), Derek Ware (Unit Sergeant), William Dysart (Reegan), Cyril Shaps (Lennox), John Lord (Masters), James Clayton (Private Parker), Peter Noel Cook (Alien Space Captain), Peter Halliday (Aliens' Voices), Geoffrey Beevers (Private Johnson).

Working Titles "Carriers of Death", "Invaders From Mars".

Cliffhangers In the space centre's computer room, Dr. Taltalien unexpectedly pulls a gun on the Doctor and Liz; the Doctor orders the Recovery 7 capsule to be cut open, even though the villains have promised a "surprise" inside; Liz Shaw, chased by General Carrington's men, tries to escape over a bridge and ends up toppling over the railing towards the water; the Doctor finds the body of Sir James in the man's office, unaware that one of the alien astronauts is moving in on him from behind the door; the Doctor's Recovery craft links up with Mars Probe 7, just as the half-mile-long alien ship appears and heads straight for him; General Carrington, finally revealed as the villain, puts a gun to the captive Doctor's head and apologises for having to do his 'moral duty'.

The Lore

• David Whitaker's original story outline, "Invaders from Mars", was first pitched in 1968 and went through various troubled re-writes before it became "The Ambassadors of Death". Whitaker's attempts to keep pace with the series format he'd helped to create were further complicated when he moved to Australia in mid-draft. Assistant script editor Trevor Ray received £150 for his dogged attempts to harmonise the various re-writes. Script editor Terrance Dicks thanked an unhappy Whitaker for all his work, and pointed out that part one had been shown at an international drama conference 'to great acclaim'. Presumably this is why that episode was spared the BBC's cull.

• Havoc, the programme's regular stunt-crew, get a whole scene of their own in episode one so that you can get to know them all by sight for future reference. They broke the record for the highest stunt fall in the UK twice in one year (Derek Ware's record from "Inferno" stood for around seven years, despite all the Bond films), and in subsequent interviews they never let anyone forget it.

• Wakefield - the anxious, bespectacled, goatee-wearing TV presenter at space control - is played by Michael Wisher, making his debut in the series. Five years later, without the glasses or facial hair, he'll be the first Davros.

7.4: "Inferno"

(Serial DDD. Seven Episodes, 9th May - 20th June 1970.)

Which One is This? A drilling project to reach the centre of the Earth releases green primordial slime that turns people into ape-creatures and then destroys the planet, but fortunately only in an "evil" parallel universe. The Doctor therefore has to explain the plot in two separate dimensions to two separate Brigadiers, one of whom has an eye-patch to prove he's a fascist.

Firsts and Lasts Last appearance of Liz Shaw, who vanishes between seasons and never even gets a proper goodbye scene. Last appearance of the original TARDIS console, which had served the programme faithfully since 1963 but disappears in the great TARDIS re-fit of Season Eight. This is also the last ever seven-part *Doctor Who* story, since by this point the BBC had concluded that if the first episode of any story got higher ratings than the rest, it made sense to do more stories every year.

The Doctor uses bizarre martial arts, specifically Venusian karate, for the first time. This means it's the first time he gets to shout 'hai!'. "Inferno" is also the first time that stuntman Terry Walsh doubles for Pertwee in a fight scene (wearing an asbestos suit).

Seven Things to Notice About "Inferno"...

1. The Doctor's various face-offs with the evil eyepatch-wearing Brigadier, with both Jon Pertwee and Nicholas Courtney clearly enjoying the job far too much. The Brigade-Leader's best line, when the Doctor insists that he doesn't exist in this world: 'Then you won't feel the bullets when we shoot you.'

2. While by contrast… the opening scene, in which two technicians exchanging pleasantries outside the Inferno station ('sounds more like a flipping dentist!'), might actually feature the worst acting in the series' whole run. And they're obviously both trying not to wet themselves laughing.

3. Unusually, for much of this story the central characters aren't the Doctor and his companion but drilling expert Greg Sutton and project assistant Petra Williams, who play out a kind of love story against the backdrop of the world / s ending. (Greg, in particular, speaks for the audience in the first few episodes. He's the newcomer around here, while the Doctor's already a permanent fixture at the Inferno project and doesn't need things explained to him. Really it's the first time the series has tried this approach since 1.1, "An Unearthly Child". Which is ironic, as the actor playing Greg also appeared in "An Unearthly Child" as one of the cavemen. He's evolved a bit since then, but he's still oozing testosterone.)

Fans of '70s television will notice that even though Greg and Petra represent the two great TV stereotypes of the era - the loud-mouthed womanising wide-boy and the pretty-but-computer-brained feminist - here they balance each other out nicely and somehow it never turns into a sit-com.

4. All the guns fired in the exterior scenes make "spaaaang" noises apparently lifted straight from a record of Wild West sound effects, while the Doctor's car makes exactly the same cartoon "screeeeech" every time it turns a corner. On a similar note, a radio news broadcast in episode five is quite clearly performed by Jon Pertwee, doing a funny voice to save the BBC the expense of paying another actor. (This scene was actually omitted from the original BBC transmission, perhaps because nobody in their right mind could possibly be fooled by it. But it re-appeared in time for the video release, as well as the version of the story shown in the US and Australia.)

5. The "fascist" version of the Inferno project has, predictably, an all-white staff. In the "normal" world there's a pleasingly nearly-futuristic ethnic mix of anciliary staff. However, nobody seems to have told them that they're playing technicians. The climax of episode seven has one in particular milling around in shot as if he's trying to see himself on the monitor.

6. As part of Season Seven's ongoing attempt to find clever new ways of messing around with the opening credits, the title "Inferno" is projected over some nice stock footage of erupting volcanoes.

7. And once again, the props people responsible for putting up signs have trouble with the spelling ("megga-volts"…).

What's Wrong with the Centre of the Earth?

According to "Inferno", (a) anybody who drills all the way through the Earth's crust will unleash forces capable of destroying the planet and (b) the core is surrounded by a mutagenic green slime which turns people into primordial ape-creatures. Leaving aside the question of why the Daleks don't release this holocaust when they start hollowing out the planet in "The Dalek Invasion of Earth" (2.2), it all seems remarkably odd even by *Doctor Who* standards, especially since the script of "Inferno" never even attempts an explanation.

The implication, however, is that this sort of thing is perfectly natural. "Inferno" was made at a time when popular culture was only just getting the hang of environmental "issues", when the world's general publics were beginning to realise that modern life was causing major eco-problems but didn't know enough science to get a grip on the consequences. The Doctor puts his finger on it when he talks about 'this planet screaming out its rage'. The suggestion is that things are going wrong because nature's been violated, and more, that the Earth itself is a form of super-organism (basically a version of the Gaia myth, always a popular theme in fantasy, especially since the '60s).

But to be honest, the Gaia-version of "Inferno" doesn't make a lot of sense, not in terms of science and not even in terms of pseudo-science. What are the powers-beyond-imagining that the Doctor refers to when he tries to stop the drilling project? Why would a single hole in the crust doom the entire world? And most of all: how could a slime buried twenty miles under the surface transform human beings into ape-people?

Unless you can swallow the idea that the Earth has some conscious, deliberate plan of its own, it's hard to imagine any naturally-occurring substance might do this. Where would it find the genetic information to transform humans into ape-things, when it must pre-date all animal life on Earth by billions of years? If it just brings out dormant apeman DNA in human beings, then how does it alter all the victim's genes and force the subsequent biological changes within just a few minutes? And if the Earth doesn't want to be disturbed, then why does the goo make the primords more determined to complete the drilling process instead of stopping it?

There is, in short, something very unnatural about all of this. Taking into account that the Daemons, Osirians, Exxilons, Silurians, Jagaroth and sundry psychic parasites massively influenced the *Doctor Who* version of Earth, and as the Gaia perspective is now tragically unfashionable, it seems more than likely that somebody *put* that green slime down there.

Though not wholly canonical, the 1990s *Doctor Who* novels have a lot to say about this, often without actually realising it. The following may therefore be described as "hugely speculative".

Neil Penswick's *The Pit* (1993) reveals that during the earliest days of the Time Lords, Rassilon's TARDIS experiments inadvertently tore awkward holes in the fabric of the universe. It was from these holes that the Great Vampires emerged (see 18.4, "State of Decay"), as well as the Yssgaroth, a particularly chronic extra-universal invader with the habit of corrupting everything it touched. According to the original background of Ben Aaronovitch's *So Vile a Sin*, Rassilon and his contemporaries put various temporal "structures" in place to seal these holes, the implication being that Earth is in some way part of one of these structures.

This idea eventually ended up being recycled for the later BBC novel *Interference*, which doesn't add much to the set-up but does explicitly establish that protective "shells" were placed around the holes made by the early Time Lords, and that these shells could eventually form the cores of planets. Presumably meaning that if these shell-worlds were to be cracked open, then the ancient evil would start to leak out again, altering the bodies of its victims in much the same way that the Great Vampires did. (It's also notable that both *The Pit* and *Interference* describe horrors like the Yssgaroth as being a hostile form of matter rather than as life-forms per se, matter which consciously corrupts human biology just by its presence. The dead giveaway is that the slime defies the most basic law of physics, the Second Law of Thermodynamics, by remaining hot no matter how long it's exposed to a cooler environment.) There would, in short, be something horribly mutagenic buried under the earth.

It may be a long shot, but it needed to be said.

This might be the time to mention that the idea of matter from "another universe" causing human mutation has a curious echo in 13.2, "Planet of Evil". Science-pedants might also like to note that the meteor (or anti-matter freighter) which hit the Earth 65,000,000 years ago, wiping out the dinosaurs, is now believed to have penetrated the planet's crust. So the primitive Silurians probably had to deal with lizard-primords as well. Unless, that is, the Silurians were *descended* from lizard-

continued on page 29...

The Continuity

The Doctor The Doctor initially sees nothing wrong with the idea of tapping the Earth's core for energy, even though he must at least suspect there's nothing in recorded history about human beings using this sort of power source. He certainly doesn't have any idea what's really down there. Nor is he aware of the existence of parallel universes before now, though he surmises that the alternative Earth he visits is a 'parallel space-time continuum' and a 'twin world'. [The existence of parallel universes is such a massively significant piece of information that it's impossible to believe the Time Lords are ignorant of it, especially as it only takes a little tinkering with the TARDIS console to move the Doctor between dimensions. Do the Time Lords suppress this sort of knowledge, or have the Doctor's memory lapses wiped out the relevant data?]

He believes he can't take people from the doomed world back to the one he knows, because it would create a 'dimensional paradox' and endanger all the universes. [This is even more peculiar. How does he know this, if he hasn't heard about parallel universes before? Does he have experience of other dimensions which aren't parallel universes, but something even stranger? And why doesn't his *own* presence in the other universe cause a dimensional paradox, since he presumably has a counterpart there even if he isn't on Earth? Are Time Lords protected from this sort of thing?] He suggests the other dimension is 'sideways' in time [much as in 26.1, "Battlefield"], and concludes there's an 'infinity' of universes, defined by the conscious choices of their inhabitants.

The Doctor can use Venusian karate to briefly paralyse or knock out humans, with just a couple of fingers near the victim's throat. [Odd that a martial art invented by another species is so good at finding the human body's weak spots. Maybe Venusian martial arts have a philosophical "zen" element, and the Doctor's just applying the same philosophy on Earth.]

His normal pulse is 170 [85 per heart?], and his hearts can beat at different rates. He personally persuaded executive director Sir Keith Gold to allow UNIT, and specifically himself, to "observe" the Inferno project. [Perhaps it's around this time that he joins the various gentlemen's clubs he claims to belong to later, e.g. "Terror of the Autons" (8.1).]

• *Ethics*. Fixing the TARDIS is still the Doctor's main concern. So much so that when nobody at the Inferno project listens to him, he gets stroppy and goes back to his experiments even though there's a lethal menace threatening the centre. [This blows a hole in the image of the Doctor as an all-out hero, and here saving individual lives isn't as important to him as we might expect. Seeing the Earth (or *an* Earth) die by fire actually seems to be a turning-point for him. In the end the Inferno acts as a kind of purgatory, reminding him of his responsibilities after he turns his back on the petty humans. The things he witnesses on the parallel Earth have become one of his greatest fears by "The Mind of Evil" (8.2), and technically he helps the Inferno project on both worlds before realising the danger of penetrating the crust, so he may even feel guilty about the billions of deaths involved.]

• *Background*. The Doctor was present during the eruption at Krakatoa in 1883, and recognises the sound made by the slime-transformed ape-men ("the primords") even though he apparently doesn't recognise the primords themselves. He regards the royal family as 'charming', and knew the Queen's grandfather in Paris. [Given the Doctor's liking for big social events, he most probably met the future Edward VII at the International Exhibition of 1889. The year Edward opened the Eiffel Tower.]

The Supporting Cast

• *Liz Shaw*. She's now helping the Doctor to work on the TARDIS console, and seems to understand the process rather than just handing the Doctor his tools.

• *Sergeant Benton*. Now acting as the Brigadier's right-hand man. It's at this point that he becomes a regular member of the Doctor's circle [although it's doubtful he has an "official" position as the messenger between the Brigadier and the rest of UNIT, since traditionally a higher-ranking officer would fill that role, as Captain Yates does in Season Eight].

The TARDIS The Doctor can use nuclear power from the Inferno project to fuel the TARDIS console, but states its storage units always have some energy left [demonstrating it's no longer "in touch" with the Ship's power source]. An energy overload sends it across dimensions [the Doctor's amnesiac

What's Wrong with the Centre of the Earth?

...continued from page 27

primords. One final piece of conjecture, then: if the object which hit the planet at the end of the Cretaceous cracked open the crust, then the crack would have happened on what's now the coastline of Mexico, straddling both the land and the water. So it's easy to imagine the resultant green slime turning ceratopsids and giant turtles into grunting, bestial reptile-people, from which the Silurians and Sea Devils - respectively - might have developed. If nothing else, this would at least explain how the Silurians got all the way from "dinosaur" to "upright-walking reptile with hands" without leaving any traces in the fossil record.

tinkerings with the controls are at least partly responsible]. After further work the Doctor believes the TARDIS console to be fully operational, and he seriously seems to think it can get him off the planet [after returning to the TARDIS first, presumably], but in fact it just shifts him a few seconds forward in time and a short distance in space.

Operating the TARDIS console involves epsilon co-ordinates, a principle which Liz seems to understand. The rotor has taken a real beating, and barely seems to be holding together.

The Non-Humans

• *Primords*. The mutagenic substance which somehow makes its way up the pipes of the Inferno project - boiling green slime, basically - has an instant effect on human tissue [c.f. 10.6, "The Green Death"; 12.2, "The Ark In Space"; and so on]. The skin is stained green-blue, and within minutes the victim begins behaving in a primal, murderously violent fashion. Before long the full transition from human to primord takes place, although it can take longer if only a small amount of the substance was touched. The slime never cools. [See **What's Wrong with the Centre of the Earth?**. The name "primord" is never spoken, only appearing in the end credits, whereas the novelisation just refers to them as mutants. Since these mutants are a previously-unknown race, the word "primord" looks more like scriptwriter's shorthand than an attempt to properly designate them.]

Primords are recognisably human, but with ape-like swathes of hair around the face and body. They're so abnormally strong and tough, they can survive for minutes after being shot. They thrive on heat and can be killed by cold, while objects they touch can remain hot for more than a day. They seem to want to carry on the primord line by exposing more people to the green goo, but even people touched by primords are "infected". [No explanation is ever given for the slime's origin. Again, see **What's Wrong with the Centre of the Earth?**.]

Planet Notes

• *Earth*. The green mutagenic slime is found twenty miles below the surface, just above the crust, and the Doctor implies that some of it may have been released at Krakatoa. If the crust is penetrated, then the energy of the Earth's core will be released. Magma will flood the world and the Doctor believes that within weeks or even days, the planet will disintegrate into a ball of gases [followers of the BBC novels will note that David A. McIntee's *The Face of the Enemy*, which is in many ways an "Inferno" sequel, contradicts this and has the planet survive as a lifeless ball of lava]. There's a high-pitched whine just before penetration, which the Doctor describes as 'the sound of this planet screaming out its rage' [he's guessing at all of this]. The primords hear a similar noise in their heads.

• *Parallel Earth*. The alternative Britain is a republic and obviously a fascist state, policed by the Republican Security Forces and employing forced labour at the Inferno project. The Brigade-Leader refers to the Defence of the Republic Act, 1943, so Britain has been in this state for some time. [Assuming that such an act would have been passed shortly after the republic's creation, fascism either took root in the country in response to World War Two or (more plausibly) the same socio-economic forces which caused the War in our world. Perhaps tellingly, the script refers to "Stahlman" as "Stahlmann" in the parallel universe. The Nazis are nowhere to be seen, so the republic was most likely established around someone like Oswald Mosley[2]. Death-camps aren't a factor, although forced labour is. There's a hint that Sir Keith Gold is Jewish - the first draft of the story calls him "Mulvaney" - but nonetheless he runs a government-led investigation.]

This Britain evidently has a single leader, a serious-looking gentleman whose photograph appears on propaganda posters. The royal family has been executed.

[What's striking about this universe is that so many little things are similar. Liz Shaw made the decision to join the military rather than become a scientist, yet the implication is that up until this point her history had been more or less the same, even though this flies in the face of logic. A fascist-run Britain should have so many millions of life-changing differences, the odds against exactly the same Inferno staff and UNIT personnel ending up together in both universes are astronomical. There are two likely explanations. One: there's a "proper" timeline, and all parallel universes tend to automatically veer towards it. Two: this universe was deliberately engineered. The novel *Timewyrm: Revelation* takes this view, suggesting the Timewyrm engineered the whole thing just to get on the Doctor's nerves.]

History

• *Dating.* [1971.] According to the Brigade-Leader's desktop calendar, it's the 23rd of July by the end of the crisis. [Some have suggested that this story should actually take place before "The Ambassadors of Death", making Liz's exit smoother. Though the start of "Ambassadors" might make more sense if Liz has seen the Doctor vanish before, the Doctor's dialogue in "Ambassadors" pretty much proves it takes place right after "The Silurians".]

The project nicknamed the Inferno is the British government's latest plan to generate energy, with Professor Stahlman hoping to tap and harness pockets of "Stahlman's gas" beneath the Earth's crust. [It's never explained how anybody knows about Stahlman's gas. The Earth's crust hasn't been penetrated before, so its existence may only have been demonstrated theoretically, hence Stahlman's insistence that his 'theories' will soon be proved correct. But there's no indication here that such a gas actually exists, as it's certainly not the green slime, which is *above* the crust.]

The drilling project is in Eastchester, England.

Additional Sources Since Liz's disappearance is never satisfactorily explained, Liz-Shaw-departure stories have always been popular among fan-writers. At least one has appeared in professional print, Gary Russell's novel *The Scales of Injustice*

(1996). Meanwhile, Paul Cornell's novel *Timewyrm: Revelation* makes its own contribution to "Inferno" mythology by having the Doctor realise that the face he saw on the posters in the parallel world - the face of the republic's totalitarian leader - was one of the faces the Time Lords offered him at his trial (6.7, "The War Games"). Since there's no trace of the Doctor anywhere else on the alternative world, this makes a certain amount of sense, although it probably still doesn't explain why Jon Pertwee's voice is on the radio.

The Analysis

Where Does This Come From? Well, mix Conan-Doyle's *When the Earth Screamed* (Professor Challenger drills into the Earth, and it's alive and rather touchy) with the BBC's *Doomwatch*, add some werewolves, and this is the result.

Raymond Williams - reviewing both this story and *Doomwatch* in *The Listener* - commented on how far the men in lab-coats had replaced the Russians as the "enemy within", since nobody knew enough to question them. At least not in Whitehall, where an ignorance of how your car works is seen as proof that you're "the right sort of chap". *Doomwatch* was Kit Pedler and Gerry Davis' solo project outside *Doctor Who*, a paranoid science-thriller in which unchecked or government-accelerated research would backfire on an almost weekly basis. (*Doomwatch* stumped up half the cost of the Recovery 7 interior in "The Ambassadors of Death", then re-used it in an episode that also needed a space capsule, which shows how much the two series were running in tandem at this point.) But then, after Concorde and the groundbreaking nuclear power generators at Calder Hall, the "Big Science" stories on the news were generally about domesticating frontiers-of-science research. New power sources included.

Ah yes, the energy race. Today it's doubtful that many writers would start a script with a bunch of scientists trying to develop a new power supply. Apart from the fact that it's so passé, these days power just isn't interesting unless it goes wrong. But in 1970, news programmes were full of sexy, dynamic helicopter-shots of the new British oil-fields. The Queen had been making glorious speeches about the UK cracking nuclear power long before the Americans or the Russians. North Sea gas was still being installed in homes nationwide, the first time since the nineteenth century that the whole country had been given a new form of power en masse (see 5.6, "Fury from the Deep").

On top of that, the environmental movement was also picking up (as it were) steam, putting ideas like solar power into the world's mass-consciousness in a way which now seems positively charming. The Stahlman project comes across as a bastard hybrid of every power-dream and power-nightmare of the era, a cheap, natural energy source that involves the same kind of drilling you'd find on the latest hi-tech oil rigs, yet releases forces even worse than a nuclear meltdown.

The other half of "Inferno" is the parallel universe storyline. Alternative-world stories have a history that goes back centuries, yet many still maintain that "Inferno" deliberately rips off classic *Star Trek* 2.4, "Mirror, Mirror", which hadn't even been broadcast in Britain by 1970. In truth, "evil double" episodes were already a staple of TV adventure serials, and the scar-faced Brigadier owes as much to ITC as to space opera.

It's worth noting, though, that whereas *Star Trek*'s idea of an "evil" universe is a universe with an empire instead of a federation running everything - inspired by the American myth of a federal country born out of a revolution against the British - *Doctor Who*'s idea of an "evil" universe is one run by Nazis... Britain being a country that lives in the shadow of World War Two, something that's as true now as it was in the '70s. (American SF tends to treat fascist takeover as a remote hypothetical matter, since none of the writers grew up with a real threat of invasion. It's not as if anyone of that generation didn't wonder how Britain would have been if the Nazis had won. Enough books on the theme were published even in wartime, and the first of them pre-dates the Second World War by two years, in the form of Katherine Burdekin's 1937 *Swastika Night*.) With its UNITY IS STRENGTH posters, this fascist Britain is straight out of *1984*, or at the very least it's straight out of the BBC's TV adaptation of *1984*. An adaptation written by Nigel Kneale, creator of *Quatermass*, so what goes around comes around.

The Doctor's response when Greg Sutton sees the TARDIS console - 'what did you expect, some sort of space-rocket with Batman at the controls?' - is much-ridiculed these days, but quite honestly, it makes perfect sense in the context of an age when space-rockets were on the news all the time and TV heroes were expected to wear utility belts.

Things That Don't Make Sense The primords scorch anything they touch with intense heat, yet they all wear clothes that don't burn and they never leave charred footprints on the floor. [When someone becomes a primord, the atomic makeup of anything they're wearing changes along with them... maybe.] The Doctor takes no time at all in figuring out that anyone who touches a primord turns into a monster, but when Professor Stahlman touches the mutant slime, the Doctor responds with a casual 'I wouldn't have done that if I were you' instead of the more sensible 'everybody get away from this man right now'. Stranger yet, he becomes convinced that penetrating the Earth's crust will be a catastrophe two-thirds of the way through episode four, for no reason that's ever explained. One moment he's happy to lie back in his cell and wait, the next he risks everything in a last-ditch attempt to stop the countdown. [Has his amnesia been blinding him to the project's consequences, and if so then is his head clearing?]

The final scene sees the TARDIS console transporting the Doctor a few seconds forward in time and several hundred yards to the east. Yet after he disappears, it only takes him twenty seconds to walk back to the place where he started. [Maybe he really went a few seconds backward in time.] And why does the TARDIS console transport both the Doctor and Bessie to the parallel universe? If it only took Bessie because "she" was within range, then why doesn't it also take bits of the floor and small furnishings? [It's been suggested that the console only transports things which don't have a counterpart in the other world, but this doesn't really make any sense, given that a version of Bessie probably exists in the alternate Earth even if the Doctor doesn't own her.]

Returning from the parallel universe, the Doctor muses that 'free will is not an illusion after all', i.e. alternative worlds prove that choices made by intelligent beings really can affect the future. Thus proving the Doctor is either very, very confused or just an appallingly bad scientist. Apart from anything else, has the man never heard of quantum theory?

This project, like Wenley Moor, seems to have been going for years with full government backing. So if energy's at such a premium, then why proceed with a Mars programme? And now the Doctor's shut down both projects, all the country's energy is presumably being produced at the Nuton Power Complex... so let's just hope nothing bad happens there, eh?

Critique Really, it's got an unfair advantage right from the start. Thanks to the parallel universe, "Inferno" is one of the very few occasions when the series is free to show what happens when the Doctor *doesn't* save the day, and - uniquely - to tell a story against the backdrop of a world that's genuinely going to hell.

"Inferno" never leaves the grounds of the drilling project for a single scene, and the result is morbid, claustrophobic and stifling, with an atmosphere so sticky that even the strangely-coloured primords can't spoil it. Low-budget as much of it is, there's a sense of horror here that's almost unknown even in more recent "sophisticated" television, and Greg Sutton's hysterical reaction as fascist-Britain goes into meltdown (complete with an angry, sarcastic salute) really is *remarkably* intense for a family adventure series. It's worth pointing out that when evil-UNIT interrogates the Doctor, they don't use some kind of exotic mind-probe device but just subject him to brutal physical abuse.

While most "alternative world" stories in SF television are played for cheap laughs or shock value (e.g. modern *Star Trek*, in which every parallel universe episode seems an excuse for the lead actors to dress up in unexpected costumes), *Doctor Who's* longer format allows "Inferno" to tell a story that's actually worth telling. Once you've got over the surprise of seeing the supporting cast as a bunch of fascists, there's still a long way to go. As with the two stories preceding it, its one major flaw is that seven episodes is too long for *any* story, and as a result the characters constantly feel the need to re-establish their personalities by arguing about the same things several times over. But then, in fairness, the episodes were originally shown across seven weeks and much of the audience probably needed reminding.

The Facts

Written by Don Houghton. Directed by Douglas Camfield (probably). Viewing figures: 5.7 million, 5.9 million, 4.8 million, 6.0 million, 5.4 million, 5.7 million, 5.5 million.

Supporting Cast Olaf Pooley (Professor Stahlman / Director Stahlman), Christopher Benjamin (Sir Keith Gold), Derek Newark (Greg Sutton), Sheila Dunn (Petra Williams / Dr. Petra Williams), David Simeon (Private Latimer), Derek Ware (Private Wyatt), Walter Randall (Harry Slocum), Ian Fairbairn (Bromley).

Working Titles "Project Inferno", "Operation Mole-Bore", "The Mo-Hole Project".

Cliffhangers Harry Slocum, formerly a project technician and now the first of the primords, bursts in on the Doctor and company inside the Inferno power room; Liz and the Brigadier enter the Doctor's hut, in time to see him vanish along with the TARDIS console; as the Doctor tries to fix the warning computer on "evil" Earth, the alternate Benton puts a gun to his head and asks whether he's going to go to the firing squad quietly or get shot here and now; while the Inferno project counts down to zero, the Doctor attempts to sabotage it but just finds himself at the end of Stahlman's pistol; trapped in the Inferno station on a disintegrating world, the Doctor is just about to suggest a way out when a primord starts to smash its way through the door; an immense wall of lava bears down on the hut where the Doctor and party are trying to re-activate the TARDIS console (an unusual cliffhanger for the series, because this is one time when you know that most of them *aren't* going to escape in the next episode).

The Lore

• Like "The Ambassadors of Death", "Inferno" was a holdover from Season Six, and appears to have been the contingency plan for ending *Doctor Who* - permanently - with the end of the world.

• Due to a misunderstanding later resolved, director Douglas Camfield refused to work with *Doctor Who's* regular composer Dudley Simpson. The music for this story is taken from stock, notably the 1967 *BBC Radiophonic Workshop* disc (listen for the crackles) and Delia Derbyshire's compositions "Blue Veils and Golden Sands" and "The Delian Mode". This is, in fact, the very last story to feature music entirely taken from stock.

• Barry Letts states that Camfield was taken gravely ill, and that he himself stepped in to direct the studio work. None of the cast recalls this, and the editing in particular shows resemblances to Camfield's style rather than Letts' (e.g. the cut from Slocum about to clout the guard to Benton hammering in a nail). Many of the cast were Camfield "repertory company" regulars, such as Ian Fairburn (technician Bromley), Derek Newark

(Greg Sutton) and Sheila Dunn (Petra Williams). Although he took a break from *Doctor Who* after this, Camfield is also said to have been instrumental in the casting of Jon Pertwee.

• The location work, done at the Wiggins Teape factory, involved a strict non-smoking policy due to the inflammable materials. Gum-chewing is said to account for the crew putting on a stone per head.

• Another connection between the BBC's version of *1984* and "Inferno": in *1984*, Big Brother was represented by a picture of Jack Kine, head of the special effects department at the time. This story's Effectsnik, Len Hutton (not the cricketer), decided to follow suit and lent his face to the UNITY IS STRENGTH posters here.

• The *real* Operation Mo-Hole (see **Working Titles**) was a ship-borne drilling project (through the Mohorovic Discontinuity, a fissure in the Pacific seabed) designed to take core-samples and provide a basis for dating mineralogical specimens. Officially. However, when writer Don Houghton tried to get any information about the project he ran into US government opposition... as did the Natural History Museum when he contacted them. Three years of this led to him speculating on what they found, hence "Inferno".

• Though it's the intention of this volume to be a *complete* collection of the lore of *Doctor Who*, the authors find themselves incapable of re-telling the anecdote about the eyepatches.

8.1: "Terror of the Autons"

(Serial EEE. Four Episodes, 2nd January - 23rd January 1971.)

Which One is This? Killer toys, killer chairs, killer plastic daffodils, killer telephone flexes, killer policemen with rubber faces and killer carnival dolls, plus a showdown at a radio-telescope with a brand new Time Lord arch-enemy and an *awful* lot of explosions.

Firsts and Lasts The story which sets up the recurring cast and recurring themes for the rest of the UNIT era, now that all the various scientific installations of Season Seven are out of the way. Here we see the first appearance of Jo Grant, *the* archetypal ask-lots-of-questions-and-get-captured companion; the first appearance of Captain Yates, the Brigadier's new right-hand man; the first time we hear "Greyhound" and "Trap One" used as UNIT radio call-signs, as well as the first time UNIT's people wear regular uniforms; and the first appearance of the "classic" UNIT lab, the Third Doctor's natural environment.

Behind the scenes it's the first story filmed two-episodes-per-fortnight rather than one a week, as well as the first in which the entire soundtrack was performed on the EMS Synthi 100 - the "Delaware" - and post-synched to existing footage instead of being composed in advance and played back during recording.

But yes, above all else: it's the first appearance of the Master.

Four Things to Notice About "Terror of the Autons"...

1. Obviously happy with the way the new CSO technique had turned out in Season Seven (see 7.2, "Doctor Who and the Silurians"), here the production team decides it can use modern effects technology to do almost *anything*. Why build sets that are only going to be used once, when you can magically slip a colour photo into the picture behind the actors and make it look as if they're really standing inside an Auton factory? Why build a complicated fully-working "death doll", when you can put an actor in a full-size "death doll" suit and use video effects to shrink him?

As a result, here CSO's used to depict everything from a shrunken corpse in a lunchbox to the views out of various car windows. (The original colour version of "Terror of the Autons" has long been lost, and the version available on BBC video (1993) has been digitally re-coloured. This is, perhaps, a mercy as the little blue lines are so much less noticeable.)

2. Episode three sees a confrontation between UNIT and the Autons in an quarry, the first time that a quarry appears in the programme *as* a quarry rather than (say) as an alien planet. Typical of *Doctor Who*, the final battle to prevent the invasion of Earth comes down to a bunch of soldiers shooting at a bus in a field.

3. The Doctor's lovely response to the Time Lords' messenger, who describes the Master's worse-than-nuclear volatiser trap as "amusing": 'Then you'd better find a witty way of dealing with it.' Not to mention the Master's sanitised account of McDermot's death, after an Auton plastic seat suffocates the man: 'He sat down in this chair here, and... just slipped away.' (Note also that for once the henchman, Rex Farrell, gets a brilliantly dry punchline to McDermott's surreal murder.)

4. But best of all... when Jo ruins his experiment, the Doctor - believing her to be UNIT's catering woman - delivers the greatest insult in television history: 'You ham-fisted bun-vendor!'

The Continuity

The Doctor Right from the start there's an obvious rivalry between the Doctor and the Master, and it's felt on both sides. The Doctor describes his opponent as an 'unimaginative plodder', even though the Master's degree in cosmic science was of a higher class than his, while the Master believes curiosity to be the Doctor's weakness [the Doctor admits as much later in his career]. The two Time Lords clearly enjoy playing games with each other at this stage, as the Master's already devising over-complicated death-traps and the Doctor admits to 'looking forward' to the coming duels between them, despite the carnage that's bound to be involved. [See the **Lore** of 11.5, "Planet of the Spiders", for more on why this might be.]

Only the tea-lady and the Brigadier's personal staff are allowed access to the Doctor's lab. Benton calls the Doctor 'sir', and the Brigadier describes him as a scientific consultant to UNIT. He claims to belong to the same club as Lord "Tubby" Rowlands, the man in charge of a ministry department with some bureaucratic influence over UNIT, although he's probably bluffing.

• *Ethics*. The Doctor didn't destroy the Nestene energy unit that survived the last invasion attempt [7.1, "Spearhead from Space"] because it would have felt 'like murder', even though he *did* kill the rest of the Nestene presence on Earth without compunction.

• *Inventory*. The Doctor seems to instinctively home in on the Master's TARDIS when he sees it, despite the fact that it's disguised as a horse-box, although he carries a small box-shaped listening device which he uses to check the machine's true nature. He has a wallet, but no money.

The Supporting Cast

• *Jo Grant*. The Doctor's new assistant, provided by UNIT, is introduced as a cute, vaguely hapless but more-than-enthusiastic girl [the emphasis is on "girl", whereas Liz Shaw was firmly depicted as a "woman"] who's just there to pass the Doctor his equipment and ask lots of questions. She's also presented as a hip young thing who probably knows all the fashionable boutiques.

Josephine Grant failed general science at A-Level and got a job with UNIT thanks to relatives in high places [10.3, "Frontier in Space", specifies her uncle], though she's trained in cryptology, safebreaking and explosives. She basically wants to be a secret agent, and she's certainly good with locks and escapology. Though she's weak-willed enough for the Master to hypnotise her [for now], she's also determined, efficient and capable of overcoming her fear when needed [by Season Ten, experience has given her a lot more self-control]. She refers to the Brigadier as 'sir' for now. The Doctor warms to her remarkably quickly [she seems to appeal to his paternal side, assuming he's got one], tweaking her chin and calling her 'Jo' without being invited.

• *Liz Shaw*. She's gone back to Cambridge.

• *UNIT*. The Doctor orders his equipment from the scientific supply section of UNIT, run by a 'dolly Scotsman' called Mr. Campbell. The Brigadier sees it as a perfectly normal part of his job to capture alien technology for use in human weapons projects. He here uses a blue non-mili-

Season 8 Cast/Crew

- • Jon Pertwee (the Doctor)
- • Katy Manning (Jo Grant)
- • Richard Delgado (the Master)
- • Nicholas Courtney
  (Brigadier Lethbridge-Stewart)
- • Richard Franklin (Captain Yates)
- • John Levene (Sergeant Benton)

- • Barry Letts (Producer)
- • Terrance Dicks (Script Editor)

tary Austin 1100 as transport, like everybody's uncle used to have.

There's a river outside the window of the lab at UNIT HQ, handy for throwing bombs into. [Benton comments 'we'll get complaints' after the explosion, as if this HQ were part of a bigger complex occupied by non-UNIT personnel. An industrial estate, perhaps?]

• *Captain Yates*. The young, fresh-faced and rather upper-class officer now working on the Brigadier's personal staff, he already knows the Doctor by this stage. He apparently cleaned up after the last Nestene incident. Jo is calling him 'Mike' before long.

The Supporting Cast (Evil)

• *The Master*. It's immediately obvious that the Master's going to be a major villain, since the dark clothes, smouldering looks and sinister beard all say "Satan" the moment he steps out of his TARDIS.

It's not clear when the Master and the Doctor last met, but the Time Lord messenger states he'll almost certainly try to kill the Doctor after 'what happened last time'. Here the Master's presented as a fallen Time Lord who revels in power above all else, displaying a casual cruelty towards the "weak" human species. Yet he's also capable of petty spite - it's implied, though not stated, that he only picks Earth as his target to annoy the Doctor - and he apparently feels inadequate when up against his old acquaintance. However, he at least acknowledges the Doctor as an interesting adversary. Though obviously intelligent and usually quite rational, he often lets his anger cloud his judgement, while the Doctor believes vanity is his weakness. At this stage he's mostly po-faced as he goes about his work, showing only occasional moments of sly humour.

The Master is an accomplished hypnotist, mesmerising human beings without saying a word and giving them suicidal or homicidal instructions moments after meeting them. [A learned skill, not a Time Lord trait; the Doctor doesn't try the same kind of trick until 26.1, "Battlefield", although so many people end up trusting him for no good reason that he may have *some* knowledge in this field. Certainly, the Fourth Doctor can instantly mesmerise one of his own people in "The Invasion of Time" (15.6) and claims to have hypnotic powers in "The Power of Kroll" (16.5).] Away from the Master's influence, the hypnotised mind constantly attempts to free itself, and strong-willed subjects can resist him altogether. He knows all about Rossini, the circus owner, as soon as they meet [research rather than telepathy, but it *does* demonstrate how careful he is in his planning].

Weapons he employs include a rod-like device which can kill a man by shrinking him to just a few inches in height [not referred to as a "tissue compression eliminator" until 18.7, "Logopolis"] and a volatiser, a small canister with roughly the same power as a fifteen-megaton bomb. He can disguise himself with realistic masks of other human beings, and has a mask of his own face that turns one of his victims into a decoy. [The masks are almost certainly Nestene plastic, but he still has some left over in "The Mind of Evil", "The Claws of Axos" and "The Sea Devils". Here, the mask seems to have the ability to disguise his height.]

He claims he's 'usually referred to' as the Master. Both the Doctor and the Time Lords know him by that title.

The TARDIS(es) The Doctor is trying to repair the dematerialisation circuit of the TARDIS in an attempt to get the Ship working. [In "Spearhead from Space" the TARDIS doesn't work because the Time Lords have changed the dematerialisation *code*; see **What's Wrong with the TARDIS?** under 9.2, "The Curse of Peladon".] Steady-state micro-welding is involved in this work.

The Master's TARDIS is referred to as a TARDIS [q.v.2.9, "The Time Meddler"]. It's evidently in full working order, at least until the Doctor steals its dematerialisation circuit, although the circuit isn't compatible with his own vehicle as the Doctor needs a Mark One circuit and the Master's is a Mark Two. The Doctor seems to expect the Master's TARDIS to work with a Mark One circuit, but not *his* Mark One circuit [implying that the Time Lords actually messed around with parts of his TARDIS rather than just blanking his mind to keep him on Earth].

The Time Lords The Time Lord tribunal which tried the Doctor is still in existence, and capable of sending a messenger, who sports a bowler hat and umbrella to blend in with the locale, to warn him about the Master. The messenger appears out of nowhere with a TARDIS-style groaning noise, hovers in mid-air and knows that the Doctor is about to trigger one of the Master's death-traps. [If the Time Lords can transport people to and from specific points in space and time, and are so all-seeing that they know where the Master's planted bombs, then why on Earth can't they just find the Master and transport him into prison? There are clearly "rules" here, governing the amount of intervention the Time Lords can make in the outside universe, but it's impossible to guess what those rules are. See 12.4, "Genesis of the Daleks", for more of this sort of thing.]

The Doctor knows the messenger personally, recognising him on sight. The messenger claims to have come 29,000 light years to Earth. [If he comes straight from the Time Lord planet then this suggests it's near the centre of Earth's galaxy. The New Adventures take it as read that the Doctor's homeworld is close to the galactic core, but see "The Deadly Assassin" (14.3) for a possible complication.] Once the messenger's on Earth, he can vanish and re-appear again with a simple "pop" instead of all that wheezing and groaning.

Time Lords are, according to the Master, expected to die with dignity.

The Non-Humans

• *Nestenes*. A disembodied, mutually telepathic intelligence, according to the Doctor. He also suspects that their form [on a planet like Earth] is analogous to a cephalopod, even though he can't pronounce "cephalopod" properly. Nestenes can channel their energy to Earth and into one of their plastic meteorite-pods through a radio telescope.

The Nestenes change the molecular structure of plastic, energising it to turn it into quasi-organic matter, but it remains inert for most of the time. The Doctor suggests they can put life into *anything* plastic [i.e. after they've changed its structure; they can't animate any plastic item at will]. Given

Why is the Doctor Exiled to Earth?

In "The War Games" (6.7) the Time Lords do a number of things which don't make a lot of sense, at least given what we later learn about them. They accept the Doctor's argument that 'there is evil in the universe that must be fought', even though this would seem to contradict a philosophy they've held for millions of years. They allow him to keep his TARDIS, even though it's apparently stolen property. And they banish him to Earth in the twentieth century, claiming he has knowledge of the planet's 'problems', despite their policy of non-intervention.

Though this isn't proper Time Lord behaviour as we later come to know it, it makes sense in terms of "The War Games" itself. The more political, pro-actively-conservative Time Lord society we see in later stories hadn't shown itself by 1969. At this stage the Doctor's people are sterile, emotionless, not-quite-all-powerful gods, who treat the outside universe as a passing concern and are prepared to change their attitude towards it after a single lecture from the Doctor himself. Serene and high-minded, they're a long way from the petty back-stabbers of stories like "The Invasion of Time" (15.6).

But somehow we have to reconcile these two species of Time Lord. We have to ask - because that's our job - exactly why they think the Doctor's presence on Earth is such a good idea. Though the writers of the later Doctor Who novels treat the Time Lords as "arbiters" of time, overseeing the smooth-running of causality and making sure that history runs to schedule, this isn't the impression the series itself gives. The Time Lords frequently ignore accepted history and interfere in the universe's affairs, not simply to stop dangerous time-travel experiments which might damage the time-line (a generous reading of their behaviour in 22.4, "The Two Doctors") but also to make the universe more hospitable for their own kind (in 12.4, "Genesis of the Daleks" they act out of fear, not out of a duty to preserve history, and 15.5, "Underworld" establishes they adopted a non-interventionist policy out of guilt rather than causal reasons).

So the Doctor's time on Earth isn't a way of ensuring that the history of the 1970s sticks to the known timetable, as some have claimed. In fact

there's evidence in the series that the history of the universe is relatively fluid, and that the Time Lords aren't even sure how it's supposed to run. This is certainly the implication in "Genesis of the Daleks", not to mention the Doctor's comment in "The Daemons" that humanity now has the power to wipe itself out 'and probably will'.

If the Earth exile isn't set up out of a sense of duty, and isn't pure altruism either, then the most obvious explanation is that it's just a question of self-interest. It suits the Time Lords' own purposes for humanity to survive, and - not for the last time - they use the Doctor as a cat's-paw to avert a number of impending crises. The threats which are "due" (or just "likely") to menace the Earth are all suitably apocalyptic. Without intervention, the human world will be brought to an end by the Nestenes, or the Silurian bacteria, or the aliens who encounter Mars Probe 6, or the Inferno project, or Daleks from the twenty-second century (judging by "Genesis of the Daleks" this would be of particular concern).

The Doctor is presumably placed on Earth to deal with all of these problems, ideally suited to this particular task on the Time Lords' "to do" list thanks to his affinity with the planet. This at least explains why he's allowed to keep the TARDIS, a device which contains so much equipment that might prove essential to the job. When the Doctor regains his freedom in "The Three Doctors" (10.1), he assumes it's his reward for defeating Omega, but it seems likely that he's done everything he was sent to Earth to do anyway. The obvious irony is that on a local level the Doctor's presence actually causes more problems than it solves, since the Master only seems to pick Earth as his target because the Doctor's there. It's a safe bet that the Time Lords didn't see this coming, which might suggest - as many fan-writers have speculated - that when he first arrives the Master has recently escaped from a Time Lord prison. Statistically, only five of the eleven threats faced by Earth during the Doctor's exile are "natural" hazards rather than the result of meddling from renegade Time Lords.

This just leaves the question of how the Doctor is exiled. See **What's Wrong with the TARDIS?** under 9.2, "The Curse of Peladon".

---

the right equipment, the Doctor can "hack" the cellular programs of the Autons.

• Autons. Apart from the standard Auton mannequins, which here wear carnival-style head-pieces in order to mask their appearance… new

Autons used by the Master include a child's toy in the form of a hideous troll, which comes to life when exposed to heat and smothers anyone in the vicinity; a telephone cord which attempts to strangle its victim on receiving a specific signal; a self-inflating plastic chair, which folds up to suffocate the person sitting in it; and Master-designed "autojets", plastic daffodils which are activated by short-wave radio and programmed on a cellular level to home in on the nearest human face.

The Master plans to activate the flowers simultaneously, each one spraying a fast-setting plastic over its victim's nose and mouth. Carbon dioxide can dissolve this plastic. [Unlike the Autons in "Spearhead from Space", most of these new Autons aren't controlled by the Nestenes but require specific signals from outside sources. This might result from the limited Nestene presence on Earth this time.]

There are no Auton facsimiles here, although Auton mannequins can wear imperfect facemasks - not as good as the Master's? - to disguise themselves as human beings. One of the Autons has the power of speech, apparently channelling the Nestenes directly.

• *Lamadines.* According to the Doctor, Lamadines have nine opposable digits and pioneered the advanced engineering technique of steady-state micro-welding. Good for them.

History

• *Dating.* [Late 1971, probably around October. The Doctor's been working on the dematerialisation circuit for three months, and he was busy with the TARDIS console in "Inferno", so some time has passed. See **What's the UNIT Timeline?** under 8.5, "The Daemons".]

There's a National Space Museum in Britain, and the Nestene energy unit has been on display there. [Apart from the obvious breach of security, it's interesting that UNIT has no problem with museums displaying alien artefacts, when it keeps the existence of aliens under wraps most of the time. Possibly there's an "official" story to go with the energy unit, in an attempt to counter public rumour about the Auton menace.] It's suggested that the circus where the Master arrives is near Tarminster.

Additional Sources The history of the Doctor and the Master before "Terror of the Autons" is hinted at in the novels of David A. McIntee, most notably *The Dark Path* (1996), in which it's suggested that the Master's name (or nickname) is "Koschei" and that he only began to turn evil during an encounter with the Second Doctor. However, even devotees of the books can find this version of

events hard to swallow.

The Dark Path depicts the Master as originally being an "interested traveller" like the Doctor, who only begins to go off the rails after a series of disagreements and misunderstandings. Yet the character we see on-screen is a primal, irredeemable force of malice, coming across as the Doctor's "evil brother" (mythically, if not literally), and it's hard to believe that someone quite so sociopathic could have changed his nature either so easily or so late in his life.

"Terror of the Autons" implies that the rift between the two Time Lords goes back much further, pre-dating the series and probably going all the way back to their Academy days... which is what the writers in the '70s seem to have had in mind, even if it's barely ever referred to on-screen. It's also worth pointing out that Virgin Publishing only commissioned *The Dark Path* towards the end of the Missing Adventures' run, just as the company was about to lose its license to the BBC. It's questionable whether the Virgin editors would have risked a "Master origin" story if they'd had to live with the consequences. (The Big Finish audio adventure "Master" also delves into the pre-history of the Master and the Doctor, but its version of events is even harder to swallow, presenting a fairy-tale-like account of their younger days which doesn't really gel with the psychology of the on-screen characters at all. Since "Master" demonstrates that even the Doctor's memories of these events are unreliable, it's possible that the entire fable is invented by the personification of Death - the Doctor's chief nemesis in this story, alarmingly - as a way of distracting him.)

The original Target novelisation of "Terror of the Autons", another favourite of the pre-video age, is notable for its cover illustration of an enormous one-eyed Nestene octopus with a single huge claw reaching out over the radio-telescope station. Most *Doctor Who* fans now imagine this to be what a Nestene really looks like, even though no such octopus appears anywhere in the actual story.

The Analysis

Where Does This Come From? The Autons make their comeback, and bring even more evil-consumer-goods angst with them. If "Spearhead from Space" gives you the sense of a time when a nation of shopkeepers was starting to get edgy about big business and cheap mass-production (see 7.1 for more), "Terror of the Autons" pushes the point that one step further.

Here there's not just a suggestion that politicians and department stores might not be trustworthy, but that the danger might already be present in your own home. Once again, it's hard to believe Robert Holmes wrote the script as a deliberate parable about inexpensive plastic merchandise taking over the world - if anything, the main point of the exercise seems to be to scare small children - but once again, it's still hard to imagine "Terror of the Autons" hailing from any other era.

On a lighter note… it's worth mentioning the deeply peculiar plot structure of "Terror of the Autons". Though most of the Earth-bound stories see the Doctor spending time at UNIT HQ, at this point it's not simply a "home base" but a permanent centre of operations. Here he battles the Nestenes from the comfort of his own lab, biding his time, conducting research and receiving reports as if he's fighting a long-term military campaign with test-tubes. There are occasional daytrips to the outside world, generally leading to the obligatory explosions, car chases and shots of stuntmen falling into quarries, but these little excursions are spurious and don't seem to follow on from each other. As a result it's one of the least adventurous of the Third Doctor's adventures, as if the programme's found a balance between its "action" and "thriller" elements by having things on the outside move very very fast while things on the inside stay perfectly still.

Things That Don't Make Sense When the Master sets up the trap with the volatiser, so that it'll hit the floor and explode if anyone enters the radio-telescope installation, the Doctor deals with it by hurling himself through the door and catching the device in mid-fall. Rather than, say, climbing into the room through the great big window and picking it up at leisure. At the very least, wouldn't it have been polite to evacuate his friends from the area before taking the risk? It's not even clear how the Master set the trap up without getting himself "volatised", as he clearly didn't use the window route; it's sealed from the inside. [He must have done something complicated with his TARDIS.]

Jo goes from making out lists of plastics factories to personally creeping around Farrell's factory and spying on the Master within seconds of screen-time. Which is particularly impressive when you realise that she has no way of knowing

which plastics factory the Master's using. [Several days pass between scenes, and she's been creeping around *all* the factories on the list].

The Master himself starts his terror campaign by using pocket-sized devices as powerful as nuclear warheads, but then tries to kill the Doctor with an enormous bomb in a large box which barely ripples the water after it's thrown in the river. In fact, if he's got at least one volatiser and a weapon identified in the novelisation as a "Sontaran Fragmentation Grenade" (aah, childhood lore), then it's strange for him to be messing around with dolls, sofas, daffodils and sundry novelty items in the first place.

The Doctor immobilises the Master's TARDIS, which means it can't go anywhere without being (for example) hauled away by a truck. And the Doctor knows where it is. So when the Master ultimately escapes UNIT's clutches, why doesn't anybody think of going back to the circus site and impounding it before the Master can get there?

And though this present volume isn't usually concerned with actors fluffing their lines, we have to mention the painfully obvious botched dialogue in episode three. Mike Yates: 'I'd just gone out to fetch some cocoa.' The Doctor: 'Fetch a tin of *what*?'

Critique The visual equivalent of four packets of Skittles, giving the viewer a tartrazine and saccharine buzz: superficially lurid and exciting, but you miss having something more substantial afterwards. A story which feels as though Robert Holmes spent weeks thinking up good ways of creeping out the audience but no time at all working on a plot to string them together, "Terror of the Autons" ultimately comes down to a long series of set-pieces as the Master and the Doctor devise and disable threat after threat after threat. This makes it one of the era's most memorable stories, full of 'do you remember that bit where…?' moments, yet it's also very hard to get into as a coherent whole. (Some of the "pieces" don't even seem to fit together. The circus is a bit of a dead end, apparently included because somebody liked the idea of the Doctor going to the circus, and clashes uncomfortably with the rest of the story's production-line theme. Why start an Auton story in a circus when there's no plastic there…?)

Perhaps its most noticeable flaw is the ending, with the Doctor convincing the Master in just two sentences that the Nestenes will turn against him - it hasn't even *occurred* to him before now? -

which isn't particularly satisfying after an hour and a half of watching them try to out-manoeuvre each other. Roger Delgado doesn't yet get the chance to let rip as an arch-nemesis, mainly because he only comes face-to-face with the Doctor in the last episode.

The Facts

Written by Robert Holmes. Directed by Barry Letts. Viewing figures: 7.3 million, 8.0 million, 8.1 million, 8.4 million.

Supporting Cast Michael Wisher (Rex Farrel), Harry Towb (McDermott), David Garth (Time Lord), Christopher Burgess (Professor Philips), Andrew Staines (Goodge), John Baskcomb (Rossini), Stephen Jack (Farrel Senior), Barbara Leake (Mrs. Farrel), Terry Walsh (Auton Policeman), Pat Gorman (Auton Leader), Haydn Jones (Auton Voice).

Working Titles "The Spray of Death".

Cliffhangers Jo, acting on a hypnotic suggestion, tries to open the Master's bomb-box at UNIT HQ; in the back of the police car that's apparently rescued himself and Jo from Rossini's circus, the Doctor pulls away the face of one of the policemen to reveal the blank expression of an Auton mannequin; the Doctor receives a telephone call from the Master in his lab, at which point the flex on the 'phone tries to throttle him (leading to yet *more* hideous gurning from Jon Pertwee).

The Lore

• "Terror of the Autons" was considered one of the most controversial *Doctor Who* stories of its decade, meaning it was supposedly the one which startled the most children. Legend (often repeated by Terrance Dicks) insists younger viewers were scared to take their teddy-bears to bed in case they got strangled during the night, while the police were somewhat irked that after going to great lengths to improve their image amongst young people, some of their number were shown as murderous plastic mannequins in disguise. Yet despite questions allegedly being asked in the House of Lords, the *real* audience reaction was generally that the programme 'wasn't as scary as it used to be'. Long-running children's request show

Ask Aspel was just starting then, and throughout the '70s featured kids saying practically the same thing every year (see 17.3, "Creature From The Pit").

• Katy Manning got the part as the Doctor's new companion after attending the wrong audition and turning up late. Although she was completely wrong for the character they had in mind, the programme-makers rewrote Jo to suit her, even though Manning left her glasses off and "guessed" the script rather than reading it (see below). Famously, the audition scene - involving an evil pentagram in a church crypt - ended up written into the script of 8.5, "The Daemons".

• Robert Holmes' starting point for the story was a Christmas gift of a German Troll doll, so hideous that he deemed it something you'd only send to your worst enemy (he never said who gave it to him...).

• Around fifty actresses auditioned for the role of Jo, with the two names most frequently mentioned being Anouska Hemple and Shakira Baksh, which gives you some idea of the original conception for Jo. Whenever either of those names was mentioned in the press, which was quite often in those days, words like "sultry" and "sophisticated" tended to crop up. Gabrielle Drake (fresh from *UFO*) and Rula Lenska (later seen in 21.4, "Resurrection of the Daleks") were also among those who auditioned.

• Manning kept her extreme myopia a secret until the first day of location shooting, when she ran into a tree. Pertwee subsequently always held her hand in chase sequences; note how much faster this story's chase is than, say, "The Sea Devils" (9.3). Production manager Nicholas Howard John joked she could still be replaced, which appears to have been the point when Pertwee really became protective of her. (The production manager's sister had, as it happens, played Liz Shaw...)

• Richard Franklin was the second choice to play Mike Yates. Ian Marter got the part but didn't realise it was a recurring character. He had a prior commitment, so he declined. Barry Letts nevertheless kept his contact details (see 10.2, "Carnival of Monsters"; 12.1, "Robot" et seq).

• Nicholas Courtney was reportedly suffering from depression at the time and, it's said, needed some persuading to return to the series after the break. During filming, Letts noted his condition and sent him to a hospital, rewriting the ending so that Yates and a double could cover for his absence. (See 8.5, "The Daemons", for a curious parallel.) The main amendation to the script was the Brigadier's objection when the Doctor seems happy for the Master to escape. Had this remained, it might have been the only instance of the Brigadier taking the moral high ground over the Doctor.

• It was during the filming of this story that Pertwee began removing pages of the script not featuring the Doctor. Notoriously, he would sometimes proclaim 'thin script this week' during rehearsals, disconcerting his co-stars. Robert Holmes, meanwhile, was writing thin scripts. His plot breakdowns were about a third of the average length, causing some problems for script editor Terrance Dicks. (These two will have many such "creative differences". See 11.1, "The Time Warrior"; 13.5, "The Brain of Morbius", 15.1, "Horror of Fang Rock"…)

• Much more material of this story was filmed than was used. Cuts include the origin of the vola-tiser (Xenthoids use them for tunnelling, it seems); the nature of the solvent used to save Jo (di-methyl-sulphoxide, of course); and a filmed scene of a policeman spotting the Auton bus and asking awkward questions. Bill McGuirk is still credited for the role in episode three, despite not appearing on screen.

• The two-and-a-half-second shot of Goodge, a Beacon Hill scientist shrunk by the Master and dumped in the lunch-box, took two hours to set up and forty-five minutes to shoot. Despite this, and qualms noted in a memo, Barry Letts still believed in CSO as a viable effects technique.

• The new UNIT uniform was to include a blue UN-style beret, but fears of CSO conflict changed this. Nicholas Courtney preferred the peaked cap, anyway.

8.2: "The Mind of Evil"

(Serial FFF. Six Episodes, 30th January - 6th March 1971.)

Which One is This? *Thunderball* meets *Porridge*, as the Master graduates from silent-movie baddie to Bond villain and starts a riot at Stangmoor Prison while plotting to start World War Three. But to long-term *Doctor Who* fans, "The Mind of Evil" is best-remembered as: "the one that's now in black and white".

Firsts and Lasts First appearance of UNIT's Corporal Bell, the first uniformed woman in the Brigadier's inner circle and who therefore has the job of answering the telephones. The first (and until 26.3, "The Curse of Fenric", the only) instance of subtitles being used in the series to translate non-English dialogue.

Six Things to Notice About "The Mind of Evil"…

1. As the Master's second story, and the first in which he doesn't share the limelight with a large number of monsters, "The Mind of Evil" gives the new Public Enemy Number One a chance to develop a proper sense of humour, letting Roger Delgado pull out all the stops in his performance. Not only does the Master get to sneer, gloat, ooze and poke fun at UNIT whenever possible, he also tries major-league villainy the human way, so he's even seen sampling a fat cigar in the back of a chauffeur-driven car.

2. More fun with CSO, as the UNIT soldiers stand in front of a photograph of a nuclear-powered missile and point at it urgently.

3. The Doctor's response, when the Brigadier rescues him from certain death at the last moment: 'Do you think for once in your life you could manage to arrive before the nick of time?'

4. Captain Yates' description of the (female) Chinese officer Chin Lee - 'quite a dolly' - is guaranteed to make you want to punch him.

5. Only the final episode of "The Mind of Evil" exists in a colour 525-line format. Opinion is divided as to whether the whole thing looks much more effective in *cine-verité* black-and-white, or whether the grainy monochrome puts far too much distance between the programme and the modern audience, and stops the story looking like the glossy piece of contemporary TV that it was always meant to be.

6. *All* the episodes basically end on the same cliffhanger, with someone about to die while the Keller Machine runs amok. The only real variety comes at the end of episode two, when the Keller process manifests itself as a big pink dragon (looking not unlike Big Bird), attacking a hammy American Senator in what looks like a brothel.

The Continuity

The Doctor Experiencing fear-hallucinations from the Keller machine, the Doctor sees a variety of old acquaintants: a Silurian, a Zarbi, an Ice Warrior, a War Machine, a Cyberman, a Dalek and Koquillion. [Koquillion, from "The Rescue" (2.3), is a minor villain by anyone's standards. However… it should be remembered that Koquillion's costume was originally a form of ceremonial dress on Dido, possibly linked to Dido's Hall of Judgement, and in "The Rescue" the Doctor states that he's been to Dido before. Did the Doctor once have trouble with the law there, so much so that he feared for his life? If not, then he may just hallucinate Koquillion because it reminds him of the time right after he lost his granddaughter.] But the most specific horror from the Doctor's mind is a world destroyed by fire. [An obvious reference to "Inferno". See 7.4 for possible reasons.]

The Doctor loses to Jo at draughts, considering the game too simple. He prefers three-dimensional chess [bloody *Star Trek* fans]. He states that simple human medicine could easily kill someone with his metabolism. [Fan-lore has always maintained that the lethal pill he's offered is just an aspirin, but this isn't at all clear.] He also states that he's been a scientist for 'several thousand -' before breaking off. [See 7.2, "Doctor Who and the Silurians", for more on his apparent age.]

• *Ethics.* He refuses to carry a gun when it's offered to him, but he's prepared to kill the Master when it becomes necessary [q.v. 9.5, "The Time Monster"]. The Keller process has been worrying him ever since he heard about it. [Which means that as hinted in "Inferno", he's begun to take an active interest in the human experiments of the era. He thinks there's something "evil" about the machine, so his instincts may be warning him about either the creature inside it or the Master.] Here he's described as 'scientific adviser' to UNIT.

• *Inventory.* He and Jo both carry UNIT passes.

• *Background.* The Doctor speaks the Chinese dialect of Hokkien, and says it's been a while since he's had the chance to use it. He claims to have had conversations with Mao Tse Tung, and given leave to use Mao's personal name [but since Chairman Mao must *surely* represent so many things that the Doctor can't stand, he could be bluffing to impress his Chinese host]. He also claims to have been in a cell in the Tower of London with Sir Walter Raleigh during the reign of Elizabeth I [in 1585], when Raleigh kept going on about potatoes. He seems to have some prior experience of the type of mind parasite found inside the Keller Machine.

The Supporting Cast

• *Jo Grant.* She's already fiercely loyal to the Doctor, considering him a genius. She's no longer calling anyone in UNIT "sir" [so it's been a while since "Terror of the Autons"; see **History**]. Jo's been trained to use guns.

• *UNIT.* It's again suggested that UNIT takes its orders from Geneva. The code-names "Venus" and "Jupiter" are used instead of the more familiar "Greyhound" and "Trap" call-signs [maybe to disguise UNIT's involvement in the diplomatically-sensitive disposal of the Thunderbolt missile].

• *The Brigadier.* Has the power to put D-notices on the press, and he's a crack shot in a crisis. Disguised as a delivery man during UNIT's assault on the prison, he's forced to pretend to be working-class and doesn't look at all comfortable.

• *Captain Yates.* Shot at, captured and ridiculed by the Brigadier, he still charms his way around logistical problems. Can ride motorbikes.

• *Sergeant Benton:* Shot at, harried by psychic forces, left for dead twice and yelled at by the Brigadier, then put in charge of Her Majesty's Prison, Stangmoor. A busy 36 hours for the Sergeant [so he's good under stress].

The Supporting Cast (Evil)

• *The Master.* Here he shows his talent for gaining the confidence of the establishment, and it's been nearly a year since he installed the Keller Machine at Stangmoor Prison.

Captain Chin Lee, a victim of his hypnosis, has a small metal implant under her ear which keeps her under his control when he's not around. The device can also transmit and amplify the power of the Keller Machine through the wearer's mind. The Master is still disguising himself with face-masks, and he's clearly acquired some wealth on Earth. He can out-arm-wrestle a hardened criminal without difficulty.

It's not clear where the mind parasite in the Keller Machine comes from [the Master's been trapped on Earth since "Terror of the Autons", so he must have had it in his TARDIS for some time, waiting for a rainy day].

How Does "Evil" Work?

In general, *Doctor Who* has always presented us with a nice, easy, medieval world view: there's good, there's evil, neither can be converted and both are states of being.

As the programme veered away from reason and empiricism as its guiding principles - and towards a tendency for the Doctor to save the world just because he happens to be a Time Lord, or just because it's taken as read that Tom Baker has supernatural powers - this became more complicated, although a definite moral dividing-line could still be found. You judged beings by whether they considered the consequences of their actions on others (except for god-like aliens, of course, who could do what they wanted simply because explaining them would remove some of their mystery; see 13.3, "Pyramids of Mars").

Almost all the '60s and '70s stories take this basic line. Evil is simply knowing what good is and not doing it, though "good" might alter a little from case to case. By the 1980s this emphasis on ethical standards was rather passé, and instead the Doctor increasingly found himself facing things which were bad because... well, they were bad. In "The Tenth Planet" (1966) the Cybermen are presented almost as an ethical argument in themselves, but in "Attack of the Cybermen" (1985) they're just generic bad guys and their *reasons* for wanting to destroy the world seem added to the plot as an afterthought.

It's worth noting in passing that the usual equation in TV fantasy, that having a body means being fallible, breaks down in *Doctor Who* almost from the word "go" (or "exterminate"). Disembodied minds are corrupting influences, and brains in jars are never to be trusted. Even when people are "purified" and develop psi-powers, they're not above being petty or vindictive (see 9.5, "The Mutants"). Thus the usual Christian-Gnostic idea, that all matter is wretched and only the spirit is pure, doesn't apply here. Significantly, there's never been any indication that there's a Heaven in the *Doctor Who* universe, although if you're lucky then someone might download your consciousness into a great big computer after you die.

In the specific case of "The Mind of Evil", most of the "evil" impulses being removed from the Stangmoor Prison criminals seem identical to the effects of testosterone. Chemical behaviour-modification was the post-war solution to all social ills, and even enlightened thinkers wanted to refine humanity's baser urges out of existence. See Huxley's *Brave New World Revisited*, or the footnotes of the Wolfenden Report of 1957, set up by the British Home Office to investigate the "problem" of gay men and their ability to compromise national security. The early '70s saw the last days of the behaviourist school of psychiatric treatment, and an obsession with anything that could "correct" abnormalities such as homosexuality (still classified as an illness in America until 1973), introspection, depression or anxiety.

In more drastic cases, prefrontal lobotomies or electro-convulsive therapy were advocated, up to and including the erasure of a patient's entire memory. One notorious incident at the Allen Memorial Hospital, Montreal - CIA-funded, natch - "depatterned" dozens of patients with LSD and repeated ECT treatment before playing them tapes of feelgood messages in their sleep. They were lucky if they regained the use of speech. A generation of benzodiazopane-addicted near-zombies later, we're less keen to prescribe pills for social problems, but this is clearly what prisoner Barnham's treatment and its after-effects in "The Mind of Evil" suggest. With *A Clockwork Orange*, Anthony Burgess was merely reporting much of what had been in the headlines, as was Don Houghton nearly a decade later.

For this story to work, evil has to be more than the absence of good. It has to have substance, which can be chemically extracted and fed to an alien mind-parasite in a popcorn machine. This is admittedly far easier for children to take in than a disquisition on the contingency of moral autonomy, but it causes problems for all subsequent stories where a character has to undergo a major change of heart (or "turn good", as it's also known). If this evil-substance is innate in all humans, then is it found in every conscious species? Does it form a necessary part of consciousness? Is it finite, in which case a population explosion would diminish the amount of evil per capita, or is it self-replicating? At what point in humanity's evolution did it turn up, since it seems unlikely that you can have evil animals? And how can characters change their moral outlook, as they frequently do, if the evil-fuel is unassailable within the head / heart / guts of the individual?

The clue may perhaps lie in the alien's unexpected ability to teleport.

This ability is, in the context of early '70s TV and cinema, routinely assumed to be proof of the mind's operation outside three-dimensional space. Compare this with the way dreams traverse time in *The Tomorrow People*, or with the *Space:*

continued on page 45...

The Master's greatest fear, exposed by the Machine, is the Doctor. The hallucination of the Doctor he sees is a mocking one, and appears larger-than-life, suggesting that the Master has a serious inferiority complex [his claim in "Terror of the Autons", that the Doctor is *almost* his equal, isn't something he really believes]. Here his motive for triggering a World War is a mixture of spite and megalomania.

The Non-Humans

• *The Keller Machine.* The device used to remove all traces of aggression from convicts is an alien 'mind parasite', attached to a Master-created control mechanism. It looks like a pulsating brain once it's exposed. The Doctor implies there's more than one of these creatures in the universe, and states that they're incredibly resilient, although an atomic explosion or massive electrical discharge can kill them.

The British authorities believe the Keller Machine can suck "evil" out of people's minds, but the Doctor initially doesn't believe a word of it. However, anyone subjected to the creature under controlled conditions *does* apparently lose the ability to hate or hurt, and the Doctor concedes that the creature 'feeds on the evil of the mind'. [Some kind of psychic energy generated by "evil", rather than an actual substance? But see **How Does "Evil" Work?**.]

He also describes it, with typical melodrama, as the greatest threat to humanity since the beginning of time.

The more "evil" the Machine takes, the stronger it gets, and it eventually gains the ability to teleport itself over short distances in search of new victims. Those it attacks experience hallucinatory terror and die of fear, but the hallucinations must in some way be corporeal, as a victim with a fear of drowning has water in his lungs and a victim with a fear of rats has scratches on his skin. Other people can witness these horrors, the Doctor describing the effect as 'collective hallucination'.

The creature is harmless and immobilised when a subject who's already been drained of his "evil" is present to act as a screen, while the Stangmoor prisoners [people with violent natures?] become more aggressive when it attacks and start to roll around in agony when things get too intense.

History

• *Dating.* [Mid-1972. The fact that the Master installed the Keller Machine at Stangmoor 'nearly a year' ago, and was posing as Emil Keller some time before that, suggests that it's been some considerable time since "Terror of the Autons"; see **What's the UNIT Timeline?** under 8.5, "The Daemons". Lance Parkin's *History of the Universe* suggests, quite feasibly, that the line about the machine being installed nearly a year ago is a leftover from an earlier draft of the script which didn't feature the Master. Nonetheless, it's there.]

The British Thunderbolt missile, nuclear-powered and with a nerve gas warhead, has been outlawed and is now being dumped at the bottom of the ocean. The Master states that gas warfare's been banned for 'many years' [but the missile's nuclear powered, suggesting a recent design… have the British been up to something shady?].

UNIT is handling the security for the first ever World Peace Conference in London, as well as escorting the Thunderbolt missile, so its original mandate to investigate 'new and unusual menaces to mankind' really has been broadened an *awful* lot by now and it's apparently just doing any work befitting an international organisation. There's tension between the west and Mao Tse Tung's China at this point, and the "Chinese dragon" is the American delegate's greatest fear rather than, say, the "Russian bear".

The Analysis

Where Does This Come From? Once again, *Doctor Who* starts to sideline the "scientific research" approach and concentrate on the James Bond / *Persuaders* / ITC serial side of things. Full of gunfights, ambushes, helicopters and prison riots, "The Mind of Evil" - like Don Houghton's only other *Doctor Who* script, "Inferno" - aims for an older target audience than the series ever had in mind in the '60s, and this time there aren't even any monster costumes to keep the children entertained. (Yet even if the violence seems a lot more down-to-earth and in-your-face than usual, the British censor rates this story as certificate "U" while the positively cuddly "Curse of Peladon" gets a "PG".)

But at the core of "The Mind of Evil" is the Keller Machine, and a plot which is at least *obliquely* about free will. It's been said that the story was intended to be *Doctor Who*'s response to

This product is not authorized by the BBC. Doctor Who and TARDIS are trademarks of the BBC.

How Does "Evil" Work?

...continued from page 43

1999 episode "Black Sun", which reveals that humans can easily survive a black hole because the human mind has the zen-power to safely navigate its way through.

"Mind" can exist without "matter" here, which is why the absorption of mind-power allows the Keller Machine to break the usual physical laws. This might also explain how people in the *Doctor Who* world retain their personalities and memories after they've been abnormally aged or youthened by time-seepage (see especially 9.6, "The Time Monster" and 18.1, "The Leisure Hive"). Despite the number of affable computers in this universe, and despite the non-appearance of a palpable afterlife, no-one ever disputes the existence of the soul... except the Master, of course, when he's disguised as a trendy existential vicar in "The Daemons" (8.5). - Indeed, for possession to happen with the depressing regularity it does in the '70s, the existence of something roughly soul-like has

to be a given. That said, the definition of "soul" is always going to cause problems. In "Image of the Fendahl" (15.3) the Doctor uses the word to refer to the entire spectrum of human life-energy, but that's not really the same sort of thing.

This being the case, we have no more chance of accessing "Evil" than of removing the soul by dissection, and "The Mind of Evil" *still* falls apart. Whatever was removed from those 112 Swiss convicts by the Keller Process (*are* there 112 hardcases in Switzerland...?) had nothing to do with the kind of "evil" represented by proto-cosmic entities like Fenric, the Black Guardian, the Gods of Ragnarok, the Great Intelligence or the Animus. In order to keep good faith with the series' overall moral tendencies - evident in stories such as "Genesis of the Daleks" (12.4), "The Robots of Death" (14.5) and "The Pirate Planet" (16.2), to name but three clear examples - it's perhaps best to assume that the alien in "The Mind of Evil" feeds on testosterone, but that censorship intervened.

A Clockwork Orange, and even that Houghton was inspired by the movie before he wrote the story, although the claim's an odd one since the movie wasn't even finished in 1971. Of course, he could still have been influenced by Anthony Burgess' original novel of *A Clockwork Orange*, and there is a link between the two. Burgess was himself inspired by 1950s criminal psychology treatments, which make terrifying reading today. See also **How Does "Evil" Work?**.

Whenever people mention "Cold War paranoia" in science fiction, they generally like to talk about *Invasion of the Bodysnatchers* and the (largely American) fear of being invaded by Communist Martians. Yet what seems to have made the biggest impression on the people of the '60s and '70s - apart from the ever-present fear of nuclear armageddon, naturally - was the *dehumanising* effect of the Cold War on its participants. Look at the semi-sci-fi adventure serials of the era. The plot-hook which comes up time and time again is "brainwashing".

As *Clockwork Orange*'s author pointed out, it's significant that the movie version was made at the tail-end of the Vietnam war, when soldiers were being drilled to fight in a conflict which increasingly few people understood and when rumours of military conditioning programmes were common. Not to mention Robert Kennedy's assassina-

tion in 1968, the one "famous" political murder that really did seem to involve some kind of dubious CIA mind-control experiment. But of course, being resolutely British, when *Doctor Who* does an "erosion of free will" story it's not a *Manchurian-Candidate*-style thriller about a brainwashed political assassin (although as it happens, the very Manchurian-looking Chin Lee *is* hypnotised by the Master). Instead, brainwashing's a way of dealing with East End villains with cockney accents.

Certainly, there's none of the usual Cold War evil-communists-are-everywhere anxiety in "The Mind of Evil". When the Brigadier meets General Fu Peng, the Englishman's hopelessly ineffectual while the Oriental's just surly... and only the Doctor, being beyond all this petty human politicking, is allowed to keep his dignity. And as in the early Bond films, it's not the west or the east that causes the trouble but a criminal third party. The Master's plan to trigger a war and take over in the confusion has "Ernst Stavro Blofeld", the cat-stroking Bond villain, written all over it.

Things That Don't Make Sense The Master uses the Keller Machine to assault the delegates at the peace conference, thus linking the attacks to his work at Stangmoor prison, when he could have just given Chin Lee a gun and told her to shoot people instead. [But then, the Master likes showing off.] Even so, for the Doctor to work out the link between Stangmoor and the conference ahead of time requires there to be only one Chinese girl in the whole of Britain.

In fact it's never explained why the Master bothers spending a year on the Keller project anyway, since it's almost irrelevant to his plan to steal the Thunderbolt. Assuming, that is, that the Thunderbolt idea qualifies as a "plan". He doesn't know about UNIT's task of destroying it until episode two, and he's aiming to destroy the planet on which he's trapped. Unless he's carrying his inoperative TARDIS around on his person, there's no way he could have escaped either the detonation or his own planned nuclear war.

Thunderbolt itself is a nuclear-powered gas missile, so the brilliant scheme to neutralise the threat is to make it self-destruct, spreading fall-out and nerve-gas across suburban England and rather conspicuously announcing its existence on the eve of a peace conference. And Jo and the Doctor are perfectly safe despite being in a helicopter above Ground Zero.

The top-security prison has a secret tunnel. Before he finds out about this, the Brigadier doesn't believe an attack on Stangmoor prison would work because you'd 'need an army' to get in. So he doesn't call the army because…?

Critique Forgotten by its generation thanks to a complete lack of men in alien costumes (there are a few shots of the pink dragon and that's it), "The Mind of Evil" is '70s *Doctor Who* at its least childlike and least straightforward. Even if the "free will" theme drops out of the picture halfway through, replaced by something that can *just about* be called a political thriller, it's still a surprisingly complex piece of work - especially when you compare it to its "action TV" competition - which succeeds in getting three different storylines working together: the Keller process, the World Peace Conference and the ongoing Doctor/Master rivalry. So much so that you can even ignore its deeply non-threatening "monster", a Moulinex blender which teleports around the prison instead of bearing down on its victims in a menacing fashion.

The Facts

Written by Don Houghton. Directed by Timothy Combe. Viewing figures: 6.1 million, 8.8 million, 7.5 million, 7.4 million, 7.6 million, 7.3 million.

Only black-and-white prints of "The Mind of Evil" exist in the BBC archive, although the BBC video release contains various re-coloured clips from episode six.

Supporting Cast Pik-Sen Lim (Captain Chin Lee), Michael Sheard (Dr. Summers), Simon Lack (Professor Kettering), Neil McCarthy (Barnham), Fernanda Marlowe (Corporal Bell), Roy Purcell (Chief Prison Officer Powers), Eric Mason (Senior Prison Officer Green), William Marlowe (Mailer), Haydn Jones (Vosper), Kristopher Kum (Fu Peng), Tommy Duggan (Senator Alcott), Patrick Godfrey (Major Cosworth).

Working Titles "Man Hours", "Doctor Who and Pandora's Box", "The Pandora Machine".

Cliffhangers Left alone to examine the Keller Machine, the Doctor suddenly finds himself under attack from it as (imaginary) flames start to lick his body; lured to the Chinese delegation's suite by Chin Lee, the American representative sees her change into an oriental dragon; handcuffed to a chair in the same room as the Machine, the Doctor begins to suffer monster-hallucinations as part of the Master's experiment (this week's opportunity for a champion gurning session from Pertwee); the active Machine, having learned to teleport around the prison, materialises in the same room as the Doctor, Jo and prisoner Mailer; Mailer aims his pistol at the Doctor during UNIT's assault on Stangmoor, and there's the sound of a gunshot.

The Lore

• Inflation taken into account, "The Mind of Evil" was the most expensive *Doctor Who* story that BBC ever made. The elaborate action scenes, complete with motorbikes, military vehicles and large numbers of stuntmen falling off things, swallowed much of the budget, but it didn't help that a day's shooting at Dover Castle was lost when the negative was scratched. The whole thing was hastily remounted, with the crew doubling up as extras. And to make matters even *worse* a day's filming for episodes one and two was scrapped after Andy Ho, the original choice to play the Chinese delegate (Fu Peng), was fired.

• The author's wife, Pik Sem-Lin, not only plays Captain Chin Lee but provided the translated dialogue.

• The mannequin for the second cliffhanger was called "Puff the Magic Dragon" by the crew. Unsurprisingly.

• In an earlier draft of the story, Senator Alcott was said to be allergic to jellied eels, and this was the "fear" with which the Keller process killed him. (Presumably he was going to be found dead with jellied eels in his system, rather than being attacked in his hotel room by a seven-foot-tall pink jellied eel.)

• The Master is listening to dreary prog-rockers King Crimson in episode three, another sure sign that he's evil.

8.3: "The Claws of Axos"

(Serial GGG. Seven Episodes, 13th March - 3rd April 1971.)

Which One is This? Lumpy red bolognese-men land on Earth in their disturbingly organic spaceship, promising to feed the starving millions and showing humanity how to make frogs grow to enormous sizes. At first they look almost human, but the Doctor knows better than to trust people who dress in gold spandex and lack pupils.

Firsts and Lasts First appearance of the new-look TARDIS console and console room, although the architecture will be re-styled at least twice over the next couple of years. (It's in a mess the first time we see it, so there's never a great moment of unveiling. The Doctor's ripped the guts out of most of the console, and even the Master's disgusted.)

First mention of two key concepts in *Doctor Who* history: time loops and the High Council of the Time Lords.

Four Things to Notice About "The Claws of Axos"...

1. When the Brigadier asks if there's anything they can do about Axos draining the nuclear reactor, the Master's response is a lovely piece of *Protect-and-Survive*-era satire: 'I suppose you can take the normal precautions against nuclear blast… sticky-tape on the windows, that sort of thing…' (N.B. Younger readers should note that in the 1970s, some members of the older generation in Britain still expected nuclear war to be like the Blitz.)

2. Having spent the last year or so telling human authorities that aliens aren't necessarily hostile and that Earth should try to make peace with them whenever possible, here the Doctor meets a bunch of apparently peaceful aliens and tries to convince the authorities to blow them up.

3. UNIT personnel at the site of the UFO landing report 'freak weather conditions', a blatant way of covering for the fact that the weather changed several times during location filming. (Not the last time the series would use this ploy, either. See 26.3, "The Curse of Fenric".)

4. In the last episode, Captain Yates and Sergeant Benton are seen sitting in front of a blue cloth inside their jeep when there should be an exterior background behind them. Almost as if somebody's forgotten to put the CSO backdrop in. Bill Filer, the token American, has the same sort of problem in episode one (see **The Lore**).

The Continuity

The Doctor He still can't remember much of his past, and for the first time it's explicitly stated that the Time Lords have put a block on his memory of 'dematerialisation theory' to stop him leaving Earth. [See **What's Wrong with the TARDIS?** under 9.2, "The Curse of Peladon".]

The Supporting Cast

• *UNIT.* The Ministry of Defence feels obliged to screen UNIT personnel. The Emergency Powers Act gives the Ministry the right to issue orders to UNIT under extreme circumstances, and to allow the regular military to take over from the UN forces. However, unilateral deals with extra-terrestrials are illegal.

Whereas UNIT used to have its own space tracking station [7.1, "Spearhead from Space"], there's now a tracking room inside UNIT HQ itself. UNIT's chief headquarters is, as expected, in Geneva.

The Supporting Cast (Evil)

• *The Master.* Quite prepared to believe that the Doctor might run off in the TARDIS and abandon Earth to its fate, so he doesn't know his old comrade *that* well [and he still hasn't got the picture by the next story]. The Master has taken to carrying a 'laser gun', which does exactly what anybody would expect a laser gun to do but can also open the lock of the TARDIS [q.v. 3.4, "The Daleks' Masterplan"]. His hypnosis works on human subjects even when there's no direct eye-contact with him.

The TARDIS(es)   The Doctor's TARDIS seems to contain a 'light accelerator', which is compatible with Earth-built cyclotrons, although confusingly an Earth-built light accelerator compensates for the deficiencies in the Doctor's dematerialisation circuit and makes the Ship operational again. It's a simple solution which has previously been blocked from the Doctor's mind, even if the Master spots it straight away. However, once the Ship is active the Doctor discovers that the Time Lords have programmed it to return to Earth anyway.

The Master believes that the Doctor's TARDIS doesn't have a proper stabiliser. The scanner, formerly a TV screen in the corner of the console room, is now built into one of the wall roundels. [It returns to its normal state for the next story.] When linked to Axos, the TARDIS can put the organism into a permanent time-loop which apparently removes it from the normal universe, although boosting the power breaks the TARDIS out of the loop and leaves Axos stranded.

The Master's TARDIS has become a chunky grey cuboid with a single door [not unlike the SIDRATs in 6.7, "The War Games"], evidently its "default" form.

The Time Lords   The Time Lords have a High Council [the first time it's ever stated, albeit just in passing here].

The Non-Humans

• *Axos*. A single alien organism, which has no [surviving] planet of its own but moves from world to world as if it were a spaceship, Axos buries itself under the ground on arrival so that only its maw-like entrance is visible. Its interior is a mass of living tissue, its walls lined with tentacles and eye-like sensory organs.

Axos thrives by distributing chunks of itself - Axonite, a substance which tries to defy analysis but which is apparently Axos material in its dormant state - across the victim-planet before draining the world of all energy and living matter. It

needs to begin its nutrition cycle within 72 hours of landing [it originated on a planet which also has a 24-hour day?].

Individuals drained by Axos are spewed out of its body dead, bleached and crumbling to dust. Its presence on Earth causes erratic weather conditions in the vicinity, and it has 'variable mass' when it's on its way to Earth, vanishing from the radar altogether when missiles are launched at it. It can read the thoughts of people in its grip.

Axos is seemingly "crewed" by golden-skinned, golden-haired humanoids, but in fact these creatures are just drones of Axos itself [their bodies presumably chosen to put humans at ease]. Reverting to their natural form, the Axons become masses of red tendril-tissue, still roughly humanoid in shape. Bullets fail to harm the "lumpy" Axons, who can fire lethal jets of gas from their arms, or extend long whip-like tendrils to unexpectedly make the target explode on contact.

In fact Axos seems able to shape bits of itself into just about anything. It can even make identical-but-bulletproof duplicates of human beings after taking the subject to the replication section of the "ship". The Axons claim that Axonite can use the energy it absorbs to copy, re-create and re-structure matter, and although this is part of their "sales pitch" to the humans there must at least be *some* truth in it. It can certainly be used to make small animals larger, or to reverse this process.

[The Axons' claim that the "ship" was grown, rather than made, is unreliable as it's part of their cover-story. However, Axos seems to think like a computer and can be linked to technology like the TARDIS, suggesting it was deliberately engineered rather than evolving naturally.] The whole of Axos suffers "pain" when part of its mass is analysed.

The organism's interest in Earth comes from the Master, though it's not revealed where it encountered him [see **The Lore**]. It seems to know about Time Lords even without his help.

History

• *Dating*. [Late 1972.] 'Freak weather conditions' aside, England's drab enough to suggest autumn or winter. [Assuming the Master's only been travelling in space rather than history, enough time has elapsed since "The Mind of Evil" for Axos to capture and return him to Earth.]

Britain apparently has emergency missiles ready to take out incoming spacecraft, while Washington has taken an interest in the Master.

Where's UNIT HQ?

(And more importantly, how many UNIT HQs are there?)

The problem, of course, is that the Doctor's laboratory looks different almost every time we see it. Leaving aside the possibility that his constant experiments with bits of the TARDIS are doing weird things to space-time inside the building, at the very least we have to assume that he keeps moving from room to room (does he keep blowing them up?), even if UNIT doesn't uproot itself and head for a new installation every few months.

In the early days of Season Seven, the only UNIT "lab" is the one seen at the start of "The Ambassadors of Death", which might *just* be the one later seen in "Terror of the Autons". Even if it isn't, the ramshackle garage set-up of UNIT HQ in this period makes it likely that the Doctor isn't particularly settled anyway. Which means there could well be only two different HQs used throughout the Third Doctor's exile, despite the unpredictable décor. The building in "Terror of the Autons" apparently isn't the building we see in "The Three Doctors", since the first of these has a handy river running past the window and the second obviously hasn't.

But we can assume that the HQ being used in "The Daemons" is the same as the HQ being used in "Planet of the Spiders", because the Doctor's using the same garage. So, two HQ buildings, and the move has to take place somewhere in the middle of Season Eight. The most likely time would be between "The Claws of Axos" and "Colony in Space". In "Axos" the HQ has a nifty space-tracking room that we never see again, whereas in "Colony" the Doctor's lab looks somewhat… under-furnished. To be blunt, it looks as if he's working in a corridor, which certainly suggests that he's halfway through moving. The lab in "The Mutants" isn't much better, but the one in "The Time Monster" seems to be the same one seen in all later tales, even if it's often seen from different angles.

This makes as much sense as anything. Moving a top secret(ish) organisation's HQ around isn't something you do on a whim. You have to think about planning permission, as well as finding a suitable building and area - secure from prying eyes but also from the risk of contaminating the locals, given that UNIT's brief includes biological warfare and radiation - that's equidistant from anywhere the organisation might be needed.

Logistically, this kind of thing is easier in wartime, when you can requisition a reasonably-sized country estate (as seems to be happening in

11.1, "The Time Warrior"). The camp in "The Curse of Fenric" (26.3), flagrantly based on Bletchley Park in Buckinghamshire, is a good example of this. UNIT seems to have limited emergency powers to do something similar when handling a crisis, but for routine operations it's like any other multi-national taking over an older estate.

So where *is* this HQ, which lasts all the way up until "Robot" (12.1) and is apparently built on the site of an attack by an Egyptian god? The most obvious suggestion would be Gloucestershire, the area where England starts to turn into Wales. Wales is said to be 'nearby' in "Day of the Daleks", and there's a possibly-intentional West Country feel to much of the location work in this era. In "Planet of the Spiders" the HQ is conclusively shown to be around eighty miles from Mortimer in Berkshire, which just about works. It's also (roughly) seventy to a hundred miles from Cambridge, according to "The Time Monster".

On top of that "Day of the Daleks" suggests that UNIT HQ is north of Auderly, and Auderly is fifty miles north of London. "Suggests" because we're assuming that 'down' means southwards and south means due south. This makes sense of a lot of odd details, like the building being on top of the ruins of a priory (13.3, "Pyramids of Mars"), a short helicopter ride from Devil's End (8.5, "The Daemons") and close enough to Devesham for Benton to arrange to meet his sister after work (13.4, "The Android Invasion"). Even the comedy copper in the chase sequence from "Planet of the Spiders" seems to confirm this, as he and Terry Walsh's "Man with Boat" have the right approximate accent.

Not all the figures add up, mind you. It takes the Brigadier three hours to drive from the HQ to South Wales in "The Green Death", and it *really* shouldn't take that long from Gloucestershire, even if he's avoiding the toll-bridge over the Severn at Bristol. That said, it's a fairly small, rural area and anyone who's driven there will know that once you get off the motorways the routes get a bit circuitous. The Doctor gets to Llanfairfach in next to no time. Gloucestershire remains the best bet, then, although if you wanted to do the measuring and come up with a site which fits *all* the numerical data then you'd have to conclude that the HQ is… somewhere in the vicinity of Birmingham, plumb between the north and south of England. (*Why* UNIT would choose to make its home near Birmingham is another matter; see 26.4, "Survival".)

[The CIA probably wants to recruit him.] Bill Filer, the American agent, is evidently so well-versed in the Master's case-file that he doesn't find the TARDIS surprising. [Filer seems to have been brought in as a possible love-interest for Jo, but he doesn't last. Imagine one of the older Osmond brothers playing Felix Leiter from the Bond movies and you've got the idea.]

The Nuton Power Complex is a nuclear facility supplying power for the 'whole of Britain'. [Much of it blows up at story's end. Ergo, much of Britain suffers an immediate energy crisis and a sizeable black-out until the damage can be repaired, leading to panic, high mortality rates, a massive increase in crime and probably a baby boom. Nobody dwells on this.]

At the complex there's a research programme which is attempting to accelerate particles beyond the speed of light and therefore develop a form of time-travel. Sadly, the Axons kill the scientist envisioning all of this.

The Analysis

Where Does This Come From? A mixed bag, this one. While most of the early Third Doctor stories proudly show off the anxieties and obsessions of their era, "The Claws of Axos" seems desperate to use *all* the standards of adventure TV without really knowing what it's saying. So we have a two-fisted American agent (as a nod to two-fisted American agent shows, c.f. "The Ambassadors of Death") with an evil Axon duplicate (the usual early '70s paranoia, c.f. "Spearhead from Space"), a nuclear power plant (for that sense of modern menace, c.f. "The Silurians") and a bunch of aliens who promise the British government an unlimited source of power (to meet the needs of the imminent energy crisis, c.f. "Inferno").

Whatever you think of "The Claws of Axos", though, what's striking is its use of colour. "The Silurians" (7.2) demonstrated that *Doctor Who* in the full-colour era was going to present a different kind of environment to the black-and-white '60s universe of spaceship corridors and arctic military bases. Yet here there's a sense that the producers and designers have finally figured out how to use colour to make things seem intrinsically *alien*. It's hard to imagine a story about something as fleshy and as organic as Axos hailing from the monochrome era, which suggested flat, grey surfaces by its very nature. (Even when the black-and-white

monsters *are* unusually juicy - e.g. the Animus in 2.5, "The Web Planet" - they're still shown in stark, shadowy, hard-edged surroundings.) Here there are aliens with golden skins, sets made out of deep red nerve-roots and psychedelic energy effects on all sides, the work of a programme trying its damnedest to justify the price of the colour TV license.

It's also worth noting that in their first *Doctor Who* script, writers Bob Baker and Dave Martin are already interested in taking the mystique out of the Time Lords. Axos becomes the first alien to know the Doctor's kind by name, and the High Council is finally mentioned, if only in passing. It's something Baker and Martin will keep doing in stories like "The Three Doctors" (10.1) and "The Armageddon Factor" (16.6).

Things That Don't Make Sense Everything said by Pigbin Josh, the tramp that Axos consumes and spits out.

Five strange things to do during a nuclear meltdown. (1) Slowly amble half a mile up the road; (2) stop; (3) turn back to watch the nuclear reactor explode, (4) through binoculars; (5) go back again. A story from a decade in which most people had absolutely no idea what nuclear power actually does, "The Claws of Axos" presents us with an energy complex so large that it powers most of Britain, and yet which blows up as neatly as an empty warehouse. No Chernobyl-style death-cloud, no fall-out, and so little radiation that the main cast can return to the site minutes after the reactor goes up... even though one of the station's staff has warned it *will* become a gigantic nuclear bomb if it explodes. (Baker and Martin always have problems with nuclear energy. Just look at 14.2, "The Hand of Fear".)

There's also a sense of human beings over-playing their own importance here, since Axos believes that the power requirements for time-travel are beyond its scope but *can* be obtained from a simple nuclear reactor on Earth. Which is not only unlikely but downright contradictory, since it was planning on draining all the world's energy anyway. It can absorb everything on Earth *except* a British-made power plant...?

But then, this just emphasises the gawping hole at the centre of the plot. The Doctor reasons that the Axons must be lying, as they're apparently able to harness any form of energy but still need resources from Earth. Yet when the horrible truth about the Axons is revealed, they want power from Earth anyway, as if that motive makes perfect sense now they've been identified as evil. If they can indiscriminately draw energy from a whole planet, then can't they just suck the power they need from a sun somewhere? Then again, Axos is an entity so stupid that after it drains the life of Pigbin Josh - a mumbling, stinking tramp who ranks among *Doctor Who*'s most unfortunate supporting characters - it dumps his body outside so that the next humans to come along can find it and get suspicious. It also somehow knows that Josh's intelligence is 'atypical' even though he's the first human the ship's picked up.

The TARDIS can be seen in the background during the humans-versus-Axons battle in the final episode, even though the TARDIS has already left the scene by then. [Let's call it a freak side-effect of the Doctor's time-loop.] How come Bill Filer, sent specifically to deal with the Master, doesn't seem to know what he looks like? How come the people inside Axos can hear Jo screaming but not Filer's gun going off, repeatedly? How come the space-borne Axos, running low on power, wastes *more* power vanishing from space-time to avoid the nice tasty nuclear-energy-powered missiles that the humans have thoughtfully provided as a buffet?

Critique And so, after its brief flirtation with adolescence in "The Mind of Evil", *Doctor Who* returns to children's hour. Legend has it that the story for "The Claws of Axos" was re-written several times over before the programme was finally made, although it's debatable whether this makes it *more* or *less* surprising that the finished product is such a mess.

On the plus side, Axos is the perfect monster for a contemporary adventure story, a great big cancerous growth in the middle of twentieth-century England which must have pleased the monster-obsessed younger viewers. On the minus side, it shovels as many SF set-pieces into four episodes as possible without doing anything interesting with them. It's a plot full of cul de sacs, of elements which either don't fit (the duplicate of Filer doesn't actually do anything) or just look silly (the exploding power station).

Yet the problems aren't confined to the script: the direction, editing and camerawork are so poor that the picture shifts with no logic, pace or reason, making it hard to know - or care - what you're supposed to be looking at. So much so, in

fact, that sometimes it isn't even clear which set the characters are meant to be standing in. The weakest of the UNIT adventures, at least in the Pertwee era, it also has the worst music of any *Doctor Who* story ever.

Apart from all of this, it's also the unmistakable point at which *Doctor Who* goes from being a TV show to being a style of acting. Paul Bathurst (as Chinn, an inquiry committee head) would have been unthinkable even a week earlier, but now he's just the most egregious member of a cast so stiff that even Richard Franklin is a welcome breath of naturalism.

The Facts

Written by Bob Baker and Dave Martin. Directed by Michael Ferguson. Viewing figures: 7.3 million, 8.0 million, 6.4 million, 7.8 million.

Supporting Cast Peter Bathurst (Chinn), Paul Grist (Filer), Donald Hewlett (Hardiman), David Savile (Winser), Derek Ware (Pigbin Josh), Bernard Holley (Axon Man), Fernanda Marlowe (Corporal Bell), Patricia Gordino (Axon Woman), John Hicks (Axon Boy), Debbie Lee London (Axon Girl), Tim Piggot-Smith (Captain Harker).

Working Titles "Doctor Who and the Gift", "The Axons", "The Friendly Invasion", "The Vampire from Space". (Barry Letts opted to change the title from "The Vampire from Space" to "The Claws of Axos" at the eleventh hour, and added dialogue in episodes three and four to justify this. A title sequence bearing the "Vampire" title was made but never used, though it appears on a tape of rushes from the story that's been circulating around fandom for many years. The only "official" appearance of the title is in Frank Bellamy's "Colony in Space" comic-strip for the *Radio Times* - see 8.4 - which was commissioned before the name-change and thus refers to the previous story as "Vampire" rather than "Axos".)

Cliffhangers Jo, exploring the organic interior of the Axon "spaceship", sees a lumpy red Axon loom out of the wall in front of her; the Doctor activates the dormant Axonite in the power centre, and he and his colleagues suddenly find themselves surrounded by irritated Axons; the Master uses the nuclear reactor's power to try to destroy Axos, but the Doctor and Jo are trapped inside as the creature goes into spasm around them.

51

The Lore

• For some inexplicable reason, a pilot script for an army-based sit-com by Bob Baker and Dave Martin was forwarded to Terrance Dicks in 1969. He contacted the writers and asked if they had any ideas for *Doctor Who*. As it turned out, they had loads. The first version of the story featured a giant skull landing in Hyde Park and offering to fulfil people's desires, for a price, by making its human-sized nerve-cells become whatever anybody wanted. Letts and Dicks honed this down into a workable script over four or five drafts.

• Baker and Martin would go on to create K9 in 1977, while Baker's most notable recent writing credit was the script for the *Wallace and Gromit* film *A Close Shave*, so obviously there's an affinity with robot dogs there.

• The frog that the Axons enlarge was originally scripted as a six-foot rat (see 14.6, "The Talons of Weng-Chiang"), while the Axons were said to have difficulty with English at first, and later to have mid-Atlantic accents. They were described as looking like "the adman's dream Coca-Cola family".

• Among the cut scenes, the Master claims that Axos ensnared him off Antares IV; Filer blags his way in to see the Brigadier by claiming the CIA sent him to interrogate Lethbridge-Stewart; Jo meets Filer in a Hollywood-style "cute" collision (the sound wasn't working); the Doctor mentions 'Greeks bearing Gifts', and later claims that his first loyalty is to science, if only as an excuse to pretend to side with the Master. The main edit worth noting is that both Josh and Dr. Winser, the Nuton complex's head of research, were filmed "imploding" after Axos sucked them dry. This was apparently too scary, so in the finished version the screen whites out on both occasions.

• Derek Ware eagerly took the part of Pigbin Josh, as he welcomed the chance to do some straight acting. No, really. His dialogue was, amazingly, scripted: 'Ur bin oughta gone put thickery blarmdasted zoines about, gordangum, diddenum?' is a typical example.

• Donald Hewlett (Sir George Hardiman), later to become famous in *It Ain't Half Hot Mum*, served with Pertwee in the Navy.

• Filming was delayed when the props man lost the keys to Roger Delgado's handcuffs.

• An attempt was made to get CSO to work on filmed material, rather than inserting film into VT.

It didn't work, hence those odd blue backgrounds in the car scenes. There was also an attempt to mix Katy Manning and Mildred Brown's faces as the young and old versions of Jo, using blue-dyed rice drizzling in front of Manning's face. Director Michael Ferguson, meanwhile, achieved many of his extraordinary effects by physically abusing the "action-replay" disc video recorder to see what would happen.

• Although the cast hated the set for Axos, it looked drastically better on-screen.

8.4: "Colony in Space"

(Serial HHH. Six Episodes, 10th April - 15th May 1971.)

Which One is This? Arguably the definitive alien-planet-in-a-quarry tale, with eco-friendly colonists trying to eke out an existence on a desolate world but being harassed by an evil mining company whose robot wears lizard's claws on its arms. There are future soap-stars a-plenty, and more 'hai!'s from Jon Pertwee than ever before.

Firsts and Lasts The first "space" story of the early '70s also introduces the early-'70s version of the Time Lords, who aren't yet the glittery-robed university graduates seen in later stories but *do* seem a lot more down-to-earth than those we met at the end of the '60s. Whereas in "The War Games" (6.7) they're solemn, po-faced demigods in minimalist clothing, now they're a lot more political and like hatching secret plans amongst themselves. The Master's TARDIS is finally shown to have its own console room.

This is also the first time the opening theme music ends the way we think it always did.

Six Things to Notice About "Colony in Space"...

1. It's the first colour-era story in which the Doctor gets to use the TARDIS, but since "Spearhead from Space" the production team seems to have forgotten how to do the "dematerialisation" special effect properly. As a result, the Ship doesn't do its usual slow-fade-from-view but just vanishes completely after a few seconds' worth of wheezing, groaning noises. (A hard-core fanboy might want to develop an explanation for this, although it's *not* a side effect of the Time Lords steering the TARDIS - as the director him-

This product is not authorized by the BBC. Doctor Who and TARDIS are trademarks of the BBC.

self suggested - since the Master's TARDIS does exactly the same thing.)

2. The IMC robot, in itself a lovely piece of clunky mecha-design, uses a hologram projector to disguise itself as a giant reptile and attack the colonists. What this means, in BBC effects terms, is that two of the colonists look out through the door of their home to find an enormously-enlarged piece of stock footage (of a normal-sized lizard, natch) waiting for them outside. Since the lizard is *supposed* to be a fake, it's debatable whether this technically qualifies as a bad special effect or not.

3. Naturally, all the twenty-fifth century colonists have '70s haircuts.

4. The name of the colony's technician and all-round repairman is "Jim", thus giving one of the characters the chance to say 'Jim'll fix it'. Non-British readers should note that *Jim'll Fix It* was a popular children's programme of the 1970s, presented by the deeply unsettling Sir Jimmy Savile, and since *Jim'll Fix It* was (like *Doctor Who*) a staple of Saturday-evening BBC entertainment this looks an awful lot like an in-joke.

Except that... *Jim'll Fix It* didn't start until 1975. Since the "Colony in Space" line is obviously presented as a joke of *some* description - two of the characters giggle at it, in a knowing sort of way - the authors of this present volume find themselves unable to explain what on Earth is going on here. It looks, in short, like an error in the continuity of the *real* world. At the very least, it should probably be remembered as the best-ever example of *Doctor Who* accurately predicting the future.

5. Nevertheless, it seems right that this sort of thing might seem funny to colonists with no discernible sense of humour and an obsession with 1970s culture, since in this era the IMC people watch footage of the Vietnam War on their 'entertainment console'.

6. The moral debate between the Doctor and the Master, refereed by a godlike alien whose power the Master desperately covets, is almost identical to the climax of the following story ("The Daemons") except that it makes more sense. In both cases, however, it's remarkably easy to make the godlike alien blow himself up.

The Continuity

The Doctor The Doctor *is* briefly tempted when the Master offers him the power to end war and suffering across the universe, though he ultimate-ly concludes that 'absolute power is evil' [he doesn't hesitate to refuse when the same kind of power is offered to him again in 8.5, "The Daemons"]. Strangely, he seems to recognise the plant Uxarieus just by looking at the scanner picture of it even though he doesn't know anything about the place [he had a crafty peek at the controls while Jo wasn't looking]. He claims to be an expert in agriculture, on top of everything else.

• *Inventory.* The Doctor still has the Master's TARDIS key [from 8.1, "Terror of the Autons", so it can't be difficult for Time Lords to make spare keys for their vehicles]. His sonic screwdriver seems to beep out a warning when he's in the vicinity of an alarm beam.

The Supporting Cast

• *Jo Grant.* Despite everything she's seen so far, Jo still has trouble believing that the TARDIS can take her to other planets. She's never been inside the TARDIS before, even though she must have been working with the Doctor for months. It's suggested that she's never really believed in the Doctor's ability to time-travel, either, and that she's always thought his stories were just jokes. [The events of "The Claws of Axos" just confused her.]

• *UNIT.* Still on the lookout for the Master, with UNIT agents sending reports of possible sightings back to the Brigadier. They've already arrested the Spanish ambassador by mistake.

The Supporting Cast (Evil)

• *The Master.* Here he's said to have stolen files from the Time Lords [before he first arrived on Earth in 8.1, "Terror of the Autons", explaining how he knew about the Doctor's exile], including the file on the doomsday weapon. Although recently he's been visiting a lot of planets in search of something [the file on the weapon was incomplete, and didn't give its exact location?]. Here he carries pellets of knockout gas and a respirator [which he used for the first time in 8.2, "The Mind of Evil"]. He doesn't even attempt to use his hypnosis powers when hostile IMC men surround him [so he can only hypnotise one subject at a time].

The Master seriously believes there's a chance of the Doctor joining him in his attempt to take over the galaxy, *if* he plays up to the Doctor's altruism and claims that the doomsday device can be used to bring peace. It's notable, though, that he makes this offer to the Doctor when he doesn't technically need the Doctor's help… suggesting that he has some real regard for his arch-rival, or at least considers the Doctor generally useful. He sees it as a basic law of life that one must either rule or serve. [His inferiority complex again. He's a megalomaniac because he doesn't want to be bettered.]

The TARDIS(es) The Time Lords state that they 'immobilised' the Doctor's TARDIS. Here the Doctor builds himself a completely new dematerialisation circuit, one which supposedly bypasses the Time Lords' 'homing control', but the Ship is steered to Uxarieus by remote before he's even set it in motion.

The Doctor describes the TARDIS as being outside the space-time continuum when it travels, and strobing lights fill the scanner while it's in flight, eventually giving way to the planet where it's about to land [see **Does the TARDIS Fly?** under 5.6, "Fury from the Deep"]. The scanner itself is now a conventional TV screen again. It takes only four people to physically shift the Ship's exterior.

The Master's TARDIS has a console room with the same decor and kind of console as the Doctor's, although it's fitted with two transparent plastic tubes for holding prisoners. The Ship can fly like a spacecraft when it takes the form of one, complete with rocket-trails. The Doctor concedes that it's a slightly more advanced model than his own. As a security precaution the Master carries a pocket-sized device which floods his own TARDIS console room with sleeping gas, and a little TV screen inside the gadget shows him what's happening there.

The Time Lords The Time Lords' files describe the Uxarieus doomsday weapon, and they consider the Master's theft of this information of sufficient threat to use the Doctor to deal with the problem. [Again, there are clearly "rules" governing the degree to which they can intervene. They're unable to track the Master themselves, but for some reason the Doctor's an acceptable agent.] The three Time Lords who make this decision wear austere black robes and seem to be some form of secret committee. [Are they members of the High Council? The Doctor implies as much later on. One of them turns up again in 10.1, "The Three Doctors", where he's seen hanging around with the President and Chancellor.]

The Non-Humans

• *The Primitives.* The natives of Uxarieus once had a highly advanced technological civilisation, creating a super-race through genetic engineering and developing their "doomsday weapon". Though never actually used, the weapon was capable of destroying suns and was responsible for the creation of the Crab Nebula during testing.

The Master believes it to be 'the most powerful weapon ever created', and even the Doctor finds it unbelievable [because only Time Lords are supposed to have that level of solar engineering; see 25.1, "Remembrance of the Daleks"]. The weapon stretches for miles within the subterranean city which used to be the centre of the aliens' culture, and its radiation has not only blighted the soil and caused the people to physically decay but reduced the natives' society to a primitive level.

Most of the primitives are more or less humanoid, with muddy green skins and faces not unlike the Easter Island heads, but within the darkened, dilapidated city live mutations of the species who have pale skins, walnut-like craniums and almost no eyesight. They're also shorter, wear ornate robes and obviously wield power as priests of some kind, but like the others they're telepathic and incapable of speech.

At the top of the hierarchy is the guardian of the weapon, who resembles an even more shrivelled version of one of the priests, around two feet tall and apparently incapable of moving from his seat of power. This guardian seems to be the only native who can speak [in English???], who can reason with the Doctor and who understands the technology of the weapon he guards. Such is the "wisdom" of this creature that after he meets the Master he's prepared to destroy the weapon, and most of his species along with it. [He may feel it's a merciful release for his people, or he possibly feels some self-destructive guilt about the damage his kind did in the past.] At one point he causes a gun in the Master's hand to instantly vanish [telekinesis or 'transmigration of object'?].

Planet Notes

• *Uxarieus.* A rocky and largely barren world, with birds and insects but no larger animal life other than the primitives. [It's doubtful that *no* animal life ever existed there, or the primitives never would have evolved. Radiation from the weapon probably wiped out most other species.] Earth Control classified Uxarieus as suitable for colonisation, but it turns out to be the richest known source of the durilinium that Earth needs for living-units, i.e. houses.

[The spelling's debatable here, since generations of fan-guides have gone for "Exarius", "Uxarius" or even "Agzarius". But "Uxarieus" is the scripted, BBC-approved version. Since *Doctor Who* planets tend to have overly-appropriate names, this may be a feeble pun on "Uxorious", meaning "like a wife". Fittingly homely for the "eco-frontiersman" colonists, who occasionally border on the Amish.]

History

• *Dating.* The colonists left Earth in 2471, and according to a calendar it's now Tuesday, 3rd of March, 2472. [Jo, not quite believing in time-travel yet, thinks that Mary's reference to things on Earth back in '71 means 1971 rather than 2471. This suggests that in her own time it's got to be 1972 at the very least.]

At this point Earth is polluted, over-crowded, devoid of grass and run by a government which locks up dissenters, although starvation isn't a problem there. 'Floating islands', rising to three-hundred storeys, are planned to house hundreds of millions [the forerunners of the sky-cities mentioned in "The Mutants" (9.4), c. 3000 AD]. There are a hundred billion people on the planet.

Space travel is common but apparently expensive, and the colonists who settle on Uxarieus aren't ever expecting to go back. Technology seen here includes hand-held medical scanners and [holographic] image projectors. Both the colonists and the IMC use old-fashioned firearms, presumably because they're cheaper, while the colony itself is made up of pre-fabricated domes and powered by a nuclear generator. Everyone is expected to carry official papers, with interplanetary travel permits and spaceship registrations being mentioned. Acts of piracy carry the death penalty by interplanetary law, and the colonists' actions against the IMC are considered treason as the IMC captain is the legally-appointed governor.

The Interplanetary Mining Corporation is a ruthless, near-militaristic organisation based on Earth. Though there's a system of justice to protect colonists, the homeworld is so desperate for resources that the IMC knows it can break the rules without anyone asking questions. The mark three servo-robot used by the IMC is a big, heavy-duty device with a variety of tool attachments, and follows the programs it's given by remote control.

Disputes on colony planets are settled by an Adjudicator, who - judging by the Master's charade - arrives on his own in an official spacecraft. Adjudicators are obviously accorded a great deal of respect, and wear elaborate black-and-silver robes of office. Usually the Adjudicators' investigations take years [the Master's version of justice isn't particularly realistic].

The Analysis

Where Does This Come From? On the face of it, "Colony in Space" is simple: it's a western. Even the people who made it thought of it as 'Cowboys and Indians in space'. The colonists are the every-day folk trying to start a new life on the frontier, and the IMC is the gang of black-hats that wants to run them out of town. The Adjudicators are the Marshals sent to keep order; and the native aliens are the Injuns, usually at peace with the palefaces but who can turn on you if you stray onto their territory. So far, so easy.

Except that it doesn't have the *philosophy* of a western. Real westerns come from a specifically American tradition, from a myth of rough, tough pioneers pushing back the boundaries of the Land of the Brave. But far from being freedom-loving trailblazers, trying to spread the human / American way across the universe (as in *Star Trek*, that other notable space-western of the period), these colonists are more like refugees; scared, desperate people who just want to get away from Earth because it's such a God-awful place.

Rather than being a tale of the wild frontier, then, this is *Doctor Who*'s first flirtation with eco-fable. Like the later stories "Frontier in Space", "The Green Death" and "Invasion of the Dinosaurs" - two of which Malcolm Hulke also wrote - what drives "Colony" is a sense of *fear*. The bleak, crowded Earth draws on a genuine anxiety, at a time when nobody used words like "environmentalism" but had to make do with "pollution" and "over-population" instead. Though many things in this story tend to strike the modern viewer as frankly funny-looking, there is a sense of seriousness here, a sense of concern about a potentially worn-out future. (Unusually, the Master is actually the *least* interesting part of the plot, since his straight-out villainy doesn't have the same bite as the Earth-in-crisis material. The eco-theme comes through a lot more strongly in Hulke's novelisation of the story, the not-at-all seriously-titled *Doctor Who and the Doomsday Weapon*.)

But even the name "Colony in Space" is telling. By 1971 the idea of colonies in space was nothing new, even to SF on television, and there'd been colony worlds in *Doctor Who* as early as 1965. Why draw attention to it here, with a title quite so blatant? The answer is that post-moon-race, the rules had changed. This isn't a story about a dynamic new age of space exploration, it's a story for a time when the glamour of the moon had faded and Earth was becoming a problem again. Even the Uxarean super-weapon's radiation seems to reflect contemporary "issues", while the (stock) footage of civil unrest on Earth makes the homeworld look as if it's been fighting the same war since the '60s. And not for the last time, the villain is a big corporation acting with government approval.

Oh, and as an aside: the Uxarean city, covered in the hieroglyphs of an ancient alien civilisation, is the first sign of the von-Danikenism (the notion that aliens landed on Earth and influenced ancient societies) that would become most obvious in "Death to the Daleks" (11.3) and "Pyramids of Mars" (13.3).

Things That Don't Make Sense The Doctor distracts the guard in the alien city with conjuring tricks before knocking the creature out and making his escape. But since the primitives are telepathic, why is the guard (a) fooled by sleight-of-hand, which relies on the magician hiding his intentions from the audience, and (b) unaware that the Doctor's about to hit him? [The Doctor can block his own thoughts?] Winton, the colony's security head, completely ignores the Doctor's warning that colonist Norton is an IMC agent in disguise, and lets him have a gun during the big firefight, even though his story about being hunted by lizards has been exposed as a lie and people keep dying mysteriously whenever he's around.

When the Doctor breaks into the Master's TARDIS, he makes it quite clear that there's an alarm beam in the doorway that will trigger if anybody walks through it, and he and Jo have to crawl under it in order to get in. But once they're inside, Jo is so determined to set it off that she *walks all the way back across the room going 'oh, Doctor, do come on' before standing in its path*. She is, in a very real sense, gagging for it. It's also strange that the Ship should have so many internal

defences, when the lock's so simple that anybody can get in with a yale key. [In the Master's world, punishment is better than prevention.]

The Master's dialogue at the end of episode five isn't the same in the recap at the start of episode six. Not for the first time, the cliffhanger's shot differently and has music added so that the audience won't expect that the problem will be resolved by the Doctor shouting 'hai!'. And given that Earth's population is as large as we're told, is the rather unpredictable Caldwell really the most reliable mining engineer the IMC can get?

Critique Nothing dates faster than the future. While the early Third Doctor stories now seem so of-their-time that re-watching them is like taking Modern Cultural History 101, "Colony in Space" was originally designed to impress the audience with its scary, non-shiny vision of future history, a long way from the smoother and cleaner space-environments of the '60s. But more than thirty years on, we've seen all of this before, and the only things we find ourselves wondering at are the sideburns.

As a result the story's stripped of most of its meaning, and we're just left with lots of people running around, escaping, arguing and occasionally shooting at each other, especially in the later episodes. And yet... Malcolm Hulke *was* an effective, humanistic writer, even if he was working in a medium which now seems chronically out-of-touch. For all its faults, it's hard to watch "Colony in Space" without feeling charmed *sometimes*. It's dull in parts and it's frequently over-laboured, but really, it's much too honest to be thoroughly disliked.

As in "The Silurians", Hulke's script starts by giving us a monster (in this case the IMC robot) which vanishes from the plot after the first couple of episodes.

The Facts

Written by Malcolm Hulke. Directed by Michael Briant. Viewing figures: 7.6 million, 8.5 million, 9.5 million, 8.1 million, 8.8 million, 8.7 million.

Supporting Cast Nicholas Pennell (Winton), John Ringham (Ashe), Roy Skelton (Norton), Helen Worth (Mary Ashe), John Scott Martin (Robot), Peter Forbes-Robertson, John Baker, Graham

Leaman (Time Lords), Bernard Kay (Caldwell), Morris Perry (Dent), Tony Caunter (Morgan), Norman Atkyns (Guardian), Roy Heymann (Alien Priest).

Working Titles "Colony".

Cliffhangers Alone in a colony building, the Doctor's examining the aftermath of a "giant lizard" attack when the IMC robot trundles through the door towards him; in the same building, the same robot bears down on the Doctor *again*, but this time under the control of Morgan, the IMC second-in-command, and with fake lizard-claws attached to its arms; the primitives take a captive Jo to the underground city, and everything goes dark as the tunnel entrance closes behind them; during the firefight at the colony, the Master points a gun at the Doctor and announces that he's about to become the victim of stray bullets ('it's always the innocent bystanders who suffer'); outside the primitives' city, the Master prepares to push the remote-control button which will kill Jo with poisoned gas inside his TARDIS.

The Lore

• This story is the first directed by Michael E. Briant, later the director of "The Sea Devils", "The Green Death" and "The Robots of Death", among others. Roy Skelton, after years as the voice of every monster worth hearing, gets an on-screen appearance as Norton. He'll be back under odd circumstances (see 10.6, "The Green Death"). Ashe - the polite, dithery and rather ineffectual leader of the colonists - is, unbelievably, played by the same actor (John Ringham) who took the role of the crazed, bloodthirsty Aztec war-priest in 1.6, "The Aztecs".

• After Malcolm Hulke submitted his original storyline, Briant suggesting changing the character of Morgan (Captain Dent's murderous, sadistic right-hand man) into a woman. Tragically the BBC's Head of Drama insisted on changing him back again, on the grounds that it might look 'kinky' in a world still obsessed with *The Avengers*. Nevertheless, actress Susan Jameson - having cancelled other commitments - was paid for the role. Tony Caunter, already in the cast as a one-line guard, was rapidly "promoted".

• The "futuristic" buggies used by the IMC were Haflinger cross-country vehicles on loan. The BBC

lost an £80 deposit, partly as a result of Jon Pertwee being rather taken with them and going for joyrides when he wasn't shooting.

• The line about the Spanish Ambassador being mistaken for the Master is a belated reference to the ITC series *Sir Francis Drake* (1961-62), in which the Spanish Ambassador was played by Roger Delgado.

• This was the first story to be accompanied by a "teaser" comic-strip in the *Radio Times*, drawn from the TV script by the legendary *Eagle* and TV21 artist Frank Bellamy, who also provided monochrome pictures beside the listings for each episode. This extra splash of publicity may at least partly explain the pick-up in the programme's viewing figures after "The Claws of Axos". The *Radio Times* illustrations continued until Season Eleven, although Bellamy still contributed occasional *Doctor Who* work after that point, including a superb version of the Skarasen from "Terror of the Zygons" (13.1) which is still how many of us like to *imagine* the Skarasen looking.

8.5: "The Daemons"

(Serial JJJ. Five Episodes, 22nd May - 19th June 1971.)

Which One is This? The Devil went down to Ambridge. The Master's a trendy vicar, stone gargoyles and Morris dancers threaten the destruction of the world, something with cloven hoofs is about to manifest itself in the church crypt and the pub landlord's hens have stopped laying.

Firsts and Lasts Season Eight (the "Master Season") ends with a story co-written by Robert Sloman and producer Barry Letts, which is something of a turning-point. From this point on *all* the Pertwee seasons end with a story by Sloman, working so closely with Letts that each year's final story tells you something about the producer's vision for the series. "The Daemons" makes some suitably apocalyptic revelations about Earth's history and finally sees the Master captured after twenty-five episodes of trouble, while subsequent season-enders - "The Time Monster", "The Green Death" and "Planet of the Spiders" - are all pitched as important moments for the Doctor's character.

This is the first time that most of the key members of UNIT are seen in civilian dress, since by this stage the Doctor's relationship with the troops is supposed to be mellowing out and they're now allowed to be people as well as "the cavalry".

Five Things to Notice About "The Daemons"...

1. One of the best-remembered - nay, *defining* - stories of the Jon Pertwee years, "The Daemons" runs the gamut of great dramatic gestures, so that one minute there's a helicopter exploding and the next the Master's dressing up as the head of a satanic coven to summon the Devil. Casual students of the black arts will notice that the Master misquotes Aleister Crowley, 'to do my will shall be the whole of the law', thus once again proving that he's evil.

2. Sadly, "The Daemons" is also notorious for having one of the least convincing endings of any *Doctor Who* story, in which the vast and all-powerful Azal - last of the Daemons - explodes when Jo confuses him a bit.

3. The moment in episode two when Yates and Benton look down from a UNIT helicopter, and see a line of gigantic hoofprints marked out across the grass of Devil's End, is suspense-building at its best. Later the Doctor's menaced by evil Morris dancers, something with which anybody who's been to a *real* English May Day celebration will be able to sympathise. (These scenes may remind some viewers of the classic British horror film *The Wicker Man*, but it's worth pointing out that this came first. However, if this story does indeed end on the 1st of May 1973 - see **What's the UNIT Timeline?** below - then at the same time the Doctor and Jo are dancing merrily around a maypole in episode five, Edward Woodward is being burned to death in a pagan rite on a small Scottish island.)

4. Local white witch Miss Hawthorne supplies some beautifully contrived exposition, when she mentions the priest who's been replaced by the Master: '*I mean Canon Smallwood, our old vicar. The one who disappeared in such mysterious circumstances.*'

5. And finally... "The Daemons" features one of the series' best-known and most-quoted lines, in the form of the Brigadier's casual, off-the-cuff order to one of his men when he's confronted with a living gargoyle at the church: 'Chap with the wings there. Five rounds rapid.'

The Continuity

The Doctor The Doctor utterly refuses to believe in magic, or even use the word, insisting that all phenomena can be explained scientifically [compare with 26.1, "Battlefield"]. Even when Miss Hawthorne argues, convincingly, that magic is the same thing as the Daemons' "psionic" science anyway. He's very bad at being polite when he's flustered, doubly so when someone accuses him of wearing a wig.

The Doctor can survive a drop in temperature which would kill a human being, and knows how to ride a motorcycle. Curiously he believes that humanity will 'probably' blow up the world [referring to future World Wars, or has he just forgotten future history?], and he has no interest in gaining the Daemons' power even for altruistic reasons, believing that humanity should be left to grow up by itself. He appears live on national television as the barrow is opened.

• *Background.* Not only does the Doctor know that something terrible's buried under Devil's End, he also knows the history of the Daemons in detail, suggesting first-hand experience. [There were failed attempts to open the Devil's Hump before - see **History** - so was the Doctor involved? An intriguing scene was cut during filming, in which the Master speculates on how much the Doctor remembers.] Here he quotes the first line of an old Venusian lullaby [the same one he uses in 9.2, "The Curse of Peladon"], which translates as 'close your eyes, my darling... well, three of them at least'.

• *Bessie.* Here the Doctor fits a radio control device, which can be used to steer Bessie from a little gadget in his pocket. He's never seen to use this again.

The Supporting Cast

• *Jo Grant.* Utterly dedicated to the Doctor by now, she's prepared to sacrifice her life to save him, even though he spends much of the preceding day being rude to her. She's distinctly superstitious and easily impressed. [By now she's become far less independent than in earlier appearances, although she's still prepared to impulsively rush off and get captured by the Master.] The Doctor never thanks her for saving either him or the world, and when she follows the Doctor's example by criticising the Brigadier for wanting to blow things up, the Doctor gives her a

What's the UNIT Timeline?

Since we've established that the UNIT stories are perfectly at home in the early '70s (for the inevitable argument see **When are the UNIT Stories Set?** under 7.1, "Spearhead from Space"), the next step is to establish a chronology that actually makes some kind of sense.

Though this present volume isn't exactly obsessed with creating a timeline for the entire *Doctor Who* continuity, and feels that's a job best left to Lance Parkin's *History of the Universe*, the dating of the UNIT stories is such a contentious area (even Parkin doesn't touch it) that it's worth looking at in detail.

Obviously no chronology is going to be *entirely* acceptable to fandom-in-general, but this is the one which - in the authors' opinion - has the minimum possible number of glitches. It also follows the general principle that most of the UNIT stories are set *one* or *two* years in the future.

c. 1967: "The Web of Fear". There's nothing in "The Web of Fear" to indicate that it's supposed to take place in the future, and the original plan to set the UNIT stories a few years ahead of time obviously hadn't been made by this point. 1967 dates it to the year in which it was written, although it was broadcast in early 1968. (The novel *Downtime* insists on 1968, which is at least feasible, and it should be noted that the Yeti incursion lasts for some time before the Doctor gets involved. See 5.5 for more.)

Autumn 1970: "The Invasion". Always controversial. The Brigadier recalls the events of "The Web of Fear" taking place four years earlier, but he *is* speaking from memory and on the spur of the moment, so here we've given him a little leeway and suggested just over three years instead (well, he might have been rounding up). The alternatives are to move "The Web of Fear" backwards to 1966, which is certainly possible but a little clumsy, or to move "The Invasion" forward. Which we don't want to do, because…

Late 1970: "Spearhead from Space". According to "Planet of the Spiders", the Third Doctor arrived on Earth 'months' after the events of "The Invasion". The reason for dating "Spearhead" to late 1970 or early 1971 is simple: the shops still use imperial currency, rather than the decimal currency introduced to Britain in February 1971. Now, the truth is that if we can believe in a world where a well-known UN division fights aliens then we can believe in a world where the British currency system changed at a slightly later date. But frankly the change was such a defining event in the British consciousness that it's a perfect historical marker. To the offspring of the '60s and '70s, altering it would be like altering the dates of World War Two.

Early 1971: "Doctor Who and the Silurians", "The Ambassadors of Death". The Doctor's settled on Earth by the time of "The Silurians", and not much time passes between that and "The Ambassadors of Death" as he's still harping on about the Brigadier's act of mass-murder. There's more imperial money being exchanged.

July 1971: "Inferno". A calendar in the parallel universe says it's the 23rd of July, so unless the dates are all wrong in the other world then this looks fairly solid.

October 1971: "Terror of the Autons". The Doctor's been working on the dematerialisation circuit for three months, and he hadn't even touched it by the end of "Inferno". Liz's departure also seems to have happened a while ago. October makes sense, since it doesn't look like summer in the story and the radiators are on inside Mr. Farrell's house.

Mid-1972: "The Mind of Evil". Now, here's controversy for you. In "The Mind of Evil" it's been 'nearly a year' since the Master set up the Keller Machine. It's unlikely that the Master could have gone back in time straight after "Terror of the Autons" and installed the Machine before his arrival, since his TARDIS wasn't working at that stage and it (probably) would have breached the Blinovitch Limitation Effect anyway. It's unlikely that he arrived on Earth months before "Terror of the Autons" and secretly worked on the project for some time before revealing himself, as the Time Lords would have warned the Doctor sooner. And it's unlikely that he even considered the Keller Machine idea before the Nestenes were defeated,

continued on page 61…

59

patronising stern lecture. There's no pleasing some people.

• *The Brigadier.* Despite his irritation at being woken up to hear that his entire staff has gone AWOL, here he responds to unusual circumstances very ably. His trust in the Doctor's gadgetry means that instead of getting trigger-happy he's reduced to grumbling that he sometimes wishes he worked in a bank. Nevertheless, the rest of UNIT act as if they've got a day off school when an impenetrable barrier separates them from him. The Brigadier sleeps alone [but see **The Lore**].

• *Captain Yates.* He and Benton are quite prepared to go off on an unauthorised jaunt in the Brigadier's helicopter and improvise rescue plans. [Yates also takes over from Jo as principal expository question-feeder here.]

The Supporting Cast (Evil)

• *The Master.* Having previously called himself "Colonel Masters" ["Terror of the Autons"], here he develops his habit of using a pseudonym that means "Master" in another language. He's not great at staying in character when trying to charm people, his impatience causing him to snap and start demanding their obedience. It's not clear how he finds out about the Daemon at Devil's End [more Time Lord files?].

The Non-Humans

• *The Daemons.* Roughly 100,000 years ago, the Daemons came to Earth from Demos, a planet 60,000 light years away on the other side of the galaxy. They originally came to help homo sapiens kick out Neanderthal man, and have been 'coming and going' ever since [so Azal's ship hasn't been there for 100,000 years]. The Doctor claims that the Greek civilisation, the Renaissance and the Industrial Revolution were all inspired by them.

The Daemons were amoral by human standards, and Earth was a scientific experiment to them. They were known to destroy their failed experiments, with Azal telling the Master to 'remember Atlantis' [see **How Many Atlantises are There?** under 4.5, "The Underwater Menace"]. Human myths of magic are just remnants of the Daemons' advanced science, Azal apparently being the inspiration for Azael, the fallen angel. The Doctor describes him as the worst menace ever to face humanity, thus shifting the Keller Machine from the number one position

after just a few months.

The Daemons were humanoid in shape, but with goat-like legs, cloven hoofs, satanic features and - of course - horns, which therefore became a symbol of power throughout human culture. Azal, the last of the Daemons [probably in the universe, although he *could* feasibly just mean on Earth], is at least twenty feet tall when he appears but can cause both himself and his technology to change size. His spaceship is only fifteen inches long when the Doctor finds it, even though it weighs around 750 tons and was 200 feet by 30 feet when it came to Earth.

When Azal's miniaturised he's so small that he's practically invisible [not to scale with the miniaturised spaceship, then, or he'd be more like an action figure]. He absorbs energy / matter from the environment around him to grow, while shrinking makes him shed the surplus energy as a heatwave. [Although it's hard to spot, the end of episode three has the Master's face covered in frost as the Daemon expands and sucks in heat.] He can also psychically generate a heat barrier, a dome of energy ten miles across and a mile high, which explodes anything it touches. Azal himself can generate lethal energy from his fingers.

The Daemon sees Earth as a failure, and he's been 'instructed' [by whom?] to destroy it or pass on his knowledge and power to someone else who'll oversee things [this suggests an unshakable scientific procedure among Daemons]. Procedure is clearly important to him, as he insists on appearing before the Master exactly three times, making his decision on his last appearance. It's not clear whether Azal's been conscious all these years, or whether he only wakes up when the Devil's Hump barrow is opened.

He's able to sense the Doctor's alien presence at long range, and considers even a Time Lord's knowledge to be inferior [but presumably the Daemons never cracked time-travel]. He believes himself so rational that when Jo tries to sacrifice herself to save the Doctor, Azal self-destructs, his own power turning against him. [No wonder he's the last of his kind. This is deeply strange, especially since self-sacrifice isn't illogical but a survival technique that even non-sentient species have adopted. The novelisation expands on this *slightly*, giving the impression that Jo's act of "irrational" intervention sets up a psychokinetic field which causes Azal's power to rebound on himself. Though this may be an over-generous way of see-

What's the UNIT Timeline?

...continued from page 59

because at this stage the Master just isn't the type for back-up schemes.

We have to conclude, then, that nearly a year really *does* pass between "Terror of the Autons" and "The Mind of Evil". (Isn't it strange, though, how we can easily accept large gaps between seasons but not between individual stories? As if the scheduling of a BBC TV programme would really make a difference to UNIT.)

Late 1972 - Early 1973: "The Claws of Axos", "Colony in Space". Some months have probably passed since "The Mind of Evil", given that the Master's had time to explore the universe, find Axos and come back to Earth. Assuming that the Master has a habit of returning to Earth in "real time" - meaning, if he's aged six months then he deliberately returns to Earth six months after his last visit, not necessary in a TARDIS but Time Lords seem to keep doing that sort of thing anyway - then more months pass between "The Claws of Axos" and "Colony in Space", as the Master visits several planets prior to landing on Uxarieus.

April - May 1973: "The Daemons". "The Daemons" unquestionably ends on the 1st of May, and again, the Master's spent some time preparing his role as Mr. Magister. Those who aren't convinced that nearly a year passes between "Terror of the Autons" and "The Mind of Evil" might prefer to conclude that it's actually May '72 rather than '73, which is feasible but leaves some awkward loose ends later on. Rugby from Twickenham is on television, so it's probably a weekend, and strictly speaking the 30th of April was a Sunday in 1972. But days of the week *never* seem to match up with dates in the *Doctor Who* universe.

September 1973: "Day of the Daleks", "The Sea Devils". In "Day of the Daleks", it's the 13th of September when Jo leaves the present day. "The Sea Devils" probably takes place shortly thereafter, since the weather looks suitably autumny, but the problem is...

December 1973. "The Time Monster". According to a 'phone conversation between Jo and Benton in "The Time Monster", it's Michaelmas, i.e. the 29th of September (but this is questionable to begin with: see 9.5 for the reasons). Since "Day of the Daleks" is set in mid-September, this means that *if* we take "Michaelmas" literally then the whole of Season Nine takes place over the span of a fortnight and that the Master sets up the TOMTIT project in about a week. And yet, one of the lab-staff involved in TOMTIT suggests she's been working with the Master for several months (again, let's keep the Blinovitch Limitation Effect in mind).

Two explanations present themselves here. One: there's more than a *year* between "Day of the Daleks" and "The Time Monster", and they're different Septembers. Two: it's not really Michaelmas. We'll assume the latter, since a lot of the stories in Season Nine are off-Earth missions for the Time Lords, and if more than a year passes then the Doctor would have to spend most of that time sitting in his lab failing to get his dematerialisation circuit in working order. (*The Discontinuity Guide* has suggested that "Michaelmas" might just refer to the Oxbridge autumn term, but it's anybody's guess how Benton might know a thing like that. Perhaps some student came up to him in the street and said 'it's Michaelmas, so buy one of my crap University magazines'. If so then it's no later than December, when the term ends. Which fits.)

Early 1974: "The Three Doctors". Another season gap before "The Three Doctors" means that it could have been weeks or months since the Master's last sighting. Jo's travels in the TARDIS after this only take a few days, so she gets back to Earth in time for...

April 1974: "The Green Death". There are *two* calendars on display here, one in a security guard's office and one at the pit-head, the first claiming that it's February and the second claiming that it's April. Since the closed-but-curiously-well-staffed pit-head is more likely to keep track of these things than a dim-looking security guard, and since the guard's calendar is clearly a hopelessly out-of-date 1972 model anyway, April's much more likely.

continued on page 63...

ing things. 26.3, "The Curse of Fenric", uses this idea rather better.]

The Master calls on Azal's psionic power through ritual or pure concentration, and his coven helps as violent emotions produce psychokinetic energy. The power can cause weak victims to die of fright; overcome the will of specific targets, turning them into murderers; create forcefields around people; or cause various poltergeist-like phenomena. Miss Hawthorn's "magical" incantations *do* seem to hold the energy back [perhaps any kind of ritual sets up a psychic countercharge, since the Doctor's Venusian nursery-rhyme keeps Bok at bay and part of the Master's invocation to Azal is "Mary Had a Little Lamb" backwards].

The Hump is opened at Beltane, a major occult festival, and the Doctor believes that this is significant. [It's hard to see how, unless the psychic force of the Daemon somehow convinced Professor Horner to open the barrow on that particular night. Or did the Master hypnotise the man?] The Master tries to bind Azal 'in the name of the unspeakable one' [maybe suggesting that there's something even older which Azal should be scared of].

• *Bok, the Gargoyle.* [Named in the script, but not on-screen.] A stone carving in the church cavern at Devil's End, once animated by the power of Azal. It's apparently indestructible - putting itself back together even when it's blown into fragments - and can disintegrate people by pointing at them. The Master can control him telepathically, but he's got a mind of his own. [It seems odd that Azal's power should choose to settle in such a definite form, since Azal has no reason to show off. Either the animation of Bok is the Master's idea, or one of the earlier witch-cults at Devil's End specifically made the gargoyle a receptacle for the Daemon's energy.] Bok can be scared off by something made of iron, the Doctor claiming that iron is an old magical defence. He doesn't believe in it, but Bok does.

• *Venusians.* Evidently they have more than three eyes.

History

• *Dating.* The barrow is opened on the eve of April 30th [probably 1973]. See **What's the UNIT Timeline?**.

According to the Doctor, the Daemons in some way inspired the horned Egyptian god Khnun

[q.v. 13.3, "Pyramids of Mars"]. In the seventeenth century, witches hid from the witch-finder Matthew Hopkins in the cavern under the church at Devil's End. In the eighteenth century, the third Lord Aldbourne performed black magic ceremonies there and it was apparently a site of religious importance to the pagans.

In 1793 Sir Percival Flint attempted to open the Devil's Hump, but his miners ran back to Cornwall, leaving him for dead. Another attempt was made in 1939, but this is described as the 'Cambridge University fiasco'. The "tomb" inside the Hump is ostensibly the same shape as the Daemons' spaceship, though smaller than it would be at full-size. [Which might indicate that human beings built the tomb around it. Throughout *Doctor Who* Britain plays an unfeasibly large part in the history of the world, and most aliens attack it first. Is the presence of Azal the reason for this? The Doctor mentions the industrial revolution, which *is* potentially the country's greatest contribution to global history.]

The Devil's End broadcast is shown on BBC3. [In the real world BBC3 didn't come into existence until the twenty-first century. Since BBC3 presenters Johnny Vaughn and Cat Deeley don't present the barrow opening, we can assume it's not the same station.] Miss Hawthorne claims that Britain repealed the last witchcraft act in 1951 [technically accurate, since the 1951 Fraudulent Mediums Act replaced the 1736 Witchcraft Act]. UNIT helicopters are worth £20,000.

The Nuton power complex [8.3, "The Claws of Axos"] seems to be operational again.

The Analysis

Where Does This Come From? It is, as Jo Grant says, the dawning of the Age of Aquarius.

By 1971 the basic principles of happy, shiny hippyness (mystic UFOs, spiritual energy and consciousness expansion) had taken a turn for the darker, leaving popular culture with a taste for the occult and a tendency to mess around with ouija boards. (See also 11.5, "Planet of the Spiders", in which pop-Buddhism summons demons as well as bringing enlightenment.) "Doctor Who and the Silurians" saw the start of *Doctor Who's* newfound interest in ancient civilisations and race memories, but "The Daemons" goes further, of once again ripping off large chunks of *Quatermass and the Pit* - "Devil's End" instead of "Hobbs End" - to tell a

What's the UNIT Timeline?

...continued from page 61

Mid-to-late 1974: "The Time Warrior", **"Invasion of the Dinosaurs"**. The Doctor's still hanging around with UNIT even though his TARDIS has been fixed, so Jo can't have left him *that* long ago (even if he's trying to fine-tune the Ship, you can't imagine him waiting until it's 100% operational before running off again). "Invasion of the Dinosaurs" takes place a few weeks later. After this the Doctor spends some time dragging Sarah around outer space, so a little while elapses before...

Early 1975: "The Ghosts of N-Space". Yes, all right. The canonicity of "The Ghosts of N-Space", as a story which is both a novel *and* a radio play, is always going to be in doubt. But it's worth including simply because it was written by Barry Letts, who should know a thing or two about when the UNIT stories were supposed to be set. The comet in "The Ghosts of N-Space" returns to Earth every 157 years, and was last seen in 1818, so 1975 is bang on the button.

March - April 1975: "Planet of the Spiders", **"Robot"**. Two stories back-to-back, although three weeks slip by during that difficult regeneration period, and the pass Sarah's issued by the SRS is dated the 4th of April. (The SRS is staffed by fascistic obsessives, so this is a lot more reliable than a security guard's calendar.)

1976, Let's Say January: "Terror of the Zygons". There's no way of knowing how long it takes the Brigadier to use his space-time telegraph and bring the Doctor back to Britain, because there doesn't seem to be any correlation between the time the Doctor spends on the TARDIS and the time the Brigadier spends on Earth while he's gone.

Awkwardly-placed Missing Adventures aside, from the point of view of the TARDIS crew it's only days between "Robot" and "Terror of the Zygons", and more time *must* pass for UNIT. Those who consider the novels to be at least semi-canonical might note that Paul Cornell's *No Future* suggests a date of January 1976 for the Zygon affair. The novel itself is set months later, in June 1976, so everything fits neatly. (It also makes a kind of sense

that in Sarah's time it's 1976 for her during "Pyramids of Mars", since her claim to come from '1980' just sounds like rounding up. Compare this with Jo's dating of the UNIT era in 10.2, "Carnival of Monsters".) The Brigadier retires shortly thereafter, and...

1977: "Mawdryn Undead". ...he's working in a public school a year later. Everything is settled, and all is right with the world.

When it comes to "supporting evidence" most of the New Adventures concur with this version of events, including *No Future*, *Falls the Shadow*, *The Left-Handed Hummingbird* and *Christmas on a Rational Planet*, although *Christmas on a Rational Planet* immediately invalidates itself as a historical source by claiming that "The Web of Fear" and "The Invasion" are set in consecutive years.

The only dissenting voices are *Millennial Rites* (which weirdly claims that the UNIT stories take place in the 1980s, despite the fact that even the most rabid "late UNIT" apologist doesn't try to set the last of them after 1980); *The Face of the Enemy* (see the **When Are the UNIT Stories Set?** essay); and *Blood Heat* (which dates "The Silurians" to 1973, halfway between the "early UNIT" and "late UNIT" versions of history, partly because Jim Mortimore didn't care one way or the other and partly because the novelisation *Doctor Who and the Cave-Monsters* influenced the *Blood Heat* as much as the TV story). Since *Blood Heat* is set in a specially-created parallel universe anyway, this can safely be brushed under the carpet.

Dancing the Code contains a reference to Watergate, and is set just before "The Green Death", which works. Virgin's Almost-a-New-Adventure *Who Killed Kennedy* supplies dates for all the UNIT stories up to "Day of the Daleks", and generally speaking they're a year out, but then again Lance Parkin's *The Dying Days* - in another of Parkin's attempts to refute any kind of early-'70s UNIT dating - claims that the British government changed the dates in the *Who Killed Kennedy* text for security reasons.

distinctly contemporary, even *faddish*, story about psychic powers and devil-worshippers. And once again, most of the standards of pseudo-occult fantasy TV are on show, so Azal even insists on bringing Atlantis into things.

As in Quatermass, here the apparently magical just turns out to be highly-advanced science by another name, but unlike the '50s version "The Daemons" has a mandate to apply the Doctor's reason-over-superstition approach to the trends of the time as well as to the big human issues. After all, Quatermass-creator Nigel Kneale never had a character like Jo Grant on hand to talk about 'the supernatural and all that magic bit'. Interestingly, in the following year Kneale returned to the subject with the BBC play *The Stone Tape*, in which ghosts are "rationalised" by being compared to magnetic tape recordings - quite a novel idea, at the time - and *The Stone Tape* also makes something ancient and nasty responsible for the phenomenon.

It's almost as if the SF writers of the day were getting thoroughly fed up with all this "spiritual" business. There's even a political spin on things here, since the Master's rant against democracy, freedom and lax morals is pitched to the local villagers as a conservative reaction against the late '60s. Of course, the idea that the Daemons' "psychic powers" are any more rational than the witch-magic of Miss Hawthorne is quite ludicrous, but it's the imagery that counts. The Doctor represents *science*, a different way of approaching the world even if the science in question is pure technobabble.

It's also worth mentioning the way episode one presents the archaeological dig as a live BBC TV broadcast, something that's really *very* clever for a decade which hadn't officially invented post-modernism. On the BBC, televised archaeology had already proven a mixed blessing. In the weekend of the first moon landing, BBC2 had offered live coverage of a dig into a Saxon barrow at Silbury as an alternative. As the weekend wore on, presenter Magnus Magnusson became less willing to cover everyone's annoyance that nothing at all had been found. Archaeologists weren't really "characters" back then. TV eccentrics were either scientists, or people who were just abrupt. In the latter category comes the now-forgotten figure of "the rudest man on TV", the long-running *What's My Line?* panelist Gilbert Harding. Professor Horner is Harding to fifteen decimal places.

Another thing often seen on BBC2 was men with little pointy beards and horn-rimmed glasses saying things like 'the soul is a very dated concept, viewing the matter existentially...'. Many of them were the advocates of the much-ridiculed "Good News" Bible, hence the appearance of the Master here. As with Miss Hawthorne, who is - shall we say - from a different denomination, the people most prone to complaining about the traditional Church of England service being "eroded" were those least likely to attend church regularly.

Things That Don't Make Sense The energy barrier around Devil's End is ten miles across, yet its perimeter is next to the one-mile-to-Devil's-End sign. [Shoddy rural signposting. Other villages nearby are called things like "Satanhall" and "Little Coven", but nobody ever detects a theme here.] The Doctor claims that the "tomb" inside the Devil's Hump is the same shape as the Daemon spaceship, but both the tomb and the spaceship appear to be roughly circular, whereas the Doctor later describes the ship as being 200 feet long and 30 feet across [he means 30 feet *deep*, but either way it doesn't give Azal much leg-room when he's at full size].

The Doctor also claims that according to classical aerodynamics it's impossible for a bumbebee to fly, which is actually a modern superstition and he really should know better. Still, his answer when Jo asks him how he knows that everything must have a scientific explanation - 'I just know, that's all' - makes you wonder whether he's understood this whole "science" concept at all. Jon Pertwee isn't sure how to pronounce "Daemons", either.

Nobody ever bothers explaining why the first victim of the Daemons' power, who dies of fright in the opening scene, is killed. [The Master doing a "test run" on someone with a weak heart?] The novelisation calls the man "Josh", the same name as the yokel who's the Axos' first victim, so it's obviously a jinx in rural areas. The scene, as broadcast, makes very little sense to anyone who doesn't know the book and looks as if it's taking place in a petting zoo. On a similarly "rustic" note, no two villagers have the same bucolic accent, while the hayseed Satanists sound bored with all the chanting even *after* the twenty-foot Daemon appears before them.

Azal suddenly turns into a computer ('DOES-NOT-COMPUTE!') during his death-throes. Jo, fleeing for her life, nips into the back-room and picks up her old clothes on the way out of the church. Many people would welcome a blouse as nasty as that being consumed by hellfire.

Critique Hardly surprising that "The Daemons" is still considered the UNIT era's definitive story, because one look shows you everything that was great *and* everything that was grim about *Doctor Who* in the early '70s, a mixture of inspired adventure TV and horrible lapses of judgement.

It's got a better sense of pop-fantasy than any other programme of its era, with a whole host of British character actors playing off each other beautifully in the face of Armageddon, but it also features some tragic padding and has one of the most God-awful endings imaginable. Azal is wonderful, a genuinely scary attempt at a modern TV "Devil" even if you can see the little blue CSO line around him, while Bok the gargoyle is just a man in a bad mask and a body-stocking.

Ultimately, like *Doctor Who* itself, it's a deeply flawed (even unfinished) piece of work but impossible not to like unless you're a sneering halfwit. The last scene, with the Brigadier and Captain Yates being as English as anybody *can* be while the Doctor and Jo take part in the May Day celebrations, is the perfect way to end a series.

The Facts

Written by Guy Leopold (pseudonym for Robert Sloman and Barry Letts). Directed by Christopher Barry. Viewing figures: 9.2 million, 8.0 million, 8.1 million, 8.1 million, 8.3 million. However, the omnibus version shown three days after Christmas got 10.5 million, a return to the popularity of the Hartnell / Dalek days. It's worth mentioning that many of this era's best-remembered stories aren't those which received high ratings the first time round, but those which were repeated in compilation form, "Spearhead from Space" and "The Green Death" being two other notable examples.

Only episode four of "The Daemons" exists in its original colour form, the other episodes released on BBC video having been digitally re-coloured. The change in film stock between episodes three and four is *hugely* noticeable. Episode three comes from three different sources, with a particularly rough twenty-second jump from Betamax to VHS and back.

Supporting Cast Damaris Hayman (Miss Hawthorne), Don McKillop (Bert the Landlord), Rollo Gamble (Winstanley), Robin Wentworth (Prof. Horner), David Simeon (Alastair Fergus), Eric Hillyard (Dr. Reeves), Jon Croft (Tom Girton), Stanley Mason (Bok), Alec Linstead (Sgt. Osgood), John Owens (Thorpe), Stephen Thorne (Azal), The Headington Quarry Men (Morris Dancers).

Working Titles "The Demons" (apparently Christopher Barry changed the spelling…).

Cliffhangers Professor Horner breaks into the Devil's Hump, and Jo finds the Doctor's motionless body in the aftermath; inside the Hump, the Doctor's about to explain everything to Jo when Bok the gargoyle prances down the tunnel after them; the village begins to quake as the Master performs the ritual to summon Azal, but even the Master recoils from the unseen apparition in front of him (the first time that a cliffhanger depicts a threat to the *Master's* life); Azal manifests himself in the cavern for the third and final time, expanding to full size in front of Jo and the coven.

The Lore

• According to *The Making of Doctor Who*, the only series guide in print for most of the 1970s, the model-work destruction of the church at the end of the story was so convincing that one viewer wrote to complain to the BBC about the ethics of blowing up historic buildings to make television programmes. For years this anecdote was treated as a tribute to the ability of the BBC's effects team, but watching the episode again with hindsight it's more a tribute to the fact that some viewers are a bit over-excitable.

• "Charlie" - one of the villagers the Master addresses at the town meeting - is played by John Scott Martin, showing his face on-camera after years of being stuck inside Daleks, giant insects and mining robots.

• The music for the TV rugby broadcast, watched by Yates and Benton at UNIT HQ, is Berlioz's *Symphony fantastique*. This is held to be a clever in-joke, but the next movement of the piece - wherein the protagonist goes to Hell - is woefully inappropriate for BBC sports. Bill McLaren's commentary seems to suggest that five different teams are on the pitch, since it's pasted together out of fragments from several different matches (why not just use one…?).

• Robert Sloman, distribution manager for the *Sunday Times*, had written for the stage before this but not for television. His next idea for a story, "The Daleks In London", was eventually rejected when the decision was taken to include the Daleks in Louis Marks' proposed time-paradox script (see 9.1, "Day of the Daleks" and 9.6, "The Time Monster"). Sloman's son was called Guy, and Leopold was Letts' middle name, hence the pseudonym.

• Just like Jo in episode one, Katy Manning really *did* get the map upside-down while guiding Jon Pertwee to location filming earlier that year.

• Jon Pertwee was slightly injured falling off the motorbike. This may have happened when he went joyriding to vent his annoyance at the protracted reshoots of the "diagram" scene. Nicholas Courtney had previously attempted to placate him, a reversal of the situation in "Terror of the Autons" (8.1).

• The line '…and it comes out here' is taken from "The Music Goes Round And Round", a hit for Danny Kaye. Pertwee had doubled for Kaye during the filming of *Knock On Wood*, and "covered" many of his novelty songs on record.

• In the script, a female hand was to have handed the Brigadier the phone when a call awakes him in the middle of the night. Terrance Dicks had created an entire life for the Brigadier, involving a wife called Fiona, which Nicholas Courtney found a bit odd. Benton, meanwhile, was supposed to have a ballroom-dancing partner called "Mavis" (possibly the kid sister he takes dancing in 13.4, "The Android Invasion"). It was the Knockout of the Southern Area Championships, if that helps those of you trying to locate UNIT HQ.

• Stephen Thorne (Azal) was originally to have mimed to the voice of Anthony Jackson (AKA Fred Mumford from *Rentaghost*) while playing Azal, but this went wrong in rehearsals.

• Marketing this story overseas was tricky, and Australian viewers may now be getting their first chance to see it broadcast. Several steps were taken to avoid offending Christian / family sensibilities at the time. God isn't mentioned at any point, and the area beneath the church is never referred to as a "crypt" (so it isn't consecrated ground), while the controller of BBC1 insisted on the removal of a shot in which the Master holds a knife over Jo while she's held down on the altar.

• The menacing shape in the opening scene is a black furry hat owned by Assistant Floor Manager Sue Heddon.

9.1: "Day of the Daleks"

(Serial KKK. Four Episodes, 1st - 22nd January 1972.)

Which One is This? The Daleks fight UNIT in an English country garden, the Doctor visits a nightmare future policed by gorillas in uniform and those pesky Chinese once again threaten to start the Third World War, all as part of one big Dalek-inspired time paradox.

Firsts and Lasts Other than the two 1960s Peter Cushing movies, it's the first time the Daleks appear in colour. (Many viewers in 1972 were surprised to discover that not one of them is red, despite what both the films and the Dalek comic-strips in *TV21* had told them.). Also, the Ogrons make the first of two-and-a-half appearances as the Daleks' lackeys. The Blinovitch Limitation Effect is mentioned for the first time, as a shameless piece of technobabble designed to gloss over complicated time-travel problems, and it'll go on to become a much-abused catchphrase of the series.

Jon Pertwee finally gets out of those black capes, and puts on something more akin to a dog-blanket or a Volkswagen seat-cover. The TARDIS console is seen outside the Ship, and installed in the Doctor's lab at UNIT HQ, for the last time.

Four Things to Notice About "Day of the Daleks"...

1. "Day of the Daleks" continues the great *Doctor Who* tradition of not giving old enemies a proper scene until the end of the first episode, even though the *Radio Times* has already publicised their return and it's hardly going to surprise anyone. Since the Daleks had been away from television for five whole years when this story was first broadcast, and since the plot involves another successful Dalek take-over of the planet, the BBC advertised "Day of the Daleks" by recycling the old publicity material for 1964's "The Dalek Invasion of Earth". Complete with hugely misleading shots of Daleks trundling across London Bridge, but this time in colour.

2. It's a great story for monsters acting out of character. When one of the gorilla-minded Ogrons is asked what happened to the human vic-

tim he was sent to kill, his reply is a slow, half-witted 'we... found... and... destroyed... the... enemy'. When a second or two later he's then asked if there were any complications, he off-handedly mumbles 'no complications' as if he's just forgotten to keep acting stupid. Though that's not as entertaining as the Daleks' shocked response, when told that someone called the Doctor is interfering with their plans: 'DOC-TOR? DID-YOU-SAY... DOC-TOR?' (Not only that, but in episode four there's the glorious sight of a Dalek gingerly pushing open a pair of French windows with its sucker-arm.)

3. When the Daleks attach the Doctor to their mind analysis device, the psychedelic "brain-pattern" we see on the screen is quite blatantly the *Doctor Who* end title sequence, in an obvious attempt to save money on special effects. Although this (weirdly) suggests that the title sequence represents the inside of the Doctor's mind, the effect is rather spoiled when the words "Doctor Who Jon Pertwee" *ever-so-briefly* flash up on screen before the episode ends and the "proper" credits begin. (The other two cliffhangers are reprised with the musical "sting" still included, as director Paul Bernard thought that was how things were usually done.)

4. One of the most memorable scenes here - though not necessarily for the right reasons - is an extended chase sequence which involves the Ogron-pursued Doctor and Jo escaping on a Honda trike that they find outside the Dalek control centre. Though the programme-makers of 1972 presumably thought a Honda trike looked futuristic enough for this sort of thing, with hindsight you just have to ask yourself who the trike

Season 9 Cast/Crew

- Jon Pertwee (the Doctor)
- Katy Manning (Jo Grant)
- Nicholas Courtney
  (Brigadier Lethbridge-Stewart)
- Richard Franklin (Captain Yates)
- John Levene (Sergeant Benton)

- Barry Letts (Producer)
- Terrance Dicks (Script Editor)

belonged to, since the Ogrons would topple over if they tried to climb onto it and the Daleks' Nazi-style policemen would lose an awful lot of authority if they tried using it to keep order. The shot of the trike pulling away from the centre, chased by a group of extras in badly-fitting helmets and black leather tunics, looks for all the world like the evil-alternative-future version of the Keystone Cops.

The Continuity

The Doctor Here the Doctor claims that a principle called the Blinovitch Limitation Effect stops time-travellers constantly going back into their own pasts and making sure that everything turns out all right for them. Sadly, somebody interrupts him before he can explain it properly. [But see **What is the Blinovitch Limitation Effect?** under 20.3, "Mawdryn Undead".]

The Doctor has no problem using the word "ghost" to describe apparitions and manifestations, provided there's a scientific explanation involved, and initially isn't bothered by the fact that Earth is on the brink of war [perhaps knowing that humanity isn't "scheduled" for World War Three yet]. He describes the Daleks as his 'bitterest enemies' and 'the most evil, ruthless life-form in the cosmos'.

• *Ethics.* At one point, the Doctor uses a stolen gun to disintegrate an Ogron who's pursuing him. This is one of the very few times he uses a gun against an opponent, and indeed, killing an "intelligent" creature by *any* means seems out of character for him. He doesn't appear to feel remotely guilty afterwards. [The impression we're starting to get is that the Third Doctor dislikes violence, but is far more willing to use it in a crisis than most of his other incarnations. Even his non-lethal Venusian karate is overly aggressive by the Second Doctor's standards. He may also feel that the Ogrons aren't intelligent enough to count as "real" people, but even so, it's an unsettling thing to watch. And it happens again in 10.3, "Frontier in Space".]

Later, he's quite convinced that killing someone to save the lives of millions is 'still murder'. He even spares the life of the traitorous Controller, persuading the terrorists / freedom-fighters that the Daleks 'would always have found someone'.

• *Background.* The Doctor claims to have given Napoleon the idea for his famous 'an army march-es on its stomach' line, having known him well enough to call him "Boney". [In "The Sea Devils" (9.3) he also claims to have known Nelson, one of Napoleon's arch-nemeses, so he likes playing both sides against the middle. A friendship with Napoleon is a lot more feasible than a friendship with Mao Tse Tung: - see 8.2, "The Mind of Evil" - as Napoleon may have been a dictator, but he came from an age when very few rulers were truly "democratic" anyway. Most of Napoleon's British opponents certainly weren't. At least Napoleon thought of himself as a scientist, and went to investigate Egypt instead of *just* conquering it.]

The Supporting Cast

• *UNIT.* Here the government is no longer using UNIT as standard security for peace conferences, but calls in the Brigadier's team when there's a "special" problem at the site of the summit. Either there's a new lab for the Doctor at UNIT HQ, or a whole new HQ. Here characters go 'down' - i.e. south - from HQ to Auderly, which is said to be fifty miles north of London, while Wales is 'nearby' [see **Where's UNIT HQ?** under 8.3, "The Claws of Axos"]. The soldiers on guard stand to attention when the Doctor arrives, but now have long hair and Frank Zappa moustaches. Once again, the Brigadier is far from camera-shy when the news media turn up.

The TARDIS The Doctor is still working on the dematerialisation circuit, trying to cut out the 'override' which allows the Time Lords to remote-control the Ship. [Here the Doctor has worked out that the High Council steered it in "Colony in Space" (8.4), but he's probably guessing, since at the very least the three individuals responsible weren't the *whole* High Council.]

While fiddling about with the console, the Doctor causes duplicates of himself and Jo to appear, but there's an explosion from the console and the duplicates vanish. The Doctor claims that this is a freak effect, and that the duplicates have gone forward into their own time-stream. [The duplicate Doctor says 'of course, I remember now' as he appears, and knows things will soon sort themselves out, implying that at some point in the future he and Jo will temporarily be transported back to this point... but if so, we never hear about it, since the reprise of this scene was cut from the story. Later in the episode he speaks of seeing himself 'a few moments ago', so the "other side" of

How Does Time Work?

On first sight, the time-paradox we see in "Day of the Daleks" is impossible.

It's the usual drill: the future timeline in which the Daleks take over the world is brought into existence by the guerilla Shura, who travels back in time from that future and causes the whole thing by mistake. Except that in the end the Doctor stops it happening, but even so, it's just a case of one impossibility cancelling out another as the Doctor returns with a warning from a future which doesn't come into being as a result of that warning. (The guerrillas kill several UNIT soldiers in the early part of the story. You have to wonder what the Brigadier puts in the official record.) Causally, none of this should happen. Since there's no reason for it, no point at which the loop begins, it shouldn't begin at all.

At least, not unless it starts from the *outside*. It only seems unlikely if the Daleks - using their newly-developed time-technology to search the universe for easy targets - already knew about the crippled Earth of the late twenty-first century and thought 'a-hah, we'll go and invade *that* in our time machine'. But if the crippled Earth came as a *surprise* to them, then there's a form of logic at work. Daleks from the future arrive in the late twenty-first century and realise, to their amazement, that some kind of apocalypse has devastated Earth. They invade while it's weak, and the apocalypse comes about as an inevitable result of their invasion, even if it happens in the past.

In other words this new structure of history, from its roots in the 1970s to its consequences in the far future, comes into existence the moment that the time-travelling Daleks enter the continuum in the twenty-first century. Admittedly this leaves the question of why the time-travelling Daleks' histories and memories aren't changed, since they come from a future that's now been cancelled out (they remember the Dalek invasion of Earth in 2157, an invasion which will never take place thanks to the new invasion). But we can perhaps assume that in the *Doctor Who* universe a time-traveller never has his / her / its history changed in the way that the rest of the cosmos does. The point is that paradoxes come into being "in one piece", as soon as time-travelling elements which *can* create paradoxes arrive in the past.

But if that's true, then a new question presents itself. Why is this paradox then removed from his-

tory again? If history immediately re-wrote itself as soon as the Daleks arrived in the twenty-first century, to take all historical events into account, then it should have taken the Doctor into account as well and realised that the "new" version of history wasn't feasible (or at least, was self-contradictory) while he was around in the 1970s. The obvious answer is that when the Time Lords dumped the Doctor on Earth, his arrival there *also* instantly changed the entire timeline, erasing the whole Dalek paradox. But this would also be contradictory. His arrival *doesn't* wipe it out, as he's still able to visit the "new" Dalek future after being on Earth for over a year. If being on Earth made the paradox impossible, then history wouldn't have settled that way at all. But it did.

Try drawing this as a diagram and it becomes much easier to get a grip on.

The conclusion is clear, but suggests something rather startling. When the Daleks arrived in the twenty-first century, history immediately re-wrote itself according to what was inevitably bound to happen. The timeline took all factors into account (and no, the timeline doesn't have to be "intelligent" to do this; blind cause and effect are enough) and created the "new" history as a stable, self-contained structure. But it *didn't take the Doctor into account*. It just didn't see him coming. History became settled around everything else, but the Doctor remained an unpredictable factor, able to collapse this whole paradoxical future but not being *guaranteed* to do it. Even a conventional time-traveller's actions should have become part of the process when history was changed. Instead, it's as if the Doctor isn't part of normal history at all.

And this ties in with certain other things we're told throughout the run of the series. In "Invasion of the Dinosaurs" (11.2) time begins to slow down for everybody on Earth, except the Doctor, who for some reason isn't affected by Professor Whitaker's time-field (Sarah suggests it's because he's a Time Lord, and the Doctor agrees). The same sort of thing happens in "The Time Monster" (9.5). The implication is that Time Lords are in some way time-proof, set apart from normal causality or even immune to the course of history. Time doesn't affect them the way it affects ordinary mortals, even ordinary mortal time-travellers. "The Two

continued on page 71...

the encounter might happen then. He also seems to imply that he's not really there, as if it's not true time-travel but a moment's confusion in causality. The Target novelisation of "Day of the Daleks" contains an epilogue in which the Doctor and Jo return to UNIT HQ and find their past selves there, meaning that the console briefly jumps into the future.]

The Non-Humans

• *Daleks.* In the late twenty-first century the Daleks invaded an already-crippled Earth, and they're still in charge several generations later, at which point the time-paradox is resolved and the invasion never took place. [See **How Does Time Work?**.

[One of the Daleks tells the Doctor that they've invaded Earth *again*, meaning that they remember their original invasion of 2157 in "The Dalek Invasion of Earth" (2.2). This confirms that these Daleks are time-travellers, who went back in time *after* 2157 and invaded Earth in the late 2000s, hence the gold Dalek's claim to have changed the 'pattern of history'. The Dalek-invaded future we see here clearly has nothing to do with the 2157 invasion, as the chronology of events is completely different. This time there's no complicated plan to extract the Earth's magnetic core, either.

[These Dalek time-travellers presumably come from a period between 2164 and 2540 (the time of 10.3, "Frontier in Space") as they don't recognise the Third Doctor on sight even though they know that his appearance can change. It might be worth noting that when the Doctor's strapped to the mind-probe, the Second Doctor is depicted with a still from "The Faceless Ones" (4.8), a story in which the Daleks lay a time-travelling trap for him. Though this *could* mean that these Daleks come from a point in Dalek history after 4.9, "Evil of the Daleks" - something mentioned in the script for "Day of the Daleks", but cut from the transmission - it could equally mean nothing at all, since the pictures of former Doctors come straight from the Doctor's own memories rather than any Dalek data-bank. The implication is that time-travel is quite new to these Daleks, though, as the idea of conquering other times is still an exciting prospect for them. It's stated that they don't understand human psychology, which also indicates Daleks from an earlier age than the human-experienced ones we see in "Evil".]

The Dalek leader seen here is coloured gold [an intermediate rank, perhaps more like "regional governor" than "supreme command"]. Normal Daleks are, as expected, silver-grey. Dalek time-technology is so good that "hand"-held modules can transport someone two-hundred years into the past, and return the user even if he's no longer anywhere near the machine. Something resembling a "mini-dematerialisation circuit" is part of the design, and the space-time vortex is mentioned [the same one the TARDIS travels through].

The technology's straightforward enough for the guerrilla resistance to copy it, although the Daleks' "time vortex magnetron" - which looks a lot like a couple of ping-pong balls sitting on top of a post - can draw anybody using one of the modules to their own control room. Once the module is used to transport someone back in time, the two time-zones seem to be "linked" somehow, as the traveller will return after the same amount of time has passed that passed for him in the time he's visiting [all part of the Blinovitch Limitation Effect].

Dalek Earth seems to be one enormous slave colony, where humans are worked to death under the scrutiny of human and Ogron guards. There's a human government, with a human controller running the district where Auderly House once stood. The Daleks' staff have shiny faces and a tendency to talk like zombies [though they don't have big clunky mind-control helmets like the Robomen in "The Dalek Invasion of Earth"]. The Doctor suggests that the Daleks still operate from Skaro in this period, and the Controller seems to agree. The Daleks' empire is currently expanding, which is why they need raw materials. [So do they ship the Earth's looted resources back to their home planet in their *own* time? And if so, then are the Daleks still in charge of Earth there?]

"Dalekanium" is a highly-effective explosive, and the remarkably well-tailored guerrillas stole its formula from the Daleks. [This isn't the same as the Dalekanium mentioned in "The Dalek Invasion of Earth", which was a non-explosive metal christened by the human scientist Dortmun. But since both are Dalek-based materials apparently named by humans in the twenty-second century, there's an obvious historical parallel between the two.]

• *Ogrons.* Large, thick-skinned and stupid, the Ogrons are higher anthropoids who used to live in scattered communities on one of the 'outer plan-

How Does Time Work?

...continued from page 69

Doctors" (22.4) suggests there's a biological element to Time Lord time-travel, a 'Rassilon imprimatur' which makes TARDIS technology possible. And since this imprimatur doesn't seem to be a vital part of any *other* species' time-travel technology - and since the Sontarans are so desperate to understand it, even though they've got a basic form of time-travel of their own - could the point of this biological advancement be to make the Time Lords *free agents* in time? Not just able to travel, but immune to the gross processes of cause and effect, so that they have some power over the outcome of history when lesser beings would just have their destinies determined by the flow of time around them?

A human time-traveller can't really change history, because even the changes s/he makes are an inevitable *part* of that history, but Time Lords actually have the power to choose. This could well be what the Eternals are getting at when they distinguish between Time Lords and 'ephemerals' like human beings (20.5, "Enlightenment"). It could be that the Time Lords' concern about the Daleks is really a concern that the Daleks will soon reach the same level.

What this means, in a universe where time-travel is not only possible but an everyday occurrence,

is quite remarkable. It means, effectively, that only Time Lords have free will. No wonder they're so important to the universe, and no wonder they guard their secrets so closely. When the Doctor states (in "Inferno", 7.4) that the parallel world he's seen proves there is such a thing as free will, maybe it's not human free will that's the issue but his own. It would certainly make sense for the "Inferno" world to be so different not because of something the humans did, but because of something the Doctor did, either through simply being absent from the planet or (as the New Adventures have suggested) because he was present there in a different form.

How the Time Lords got to *be* immune to history, when any scientific discovery which might put a species outside of normal time would logically be a part of history in itself, is another matter. But then, if you take the view that the Time Lords are very old rather than very *futuristic* then they probably remember a time when the rules were different. Or maybe there's some kind of natural process built into the structure of time, which demands that one race of people should be exempt from normal history, just so someone can stand on the outside and make sure everything runs to plan.

It's amazing how much you can infer from "Day of the Daleks".

---

ets'. Though they don't exactly have much to offer in the way of initiative, the Daleks use them as "policemen" because they're loyal, or at least not intelligent enough to be dishonest. [See 10.3, "Frontier in Space", for more on the possible history between Daleks and Ogrons.] The Daleks have equipped them with ultra-sonic guns which completely disintegrate their targets. It's implied that the Daleks themselves are disintegrator-proof.

History

• *Dating.* [September, probably 1973.] Jo Grant establishes that it's the 13th of September when she leaves the twentieth century [and annoyingly the Controller says that she's already told him the year during their off-screen conversation, thus stopping anybody conclusively dating the UNIT stories].

At this point there's a summit conference in Britain, this time hosted by Sir Reginald Styles at

Auderly, a government-owned country house fifty miles north of London. [The name of the house is a matter for some dispute. The novelisation calls it "Austerly", the Brigadier pronounces it "Alderney", but the on-screen caption seen with broadcaster Alex MacKintosh reads "Auderly House".] Styles, the 'Chief Representative at the UN', is apparently the only diplomat capable of convincing the Chinese delegation to reconsider their withdrawal. The world is shown as being closer to the brink of war than ever. [This was feasibly the Time Lords' biggest single reason for exiling the Doctor to Earth in the 1970s. His presence here means the survival of a free human species, but more significantly, a less powerful Dalek empire.]

Observation satellites report troops massing along the Russian / Chinese frontier. In South America and southern Asia, fighting has already broken out in many areas. UNIT is put on maximum alert [there are news cameras at Auderly when the Daleks arrive, so presumably the Brigadier has to slap another D-notice on the press]. The Brigadier, being stiff-upper-lip British, seems to believe that China was just being stubborn in refusing to negotiate. [See also the twentieth century history in 2.8, "The Chase".]

In the alternative future, a series of wars in the late twentieth century led to a hundred years of destruction. Seven-eighths of humanity was wiped out before the Daleks took over.

The Analysis

Where Does This Come From? There has, it's got to be said, already been an awful lot of discussion about the links between '60s / '70s adventure serials and Cold War paranoia. It's worth pointing out, though, that the Cold War went on for rather a long time and that the word "paranoia" covers at least four different things.

In the late '50s, Cold War anxiety was mostly a fear of communist infiltration, warping the minds of Our Children and turning the free-thinking people of the West into robots. In the early '60s it was the sheer, stark terror of the atom bomb, the horror of believing that faceless foreign powers were going to kill everybody on Earth for their own inscrutable purposes. In the late '60s, when things had quietened down, the emphasis was on technocrats running a calculation-war based on Game Theory (although the general public would probably have said that "spies" were a major concern, too). And then, in the early '70s, there was the "bureaucracy" phase. A realisation that if nuclear war came, it wouldn't be a result of evil empires oppressing the Free World but of sad, blustery old men - on *both* sides - not being able to sort out their petty differences in time. Suddenly, it was Summit-Conference-frenzy.

"Day of the Daleks" is the product of that bureaucrat-fear. As in "The Mind of Evil", the world is hanging by a thread not because something terrible is bearing down on it (even the Daleks are just opportunists, ready to take over the world *after* humanity has blown most of it up) but because of the actions of a handful of diplomats. If one moustache-wielding Englishman fails to appear, then it'll mean disaster for us all. No wonder the last scene, with the Doctor imploring Styles to make sure the delegates work out their problems, looks so much like a plea from the heart. You can almost hear the voice of the writer saying 'for God's sake, what's *wrong* with you people?'. The Doctor's casual insult in the middle of the Dalek crisis - 'try and use your intelligence, man, even if you *are* a politician' - seems perfectly normal now, but ten years earlier a man like Sir Reginald would have commanded a great deal more respect even in a work of fiction.

Meanwhile the news reporter seen at Auderly House is real-life BBC man Alex MacKintosh, which gives the whole thing that extra smack of feasibility (see 3.10, "The War Machines"). Unlike the botched attempt at *verité* in "The Daemons", the whole scene is shot as if it were early '70s news footage, with captions superimposed. Albeit in the same lettering used for the end credits.

And what's notable here is that the effects as well as the causes of the Third World War have become more "human". The world isn't a lifeless, radioactive mess after the apocalypse, and the word "nuclear" isn't used anywhere in the script. The environment looks much as it did in 1972 (although confusingly, there are actually more flowers around in the future than in the present), *but* it's run by fascists, traitors and gorilla-faced policemen.

If it seems like an optimistic vision of Earth after the holocaust, then that's only because the Cold-War-culture of the early '70s had difficulty imagining a completely scorched Earth. In the popular psyche a Third World War brought on by evil foreign empires *looks* apocalyptic, but a Third World War brought on by a failure in peace talks just looks bland and sterile.

One of the worst-case scenarios of the time was that instead of a full-on nuclear conflagration, a series of "brushfire" wars between client states would stretch the West to the limit of its military capacity. It's well-known that the Arab-Israeli conflict at the time was a proxy superpower contest, and civil wars from Mozambique to Bangladesh were similarly exploited. Meanwhile Soviet or US sympathisers were staging coups in Chile, Argentina, Greece and the Philippines. The Daleks inherit a future that's been burnt-out, not burnt-up. Hardly surprising that the Doctor tends to sympathise with the rebels rather than the politicians.

So as in "Colony in Space", the future's more like the nightmare vision of the late '60s than a true atomic wasteland. In the US, it wasn't unusual for the publications of the civil rights and anti-

Vietnam movements to depict the police as trained gorillas in uniform. And in the twenty-second century, the Daleks keep the peace with Ogron "policemen", who… well, just *look* at them. The script also seems to be having great fun with the "guerrilla" / "gorilla" homonym. Given that the media of the era was obsessed with (1) terrorism and (2) *Planet of the Apes*, you've *got* to assume that the pun's deliberate. This was the age of the PLO, of the Black September movement and of "celebrity" terrorists like Leila Khaled (whose first name was borrowed by Chris Boucher for 14.4, "The Face of Evil", and whose surname… well, we'll come to that in Season Twelve). "Urban guerrilla" was becoming a household phrase. It was so chic that even Patty Hearst joined in, and lo and behold, in "Day of the Daleks" it's finally a woman who's in charge of the strike-team.

Ironically, in the *real* world relations between East and West were just about to get slightly better, since Nixon went to China only a month after the story was broadcast.

Things That Don't Make Sense A conference to save the entire world is being held at Auderly, so when it becomes clear that the house is a security risk the Brigadier's men are desperate to keep things under control despite all the ghosts, ape-men and vanishing UNIT personnel. Nobody suggests moving the conference to another building instead.

Styles himself is a man so in denial that he won't admit to seeing his "ghostly" attacker even when he's presented with hard evidence, and won't allow the conference to be moved out of the house even when he can hear gunfire outside. As a British politician of the 1970s, *surely* he's familiar with the word "terrorism", so why all the dithering? The Daleks are similarly confused, barging into the house without considering the notion that the people inside might have seen them coming and left, even though they know the Doctor's already gone there with a warning.

The Doctor explains his plan of escape to Jo in a prison cell that's fitted with surveillance cameras, which relay the image straight to the Dalek control room… where the Daleks are watching it with the sound off and talking amongst themselves, making them look (a) incompetent and (b) like Cadbury's Smash Martians. At this point they're actually discussing the question of whether the Doctor really is the Doctor, so at the very least you'd have thought they'd be interested in what

he's got to say for himself.

The Ogron guns aren't Dalek-issue, as the Doctor recognises them as being Earth-made twenty-second century technology, i.e. part of known history. But if they come from a twenty-second century in which global war sent humanity into a new dark age, then why do they end up being produced on Dalek Earth?

Searching the house for the missing Doctor, Yates and Benton don't bother looking in the cellar (where he's being held at gunpoint) even though they know he's been raiding it for bottles of wine since he moved in. Later, on being told that the "last hope for humankind" conference is going to go ahead after all, Yates asks 'oh, when's it on?' as if somebody's just told him there's going to be a live Barbra Streisand concert on BBC2.

And when the Doctor's a prisoner of the camp-but-beastly security guard with the big black truncheon, the guard states that he's been given 'a free sample' of the brutal treatment he can expect if he doesn't co-operate. Nice to know that in this pitiless future, where the entire human species is nothing more than slave labour for the Dalek master-race, capitalist free enterprise is still common enough for people to know what "free sample" means. Do slaves get complimentary sachets of Ogron musk through their letterboxes? No wonder the guerrillas find it so easy to get hold of proper camo gear.

Critique These days *Doctor Who* fans like to think of "Day of the Daleks" as the perfect model of a "straightforward" story - four parts, sparkly monsters and lots of moral anguish from the Doctor - and you can see the appeal. It may have a plot full of whacking great holes, a central concept that wasn't terribly inventive even in 1972 and some truly bizarre notions about the future (shiny-faced computer controllers, global wars without fall-out, power-tricycles…), but it's also a neat, self-contained piece of storytelling which works by being *busy*. With none of the endless padding and arguing of the longer Pertwee stories, this is a four-part story with four parts' worth of material, the only exception being the pointless escape-and-recapture sequence halfway through episode three.

It doesn't hurt that both Auderly House and the '70s-tower-block world of the twenty-second century suggest some kind of human atmosphere, not something you can say about a lot of the installation-bound UNIT stories. The Daleks are smartly used to add weight and colour rather than being at the heart of the plot; ignore anybody who tells you they're not necessary, as the future-evil story-line would lack any kind of focus without them. And there are few moments more iconic than the sight of the Dalek / Ogron procession (forming an Auderly queue?) emerging from under the bridge in the final battle. Anna Barry puts in a memorably likeable performance as the guerrilla strike-team leader, in defiance of some stilted material that doesn't allow the people of the future to use contractions.

The Facts

Written by Louis Marks. Directed by Paul Bernard. Viewing figures: 9.8 million, 10.4 million, 9.1 million, 9.1 million.

Supporting Cast Aubrey Woods (Controller), Anna Barry (Anat), Jimmy Winston (Shura), Scott Fredericks (Boaz), Wilfred Carter (Sir Reginald Styles), Jean McFarlane (Miss Paget), Alex MacIntosh (Television Reporter), Oliver Gilbert, Peter Messaline (Dalek Voices).

Working Titles "Years of Doom", "The Ghost Hunters", and ostensibly "The Time Warriors" (though there's precious little evidence for this last one).

Cliffhangers After getting a fix on the twentieth century, the Daleks in the control room loudly insist that all their enemies will be exterminated; the Doctor pursues the time-travelling guerrillas into the tunnels near Austerly House, and is startled to see a Dalek materialise in the shadows; the Doctor loses consciousness on the Dalek mind analysis machine, while the Daleks once again chant 'exterminate' at him.

The Lore

• When writer Louis Marks first submitted "Day of the Daleks", it was a straightforward time-paradox story with no Dalek involvement whatsoever. Daleks were added by popular demand, and Dalek creator Terry Nation - now too busy with his own projects to try to get his much-mooted Dalek series started on US television - agreed. He received £25 per episode and the credit "Daleks Originated by Terry Nation"; the strange choice of verb, "originated" rather than "created", may well have been intended to gloss over the dispute between the BBC and Dalek designer Ray Cusick. Their late addition to the plot explains why the Daleks appear, on average, for only two-and-a-half minutes in each episode. (The original Dalek-free version looks remarkably similar to "Conquest of the Planet of the Apes" (1972), a time-paradox story about an anthropoid future after a nuclear war caused by people trying to prevent it. However, "Day of the Daleks" got there first. In fact the version with Daleks ends up sounding a lot more like The Terminator, but without any of the hideous macho posturing.)

• The decision not to feature the Master throughout Season Nine was welcomed by Pertwee, who was reported to feel slightly threatened by Delgado's popularity. The decision to use the Daleks was less pleasing to the star, who hated them.

• Director Paul Bernard, new to the BBC from Thames TV, brought with him the use of yellow CSO backdrops and a more overtly "art-school" manner of designing. Many of his sketches were simply turned into solid objects by the "official" designer or costumer. An entire day of experimental shooting with yellow is one reason that the finished story often seems under-rehearsed.

• The Doctor's encounter with Napoleon, first mentioned here, formed the basis of the test-reading for actors auditioning to be the Eighth Doctor in 1995. (The scene, specifically written to show off all the important points of the Doctor's character, was filmed several times over. See 27.0 for a list of some of those who tried it.)

• Considering the ratings boost from the omnibus edition of "The Daemons", it seems strange to note that as this story was broadcast the BBC commissioned a potential replacement for Doctor Who. This was The Incredible Robert Baldick, from Terry Nation, his first BBC gig since "The Dalek Masterplan" (3.4). Despite starring Robert Hardy (later of All Creatures Great and Small fame) as the eponymous Victorian scientist / adventurer, the series bombed. Nation, on its transmission in October 1972, immediately re-approached the Doctor Who production team (see 10.4, "Planet of the Daleks").

• Jimmy Winston, who plays the guerilla Shura, was the original keyboard player for the Small Faces.

9.2: "The Curse of Peladon"

(Serial MMM, Four Episodes, 29th January - 19th February 1972.)

Which One is This? *The Hound of the Baskervilles* re-told in a style that's half medieval and half Glam Rock, with mythical beasts, torch-lit dungeons, bearded men in robes and more alien delegates than you can shake a spinning mirror at. Plus, Ice Warriors.

Firsts and Lasts The Ice Warriors return to the series after a three-year break (see 6.5, "The Seeds of Death") to make their colour debut, and it surprises absolutely no-one to learn that they're green. Some of the characters seen here - along with most of the props and sets - turn up again in the story's sequel, "The Monster of Peladon" (11.4). Pay particular attention to the art nouveau throne, which crops up on most subsequent pseudo-mediaeval planets in the 1970s. The eagle lectern in the TARDIS console room will also become a regular fixture, in "The Time Monster" (9.5), "Image of the Fendahl" (15.3) et seq.

First of the endless uses of the word "interstitial" in this season.

Four Things to Notice About "The Curse of Peladon"...

1. "The Curse of Peladon" comes equipped with five different kinds of monster, a supporting cast dressed in Tolkien-cum-*Flash-Gordon* fantasy-wear, an extended fight scene in an arena and a great big fortress on a lightning-wracked mountainside. It is, therefore, *the* perfect story for eight-year-old boys.

2. Set against this "epic" backdrop there's even an attempt at a love-story between King Peladon and Jo Grant, which leads to some of the most unlikely romantic dialogue in television history. 'My mother was an Earthwoman, so you see, there is a bond between us' is always a favourite, as are 'I was brought up by wise old men, I hardly ever see anyone young or beautiful' and 'one minute you're condemning the Doctor to death, the next minute you're proposing to me'. Anakin and Padmé just aren't in this league.

3. This story and "The Monster of Peladon" were the only Pertwee tales with no location filming. However, two scenes were shot on film at Ealing Studios for that "on location" look, one being the stormy mountainside set and the other

being the gladiatorial battle that nobody can watch without humming the "Kirk fighting" music from *Star Trek*. (This scene may or may not have been designed to look as if it's "outdoors", as it apparently has a roof and the spectators are all shot on video. Yet it's telling that the novelisation depicts the arena as an enormous outdoor stadium.)

4. And the Alpha Centauri delegate, with his great big domed head and single enormous eye, is one of the great "rude-looking" *Doctor Who* monsters. The moment when the Ice Warriors menace him into voting their way, and he sheepishly raises all his right pseudopods in favour of the motion, is quite lovely.

The Continuity

The Doctor The Doctor is prejudiced when it comes to Ice Warriors, believing them to be 'savage and warlike' before he finds out the truth. It's one of the few occasions when he's seen to be utterly wrong. He seems to enjoy the process of accidentally getting mixed up in interplanetary politics. Even without Venusian martial arts, he's skilled enough in armed combat to hold his own against the King's Champion.

• *Inventory.* The Doctor carries a spinning mirror which, when fixed to the end of his sonic screwdriver, creates a strobing light and a soothing noise capable of calming a large, angry animal. [At least, it *looks* like his sonic screwdriver. But see 9.3, "The Sea Devils".] The same device almost hypnotises Jo, and even causes some more impromptu gurning from the Doctor himself [so it's not *just* a spinning mirror]. The Doctor calls this 'a kind of technical hypnosis', but also refers to a 'telepathic understanding' [between him and animals?].

• *Background.* He attended the coronation of either Queen Elizabeth I or Queen Victoria, but isn't sure which. Either way, he doesn't see any reason that he shouldn't go back and attend it again. [See **What is the Blinovitch Limitation Effect?** under 20.3, "Mawdryn Undead".]

He knows all about the people of Alpha Centauri [and 12.1, "Robot", hints at a prior visit].

The Supporting Cast

• *Jo Grant.* Jo was planning on a night out on the town with Mike Yates before the Doctor dragged her off in the TARDIS [does this hideous relationship ever get anywhere...?]. By now she's self-confident enough, without even flinching, to bluff a throne-room full of alien monsters into thinking she's a princess. There *is* an obvious attraction between her and King Peladon, and just for a moment it looks as if she's genuinely tempted to stay [c.f. 10.4, "Planet of the Daleks"]. She's also visibly shaken by the death of Hepesh, the high priest, having earlier taken his side against Alpha Centauri in an argument.

The TARDIS   It's still apparently under the Time Lords' influence, although the Doctor once again believes he's in control and says that this is the first test-flight since he got it 'working again'. [It seems the TARDIS can now travel around as much as it wants, but only to places where the Time Lords think the Doctor's presence might be useful. See **What's Wrong with the TARDIS?**.] It's dematerialising properly again [after that little problem in 8.4, "Colony in Space"].

The Doctor believes the TARDIS is 'indestructible', or at least, it can fall off a mountain without suffering damage. [Yet the Doctor seems to think Jo is safer outside than in, so a lot of objects inside the Ship must be smashed to pieces. See **Just How Indestructible is the TARDIS?** under 6.4, "The Krotons".] The scanner's on the blink, thanks to a tiny fault in the interstitial beam synthesiser, an element that's found underneath the console.

The Time Lords   Having set Peladon on the path to joining the Galactic Federation, the Doctor believes it can't have been a coincidence that he arrived here at such a critical time in the planet's history and concludes the Time Lords sent the TARDIS there. [The Doctor's suspicions are never confirmed, but it's a reasonable assessment, even if arriving at critical points in planets' histories is what he *always* seems to do. It's not clear why the Time Lords should want Peladon to join the Federation. But since the rise of the Daleks is such a concern for them (see 12.4, "Genesis of the Daleks" and arguably 9.1, "Day of the Daleks"), since the Federation needs Peladon's resources to fight Galaxy Five (in 11.4, "The Monster of Peladon") and since Galaxy Five will one day ally itself with the Daleks (3.2, "Mission to the Unknown" and 3.4, "The Daleks' Masterplan"), they might be making an early attempt to curb Dalek influence here.]

The Non-Humans

• *Ice Warriors*. Since the Doctor last met them in the twenty-first century, the Ice Warriors have rejected violence 'except in self-defence' and are loyal members of the Federation: see **History**. Here they don't identify themselves *as* Ice Warriors.

The two-man Ice Warrior delegation is headed by Lord Izlyr, his aristocratic rank denoted by a smoother helmet, less armour and what look like marks of status on his chest-plate. [The phrase "Ice Lord", oft-used in fandom, is never mentioned here.] Despite being at peace these days, Izlyr still demonstrates a distinctly military sense of nobility, and sub-delegate Ssorg carries a large firearm that can apparently kill any living creature. The weapon is no longer physically incorporated into the armour.

Trisilicate, a metal used by the Ice Warriors, can only be found on Mars [but see "The Monster of Peladon"]. Mars and Arcturus are said to be old enemies [so at some point after the twenty-first century, all the Ice Warriors on Mars presumably come out of hiding and create their own "empire"].

• *Alpha Centauri*. A 'hermaphrodite hexapod', referred to as a "he" but with a profoundly effeminate voice, the delegate from Alpha Centauri is a yellowy-green thing with one huge eye in the middle of his bulbous head and no other facial features. He has six maggoty arms protruding from the front of his body, and as he wears a robe it's not clear what he's got for feet. ["Hexapod" means six limbs, all of which we can see, so he probably shuffles like an upright slug. Uncomfortable in Earth-like gravity, the species may be aquatic, which would also explain the high voice.]

Centauri is flustered by the very thought of violence, and the implication is that the people of Alpha Centauri are peace-loving, although he has a tendency to see other cultures as primitive and doesn't try too hard to stop them killing each other.

• *Arcturus*. A spider-like being with a humanoid face on a body just a few inches long, the delegate from Arcturus occupies a clunky robotic "body" with a life-support system that includes a helium regenerator [so Arcturans can't breathe Peladon's atmosphere]. Arcturus lacks mineral deposits, explaining why the delegate wants to make a private deal with Peladon instead

Why Doesn't the TARDIS Work?

As all interested parties will know, between Season Seven ("Spearhead from Space") and Season Ten ("The Three Doctors") the Doctor is incapable of leaving Earth, in accordance with the terms of his exile. What's less clear is how the Time Lords keep him there.

When the Doctor's freedom is returned in "The Three Doctors", he receives a new dematerialisation circuit *and* gets his missing memories back, but before this there's some confusion about what's actually wrong with the Ship. In "Spearhead from Space" (7.1) the Time Lords are said to have changed the 'dematerialisation code' of the TARDIS, but in "Terror of the Autons" (8.1) the clear implication is that the Doctor only needs to fix the dematerialisation *circuit*. And although his memory's erratic throughout Season Seven, it's not until "The Claws of Axos" that he admits his knowledge of TARDIS technology has been compromised.

Taking all these things together, perhaps the simplest assessment is that the dematerialisation code is programmed into the dematerialisation circuit; that the code must be synchronised with the rest of the TARDIS in order for the Ship to work properly; and that this would be a lot easier for the Doctor if he could remember what he was doing. (In "The Three Doctors" he talks about dematerialisation *codes* coming back to him, perhaps meaning that he knows a number of different codes but couldn't remember them well enough to program the TARDIS with the right one to match the circuit. Well, we did say *perhaps*.)

The time vector generator needs to be reactivated in "The Ambassadors of Death", suggesting that it's been shut down, so possibly it's been off-line since the codes were changed and the Doctor's trying to find a way of kick-starting it without the circuit. He succeeds, and the console's capable of making short space-time hops as a result, so by the end of "Inferno" he (wrongly) believes it's fully functional again.

It's after this failure, in "Terror of the Autons", that we find he's spent three months tinkering with the dematerialisation circuit itself; probably trying to tune the code to the TARDIS instead of tuning the TARDIS to the code. Then again, he seems to imply that the dematerialisation circuit from his TARDIS *would* work in the Master's TARDIS if it weren't "broken", which might mean that the Time Lords have physically sabotaged the device on top of everything else. They really don't want him getting off this planet.

In "The Claws of Axos" (8.3), the Master gives the Doctor a way of overcoming the problem with the dematerialisation circuit using remarkably simple Earth technology, but the Doctor discovers that even when his circuit works - or sort-of-works - the TARDIS is still programmed to return to Earth whenever he tries to escape. (We can assume that this programming is built into the circuit, since it no longer applies when he gets a new one.) In "Colony in Space" (8.4) the Doctor makes a permanent change to the circuit, perhaps based on the Master's advice, thinking that it'll overcome the 'homing control' and allow him to leave the planet. The circuit seems to work, but only by the grace of the Time Lords, who operate the Ship by remote and take the TARDIS to Uxarius. It's later stated that there's an 'over-ride' in the circuit which allows them to do this, and the Doctor spends his last few months on Earth trying to bypass it.

What's notable, though, is that when the Time Lords steer him to an alien trouble-spot they have to wait for him to get into the TARDIS first. In "Colony in Space" he's just *about* to make the Ship take off when the remote-control kicks in, and in "The Curse of Peladon" the TARDIS is apparently hi-jacked in mid-flight. So if the Doctor kept making trips instead of leaving the TARDIS in pieces at UNIT HQ, then would he keep having Time-Lord-sponsored adventures? Does the High Council still think there's an infinite amount of work to be done in the universe...?

of seeing it join the Federation. [Is he acting for selfish reasons, or on behalf of the Arcturan government?] He's capable of entering a metabolic coma, and has built-in weapons in his tank with which he can perform extremely slow quick-draws on furniture provided by his hosts. The removal of the sensory array not only triggers the coma but affects the 'memory circuits' [the mention of 'memory circuits' suggests that this is a true cyborg, not an organic occupant of a tank, even if Arcturus is lying about his memory-loss as part of his scheme].

• *Aggedor.* The Royal Beast of Peladon, a large, shaggy, bear-like creature with a snout like a boar's, a single horn in the middle of its forehead and lethal claws. It's believed to be the last of its species, and up until this point was thought extinct, not surprising as young men used to hunt it as a rite of passage. The Doctor treats Aggedor as a male specimen, though it's not clear how he knows [it just acts male]. Aggedor is not only the "heraldic animal" of the Peladon royal line, but also has a kind of religious significance, with its own sacred temple in the King's citadel.

Planet Notes

• *Peladon.* A planet with an Earth-like atmosphere and Earth-like inhabitants, Peladon has a culture and technology level which appear medieval, but its people know about the existence of aliens and it's on the verge of joining the Galactic Federation.

Indeed, the world seems to have had alien visitors for some time, as the current ruler's mother was from Earth. [This royal inter-breeding might qualify the planet for Federation membership, although it could be argued that Peladon is a former Earth colony which has lapsed into a pre-industrial state. The letter "H" looks the same on Peladon as it does on Earth, which might suggest human ancestry… unless the King's mother introduced a human language as the language of court. Alternatively, the mysterious force which translates everything into English for our benefit might just be converting the symbol as well.]

The planet is rich in minerals, and is many light-years from Earth, which Centauri describes as 'remote' [from Peladon, obviously, since Earth is less then five light-years from Alpha Centauri itself].

Peladon has a single ruler, currently the young King Peladon, whose court includes a Chancellor, a High Priest and a very macho Champion. Superstition is common, sacrilege is punishable by death and trial by combat is still possible for nobles. The royal citadel is, charmingly, lit with flaming torches. As on Earth, purple appears to be the royal colour.

• *Venus.* The Venusian lullaby previously used by the Doctor [8.5, "The Daemons"] now has a tune, which sounds remarkably similar to "God Rest Ye Merry Gentlemen".

History

• *Dating.* At least a thousand years in the future, probably a lot more. [Earth is a key member of the Federation, so this is after the fall of its Empire, c. 3000 AD. The Virgin novels take the view that the Peladon stories take place in the thirty-ninth and fortieth centuries, which works.]

The Galactic Federation includes Earth, Mars, Alpha Centauri and Arcturus. Earth is important enough for its delegate, Amazonia, to chair the Committee of Assessment. Alpha Centauri describes himself as a member of the Preliminary Assessment Commission [just on Peladon, or is it a standing body?]. Political conflict is said to violate Federation law. Despite its supposed commitment to peace, if Peladon were to execute a Federation representative then it would constitute an act of war and Federation ships would level the planet. Under the Galactic Charter - Galactic Articles of Peace, paragraph 59, subsection two - the Federation can't over-ride Peladon's holy laws [does this apply to all local laws, or just religious ones?], and nor can it involve itself in internal politics unless a unanimous decision of delegates calls on emergency powers: Federation law only accepts unanimous decisions. The organisation's evidently rife with internal divisions, as a war would ensue if the Ice Warriors were accused of killing the delegate from Arcturus.

The Analysis

Where Does This Come From? Sometimes you can read too much into this kind of thing; sometimes you can end up treating every detail of a Dominator's costume as a subtle political metaphor. In "The Curse of Peladon", however, there's no ambiguity.

In 1972 Britain was on the verge of joining the EEC, with the Common Market giving the country closer links to Europe than ever (and, indeed, closer links to Europe than many people wanted). By its writer's own admission, "The Curse of Peladon" is *Doctor Who's* version of a "current events" story.

The people of the UK might not have believed that the Ghost of the British Bulldog was going to get them if Prime Minister Ted Heath kept negotiating with the European community, but the High Priest's conviction that the Federation will wipe out all his petty, pig-headed little superstitions *does* smack of Britain's distrust of anything "foreign". Like General Carrington in "The Ambassadors of Death" (7.3), he's just obsessed with his own piddling local concerns. So it's a fable rather than a work of satire, which doesn't have any particular political point to make but comes across as a cautionary tale about the fear of accepting the alien. And since "accepting the alien" is one of the cornerstones of *Doctor Who*, it's no surprise that the Doctor's on the side of the Federation.

Ah, yes. The Federation. It's been said that the Federation's appearance here is another sign of *Star Trek* influencing *Doctor Who* (i.e. original *Star Trek*, 60% less evil than the modern kind), but there's a much more European slant on things here, meaning that any planet in *this* Federation is bound to find itself surrounded by neighbours instead of a wild frontier.

And lest we forget, in 1971-72 the word "Federation" was constantly being used in the British media in relation to Europe. The *Star Trek* Federation, even in the original series, is much like America's view of the UN. The humans / Americans are the important ones, and the other species are just funny-looking people from a long way away who occasionally turn up in the background.

Whereas the Federation assembly on Peladon looks for all the world like a committee meeting in Brussels, except with better outfits. A group of diverse races, all with different agendas but forced to live alongside each other, and constantly at each others' throats as a result... it's a much more "international" view of the universe, a much more political vision. And *this* Federation even feels comfortable threatening primitive planets with warships, which is something the *Star Trek* one probably wouldn't do, unless the planets in question were full of thinly-disguised Middle Eastern terrorists.

The overall impression: someone was given an Ursula K. le Guin book for Christmas, and half-read it while watching the Prime Minister make excruciating speeches in bad schoolboy French.

Things That Don't Make Sense The Earth delegate looks astonished when she sees the TARDIS dematerialise, as if nobody in the far future has ever seen something teleport before [unless she's got a background in history, and can't believe she's looking at a police box]. Jo seems remarkably well-groomed when she climbs back into the citadel after clambering around on its rain-swept

window-ledge, and the guestrooms aren't in bad shape either, being warm, dry and completely free of "weather" noise even though the windows are just holes in the walls. The Ice Warriors' quarters only has one bed, so either their proud martial tradition requires one of them to stand up all night or they've got an equally proud martial tradition of snuggling up together (see 6.5, "The Seeds of Death", for more Red Planet pinkness).

And back in the 1970s - when we were smaller but no less pedantic - many of us found it deeply irritating that while the delegate from the Alpha Centauri system is called "Centauri" and the delegate from the Arcturus system is called "Arcturus", nobody tries calling the Doctor "Sol" or even "Earth". [Mind you, as the King of the planet takes the planet's name, this might just be a non-mandatory local custom. English monarchs used to do it with visiting nobles, q.v. *The Merchant of Venice*.]

Critique Yes, it's easy to mock, isn't it? A story which is often silly-looking (to adult eyes, at least) and turns the complexities of European politics into an adventure story about phallic alien ambassadors, "The Curse of Peladon" is just gagging for criticism from an older, more aggressive audience. But this *isn't* hard-core science-fiction, this is a children's fable, and it's staged as a fairy-tale instead of a political epic. (The children of the '70s loved it. The next generation of *Doctor Who* fans, living in an era of "serious" cult SF, poured scorn on it. We might predict that the next generation, raised on popular fantasy and force-fed the movie version of *The Lord of the Rings*, will find it a lot more acceptable.)

Like most of the Doctor-as-peacemaker stories of the Pertwee era, it remains eminently loveable in spite of the worst excesses of the BBC's hair stylists, with the *Hamlet*-by-torchlight citadel of Peladon giving the whole production a homely costume-drama feel even when the story starts to flag. The use of the Ice Warriors, as enormous red herrings who turn out to be wholly "reformed", is one of the first examples of the series messing around with the audience's expectations of it.

The Facts

Written by Brian Hayles. Directed by Lennie Mayne. Viewing figures: 10.3 million, 11.0 million, 7.8 million, 8.4 million. It's worth mentioning that the sudden drop between episodes two and three was mostly due to power-cuts. See **The Lore**.

Supporting Cast David Troughton (Peladon), Geoffrey Toone (Hepesh), Alan Bennion (Izlyr), Sonny Caldinez (Ssorg), Stuart Fell (Alpha Centauri), Ysanne Churchman (Voice of Alpha Centauri), Murphy Grumbar (Arcturus), Terry Bale (Voice of Arcturus), Gordon St. Clair (Grun), Nick Hobbs (Aggedor), Wendy Danvers (Amazonia).

Working Titles "The Curse".

Cliffhangers At the entrance to the throne-room, the King's Champion tries to push the huge stone statue of Aggedor down onto the delegates' heads; after the Doctor commits sacrilege by entering the temple of Aggedor's inner sanctum, the King has no alternative but to sentence him to death; the Doctor beats the King's Champion in the arena-pit, but in the gallery a weapon slides out of Arcturus' casing and there's a sudden shot from Ssorg's big ray-gun.

The Lore

• Stop me if you've heard this one before… director Lennie Mayne, a rather outspoken Australian, was irritated with the "polite" way in which the cast reacted to the mythical beast entering the royal chamber. He castigated them, insisting that they should be thinking 'holy f***ing cow!'. After a break, and as Barry Letts showed a party of (according to some sources) boy scouts and / or a vicar around the set, they filmed the scene and - en masse - an entire cast of character actors as aliens shouted 'holy f***ing cow!' at Aggedor.

• The power-cuts which affected most of Britain in early 1972 led to continuity announcers giving "story so far" summaries before each episode. Even so, the ratings show that more people saw this story than "The Sea Devils".

• David Troughton (King Peladon), returning to the series after his cameos in "Enemy of the World" and "The War Games", was sharing a flat with Colin Baker at the time. There are many stories about this period, but it'd be rude to print any of them.

• This is the first story to credit "Profile", the stunt troupe founded by veteran stunt artiste

Terry Walsh, and episode three credits Walsh alone.

• In the original script the "Venusian lullaby" that the Doctor uses to soothe Aggedor was the Tibetan chant 'om mani padme hum', because there really were an *awful* lot of Buddhists working on *Doctor Who* in the '70s.

9.3: "The Sea Devils"

(Serial LLL. Six Episodes, 26th February - 1st April 1972.)

Which One is This? Obviously, it's the one with all the Sea Devils: seven-foot-tall turtle-men, coming out of the ocean to launch commando raids on naval institutions. The Master makes plans from his sea-view prison, there are plenty of speedboats and hovercraft, and you should hear the *noise* this programme makes…

Firsts and Lasts As the serial code suggests, "The Sea Devils" was filmed before "The Curse of Peladon" but shown afterwards, the first time that *Doctor Who* stories had been shot out of sequence. Which says a lot about the way the programme had changed since the '60s. Episodes used to be produced on a tight schedule, filmed (and sometimes written) on a week-to-week basis, but now the production team had time to stop and think about little things like running orders. This was, on the whole, becoming a much more structured kind of programme. At least in theory.

On-screen it's the first of two outings for the Sea Devils, the marine branch of the Silurian family. For the first (and only) time during the Jon Pertwee era, there's a menace to modern-day Britain and UNIT doesn't get involved. Presumably because UNIT doesn't have a naval division at this point.

A nation's eight-year-olds sob as, for the final time, the caption "Action by Havoc" appears on the credits.

Six Things to Notice About "The Sea Devils"…

1. The most *memorable* moment is the assault on the island in episode four, in which a whole legion of reptile-people marches out of the ocean and onto the beach. Anyone who was a child when the episode was first transmitted will tell you that this was, honestly, one of the best things *ever*.

 This product is not authorized by the BBC. Doctor Who and TARDIS are trademarks of the BBC.

Just How Important is the Music?

Time, and familiarity, have made the world forget just how remarkable, how bizarre and how *important* the music of *Doctor Who* really was. So much so that when the 1996 TV Movie re-recorded the theme tune in the *Star Trek: The Next Generation* style (big orchestra, bombastic military sound, absolutely no hint of anything futuristic or experimental whatsoever) it was accepted as a perfectly normal part of a modern science-fiction series.

Rather than, say, an abomination.

It wasn't always that way. While Karlheinz Stockhausen and Pierre Schaeffer were getting all theoretical, and Leon Theremin's baby was made a novelty item, films like *Forbidden Planet* had happily made valve-modulators and "electronic tonalities" the standard vocabulary of space. The arrival of tape made sound a physical, manipulable object. Part of the deal, when a film or TV show took you somewhere else, was that you could be made to *hear* another world. If producers like George Martin or Joe Meek could do it, you'd think that aliens could.

Listen to the original 1963 theme again, bearing in mind the time in which it was made, and one thing has to strike you. *This was like nothing else on Earth*. The BBC's Radiophonic Workshop had been producing electronic music since 1957, not only composing scores for TV and radio but devising their own instruments out of spare parts. Yet until that point the tendency was to produce pieces so avant-garde as to be almost incomprehensible to the general public (e.g. the Workshop's theme for the BBC afternoon news, not so much a tune as a series of skittering, lurching atmosphere-effects which many listeners found quite disturbing).

The *Doctor Who* theme was a genuine landmark, an alliance between the very best of the Workshop's "experimental" material and the kind of dramatic, approachable soundtrack that befitted a contemporary adventure serial. We're used to it now, but the children of the early '60s have frequently called it 'bloody terrifying' and that's hardly a surprise. It pre-empts the psychedelia of the late '60s by some years. Even today, synthesisers would have trouble matching it.

Every episode of the programme bears the credit "Title Music by Ron Grainer", but it's Delia Derbyshire's radiophonic arrangement and production (a "realisation" which Grainer himself had nothing to do with, and found utterly bewildering), that really makes it. Derbyshire created a form of electronic music with a texture unlike anything recorded *anywhere* else before 1963, and what's more she made it truly populist. Yet until recently a lot of fans didn't even know her name.

Since the series' reputation was damaged so badly by the worst mistakes of the '80s, and since the programme's nature was completely mis-remembered by the media of the '90s (so that it became a kind of kitsch, cynical, post-modern experience, always accompanied in the popular imagination by jokes about Daleks not being able to get up stairs and memories of all the programme's *worst* special effects), even the programme's fans now forget how startlingly creative so much of it was.

There was a time when it was considered the most technically sophisticated programme on television, not because of the plastic spaceships or wobbly monster costumes but because of the little things that nobody chooses to recall. Documentaries on the making of *2001: A Space Odyssey* somehow skip the fact that the film's effects team consulted with director Douglas Camfield after seeing "The Daleks' Masterplan". But it's in the field of music that the series was most experimental. In the '60s and '70s, the people working on *Doctor Who* were not only layering episodes with weird, avant-garde soundtracks but inventing instruments capable of playing them.

Today stories like "The Silurians" and "The Sea Devils" are considered to sound a bit peculiar, full of erratic stabs and electronic / prehistoric kazoo solos, but… wasn't that the point? Take away the years of familiarity, and a Dalek or a Cyberman doesn't look stupid or badly-made, it just looks *strange*. The music matches that strangeness perfectly. Just the *noise* made by the programme suggests peculiar, alien landscapes, which is more than you can say for *Stargate*.

Beyond the titles, every story had a different score, not just different tunes and arrangements but a different relationship with music. A story like "The Savages" (3.9) has a different texture to one with stock music. A Dudley Simpson score from 1971 is different to one from 1967 or 1978 because of the mixture of "conventional" and electronic approaches. It was part of the process of going to another world every month or so.

Here in the twenty-first century, music in television (and fantasy television especially) is even more standardised, even more banal than it was in the worst adventure serials of the '60s. Modern SF isn't supposed to sound peculiar, or alien, or alarming. It's supposed to sound like Jerry Goldsmith,

continued on page 83…

2. But with hindsight, even better is the moment when we find the Master alone in his quarters on the prison island, watching BBC children's programme *The Clangers* and - obviously amused - trying to copy their language. (The look on his face, when the prison governor feels the need to explain to him that 'they're just puppets' as if he wouldn't have worked it out on his own, is utterly wonderful.)

3. It's impossible to talk about "The Sea Devils" without mentioning the music. As in "The Silurians", it divides opinion between those who feel it's daringly inventive and those who feel it's just a God-awful noise. Recorded in the days when synthesisers were bringing whole new working methods to the BBC Radiophonic Workshop, at times the soundtrack sounds like a Kraftwerk-style assembly of pseudo-random sonic effects and at other times it sounds like somebody blowing off into a vocoder. On balance, you'd at least have to give it full marks for trying. See also **Just How Important is the Music?**.

4. The Doctor sabotages the Master's electronic lash-up by reversing the polarity of the neutron flow, something that's due to become another catchphrase of the series even though this is the only time it's used during the 1970s.

5. Jo gets the "exposition" duties this time, reminding the audience about the Silurians by asking 'that was that race of super-reptiles that had been in hibernation for billions of years, wasn't it?' without even taking a breath. (And: *billions?*)

6. This week's opportunity for Jon Pertwee to do some professional gurning: being half-strangled by a Sea Devil at the start of episode six. There's also something very endearing about the way the Sea Devil does a double-take when it first comes face-to-face with him in episode two, and as for the way one of them runs away from him in episode four, like a girl in a game of kiss-chase…

The Continuity

The Doctor   He's an accomplished swordsman, a trained diver and good at playing golf while blindfolded. He's moved on from shouting 'hai!' when performing martial arts moves to shouting 'akira!', and is prepared to make a point about his superiority in combat by handing a weapon back to the disarmed Master in mid-combat. The Doctor states that the Master used to be a 'very good

friend' of his, and establishes for the first time that 'you might say we went to school together' [Prydon Academy, according to 14.3, "The Deadly Assassin"]. The Doctor admits to feeling sorry for the captive Master, though tellingly the Master can't conceive of this and believes the Doctor's just suspicious.

• *Ethics.* Here the Doctor's prepared to destroy the Sea Devils, killing thousands of them by blowing up their base, but only when he believes that war is inevitable otherwise. [Compare this with 21.1, "Warriors of the Deep".]

• *Inventory.* The sonic screwdriver is capable of detecting and detonating landmines. The Doctor's UNIT pass is numbered "10". [The photo is the publicity shot from "Doctor Who and the Silurians" of Jon Pertwee swinging around in an action-pose.]

• *Background.* The Doctor claims that Nelson was a good friend of his [q.v. 9.1, "Day of the Daleks"]. He implies that he may have been involved in the Crimean War, and - though he never states he was there - casually mentions the battles of Gallipoli and El Alamein [First and Second World Wars, respectively] in the same breath.

The Supporting Cast

• *Jo Grant.* Impressively, she knows enough karate to knock out a highly-trained guard with one chop. Her attachment to the Doctor is such that when he insists on putting himself in a dangerous situation, she looks down at her shoes and very nearly starts sniffling. [At the very least it's become a kind of father / daughter relationship by now.] She can abseil, drive a hovercraft, politely avoid Trenchard's rather slimy advances and get a naval officer she barely knows to call her 'Jo'. She's read a number of files on UNIT cases before her time and must have phenomenal eyesight, being able to spot the Master from very high up and several hundred yards away.

The Supporting Cast (Evil)

• *The Master.* Like the Doctor, he knows how to handle a sword even though he's put on weight in prison. He uses *another* mask of his own face to fake his death, the last time he's ever seen to do this. His motive for helping the Sea Devils is pure malice, wanting to hurt the Doctor by eradicating the human species.

Just How Important is the Music?

...continued from page 81

and that's about all.

The TV Movie version of the *Doctor Who* theme is a truly terrible piece of work, not because it isn't "like" the original - this is, after all, a series which thrives on change - but because it's "like" everything else you hear these days. That simply defeats the whole point of the programme. *Doctor Who* began life as a series about a moody, eccentric technocrat with a talent for building improbable machines out of bits of futuristic rubbish. And the people who defined its atmosphere better than anyone else, the BBC radiophonics experts, were *all* moody, eccentric technocrats with a talent for building improbable machines out of bits of futuristic rubbish. The "love of the amateur", a cornerstone of British culture and a particularly vital ingredient in the success of *Doctor Who*, comes across in its soundtrack more than it does anywhere else.

It's once again implied that the Doctor is a much better scientist than the Master, who's apparently becoming less and less of a genius as time goes by and increasingly relying on the Doctor for technical assistance. It might be argued that his obvious enjoyment of *The Clangers* proves he isn't completely sociopathic.

The Time Lords The Master knows about the Sea Devils from the Time Lords' files, so the species must be of note to the Doctor's people. [The Master can't possibly have stolen *all* the files of the Time Lords. He may have taken a particular interest in those files which relate to Earth, after discovering that the Doctor was there, which would explain his knowledge of Azal in "The Daemons" (8.5). If so then the Time Lords may have expected the Doctor to come across the Silurians, and cross-referenced the "Silurian" file with the "Doctor in exile" one.]

The Non-Humans

• *Sea Devils.* A half-delirious witness to the attack on the sea-fort coins the term "Sea Devil", so it's not the name used by the Devils themselves. [But again, see "Warriors of the Deep". They could just as well be called "Green Gilberts", which is how the captain of the submarine describes them.] The Sea Devils are reptiles, marine relations of the creatures from the Wenley Moor caves, generally known as Silurians even though the Doctor now believes they should have been called "Eocenes" [see **What's the Origin of the Silurians?** under 7.2]. The Doctor believes they're a different species [with a common ancestor, but not capable of inter-breeding], adapted for life underwater.

Lacking the third eyes of the Silurians, their faces resemble sea-turtles, with fin-like growths instead of the Silurians' crests and skin which appears either orange or green. [This could be a racial difference. Then again, they tend to be green when they're on land and orange when they've just come out of the sea, so possibly it's something to do with damp pores.] They breathe air, but can obviously survive underwater for some time.

Like the Silurians, the Sea Devils are generally aggressive but aren't obsessed with war, their leader prepared to consider peace with the humans until he's attacked. There are thousands of Sea Devils in their underwater base off the coast of Britain [no more than a few hundred miles from the Wenley Moor caves, so these two species were common in western Europe], and potentially millions more in installations around the world.

The leader seems sure that the Doctor's telling the truth after mysteriously holding his hand over the back of the Doctor's head, so either this is some form of rudimentary telepathy or just Sea Devil posturing. It's not clear whether the Master or operations at the sea fort woke them, but their hibernation devices have deteriorated over time and the reactivation mechanism doesn't work. Unlike the Silurians, they apparently just need a certain signal to wake them up, and they don't have to drain power from other sources. [It seems odd, though, that the hibernation devices in all the installations across the world have somehow broken down. The Big Finish audio adventure "Bloodtide" claims that the wake-up mechanism was deliberately sabotaged, yet even *this* doesn't explain why the Silurians thought it'd be a good idea to connect every single hibernator on Earth to the same control system.]

Unlike their 'cousins', the Sea Devils clothe themselves, wearing mesh-like garments not unlike large - but fetching - string vests. Their technology resembles that of their land-going relatives, since the "diving bell" they use to take humans into their underwater lair is almost organic in appearance, and like Silurians they can be called by a distinctive sonic signal. They use ultrasonic communicators to rouse themselves, and the Master uses this to give commands, but only their leader is heard to use speech; the rest utter eerie cries when injured. Their standard side-arm is a weapon which projects a concentrated beam of heat, intense enough to burn through rock or metal. They have some way of immobilising a submarine at long range, and their base can be entered via a huge undersea cavern, the mouth of which can be closed off by a force-field.

Oh, and Sea Devils "shake hands" by pressing one palm against the palm of the person they're facing.

History

• *Dating.* [1973, probably autumn. The Master speaks of colour television as if it's still something of a luxury, which again suggests that it's the early '70s rather than the late '70s.]

The Master is held prisoner on Fortress Island, conveniently close to the Sea Devil base. Many people wanted to see him executed, although the armed forces don't seem to know about him. [The novelisation expands on this, claiming that the Doctor argued for mercy during the trial. It also claims the public were aware of the case - but not that the Master was an alien - and that the Brigadier wrote the Prime Minister a letter about the problem of keeping him confined.] He's being held in remarkably luxurious conditions, even taking into account the hold he has over the governor, and the guards call him 'sir'. [Is the British government buttering him up for some reason?].

Walker, the Parliamentary Private Secretary, has the Minister's authority to blow up the Sea Devils. He's familiar with UNIT's file on the Silurians, and suggests there's an "official line" that these creatures are to be destroyed.

The Analysis

Where Does This Come From? As we've already seen (in 7.4, "Inferno"), there was a time when dynamic new power-sources and thrusting scientific research projects were thought to make sexy TV, not least because of the British-owned oil being drilled out of the North Sea. The popular media was obsessed with oil rigs (maybe it was a down-to-Earth alternative to all those American space missions), and all the attendant machinery. Michael Buerk, as the BBC's "energy correspondent", was rarely seen outside a helicopter.

In "The Sea Devils" we have abandoned seaforts and secret naval research projects rather than actual oil rigs, but the imagery's so close to contemporary news reports that in 1972 the story must have seemed downright topical. Whereas the earlier story "Fury from the Deep" (5.6) used the *concept* of futuristic new power projects at sea - it was made in 1968, when everybody knew that North Sea Gas was coming but it was still vaguely abstract - "The Sea Devils" is more like reportage with extra added sea-monsters. All the best "toys" of British industry are proudly on show, not only helicopters and submarines but an ever-so-modern hovercraft as well. Jon Pertwee always had a thing for fast-moving machinery, so here's a story that satisfies his urge to play an action-hero Doctor *and* seems nice and fashionable.

(Incidentally, it's worth pointing out… the scene in which the Doctor tries to turn a transistor radio into a transmitter, and ends up listening to the DJ on the morning music programme, was made at a time when pop radio was entering its heyday and when British DJs were deliberately grooming themselves as celebrities. So even that suggests a deliberate nod towards the shiny and the new, as does Jo's maximum-chic dress sense. This may technically be the Silurians' second outing, but there's none of that ancient-mystical-horror business this time. This is the present-day, and then some.)

And as in so many stories of the early '70s - "The Silurians", "The Claws of Axos", "Day of the Daleks" - there's a mistrust of bureaucracy that's typical of a country figuring out how ridiculous the world's political situation really was / is. As ever, the crisis between humans and aliens is brought to an unhappy end not by a Nazi megalomaniac but by a bloody-minded civil servant who's obsessed with toast.

Unusually, though, this time it's the Doctor himself who delivers the killing blow.

Things That Don't Make Sense There are some swords on the wall just outside the quarters where the Master's being held, and yet this doesn't tip anybody off that he may not be *quite* as imprisoned as he's meant to be. When the Doctor sabotages the Master's device for waking up the reptile-

This product is not unauthorized by the BBC. Doctor Who and TARDIS are products of the BBC.

people, and causes all the Sea Devils in the area to roll around in agony to a painful high-pitch shriek, it goes on for well over a minute before the Master thinks to ask what's going on.

The Sea Devils seem to believe that attacking any ships which come into their waters is a good way of wiping out the human species, rather than being a good way of drawing attention to themselves [the Master's *really* misinformed them about modern humanity]. It's never explained why the Sea Devils capture the submarine that's sent to investigate them, instead of just blowing it up the way they do with everything else. [They want to inspect state-of-the-art human technology…?] The surviving lifeboat from one of the early Sea Devil attacks, supposedly kept at the top secret naval base as evidence in the official investigation, is lying around on the beach exposed to the weather. British forensic science… no longer a world leader.

Furthermore, three ships have been sunk in a month. In the English Channel, no less. Not only has this not made the headlines (as it did when two were damaged in the same month in 2003), but UNIT haven't heard a dicky-bird about it. In fact *everybody* seems badly-informed, since Captain Hart knows Trenchard well enough for them to be talking about golf but doesn't know that he's there to guard someone called the Master. Not even a "Have You Seen This Man?" poster, in case the Master should happen to break out and head for the nearest supply of electronic components and weapons.

Ultimately the Master escapes by hovercraft into a narrow section of sea with half the Royal Navy massing there, unless they all went home ten minutes after preparing to bombard the Sea Devils. And the main mode of official transport is a fleet of Citroen 2CVs with no doors. Haven't they considered the possibility of it raining?

But most gloriously of all, in episode three Security Guard Barclay (Terry Walsh, of course) has apparently been crouching in the middle of a field for some time on the off-chance that escaping UNIT personnel might try heading for a precipice behind him.

Critique Throughout the run of the '70s series, you can almost take it for granted that any given *Doctor Who* story will be too long. The original (serial) nature of the programme, as well as it being made at a time when people were slightly less familiar with the conventions of television

and slightly less willing to take everything in at high speed, guarantee that most six-parters would be better off with four parts and that an awful lot of four-parters would be better off with three. But really, some stories just *beg* you to mention it.

"The Sea Devils" is, like "The Silurians", a story full of great moments which also goes out of its way to slow itself down at every turn. Episode three is at least two-thirds padding, while episode four spends several minutes showing us the process of the Doctor's diving bell being lowered into the water and pulled up again. (But then, this is all part of *Doctor Who*'s semi-educational streak, a way of demonstrating modern naval technology to the audience. And perhaps part of the deal to get access to the Navy's hardware.)

The strain really shows in episode six, when an escaping Jo gets to whisper through a window to the captive Doctor *just like she did three episodes earlier*, while sadly both Walker and Colonel Trenchard are as annoying for the audience as they are for the characters. If somebody took a pair of scissors to the footage and sliced it down to an hour and a half, it'd be seminal. As it *is*, it's best to keep fast-forwarding to the good bits.

In its defence, it's the last real effort at getting the details right. Every aspect of naval protocol, right down to what they call a cup of tea, is solidly grounded in fact. Unlike the next "proper" Britain-in-Peril story, "The Green Death" (10.5), no-one is caricatured or patronised. Trenchard is a fool, but an honest one. Walker serves to show humanity at its least admirable just as the Doctor's trying to defend us, but he's doing a job recognisably like that of a real civil servant. People in Malcolm Hulke stories have first names and accurate ranks. Michael Briant's direction is often criticised as "comic-strip", but it is an effort to keep something planned as pseudo-documentary (with borrowed stock footage from promotional films) visually and aurally interesting, despite the script's longeurs.

In terms of character, the *real* sour taste is how this story compares to "The Silurians", where intelligent, unsettling beings jockeying for position were shown as having varied points of view. The Master's calling-device is no marvel of an alien technology but a remote-control to move a monster around a minefield like Sonic the Hedgehog. Nonetheless, John Friedlander's Sea Devil masks are among his loveliest creations, even if they're not terribly "realistic".

ABOUT TIME 1970-1974

The Facts

Written by Malcolm Hulke. Directed by Michael Briant. Viewing figures: 6.4 million, 9.7 million, 8.3 million, 7.8 million, 8.3 million, 8.5 million.

Supporting Cast Roger Delgado (The Master), Edwin Richfield (Captain Hart), Clive Morton (Trenchard), June Murphy (3rd Officer Jane Blythe), Alec Wallis (Ldg. Telegraphist Bowman), Terry Walsh (Castle Guard Barclay), Donald Sumpter (Commander Ridgeway), David Griffin (Lt. Commander Mitchell), Christopher Wray (Ldg. Seaman Lovell), Colin Bell (CPO Summers).

Working Titles "The Sea Silurians" (don't they *ever* learn…?).

Cliffhangers Marooned on the sea-fort, the Doctor and Jo have just found a crewman's dead body when they hear something shuffling down the corridor towards them; having lost his sword-fight with the Doctor, the Master unexpectedly produces a knife and hurls it at his opponent's back; as the guards pursue the Doctor and Jo across the beach, the Master activates his calling-device and a Sea Devil emerges from the water in front of them; the Doctor's diving-bell is pulled up out of the sea, and Jo realises that it's empty; the Doctor, Jo and Captain Hart are heading across the naval base when a Sea Devil - one of the first to attack the facility - appears in front of them and takes aim.

The Lore

• The Sea Devils were originally meant to be stark naked, but director Michael Briant felt they looked funny that way and insisted on giving them the mesh robes. Terrance Dicks has always maintained that this was a mistake, and that the monsters looked 'bloody stupid' when dressed, which goes to show that Dicks' judgement on '70s *Doctor Who* isn't *always* on the button. A nude Sea Devil just wouldn't be as interesting, somehow.

• Despite morally blackmailing the Royal Navy into donating manpower and facilities (by mentioning how co-operative the Army had been with 6.3, "The Invasion"…), the production team wasn't given too many details about submarine designs. Working out that the propeller specifica-

tions were stupidly small, the designers made something that *looked* right, and the MOD promptly asked them very serious questions concerning a possible security breach.

• Jon Pertwee injured himself again, this time bruising his ribs on the sonic screwdriver while lying flat on the barbed wire. Although he wasn't drastically injured, this was his last significant stunt scene until "The Green Death" (10.5). His back injury, a long-term complaint from - as he put it - 'too many prat-falls', would make the action increasingly difficult. Surgical supports would eventually be involved.

• In fact the sonic screwdriver seen here is a new prop made for this story, leading some to think that the old prop was recycled as the gadget for hypnotising any hairy beasts the Doctor might run into (see 9.2, "The Curse of Peladon").

• Stunt-team "Havoc" went out with a bang, although Alan Chuntz doubles for Katy Manning in both motorbike and abseiling scenes. Terry Walsh, Pertwee's (and later Tom Baker's) regular double, formed "Profile" but never got an on-screen credit during the next seven years of work.

• Malcolm Clarke's ever-controversial soundtrack was a late replacement, as John Baker had originally been scheduled to provide the music. Within the Radiophonic Workshop, Clarke was said to have had the best "rapport" with the new EMS Synthi 100 (or "Delaware"). Baker was one of the old school, happier with tape and scissors than banks of potentiometers. Recently the score has become something of a touchstone for devotees of "electronica".

• The record playing on the fab-and-groovy DJ's show was the (non-copyright) backing track from "Johnny Reggae" by the Pipkins, a Jonathan King project. The version with words would have been (a) too rude and (b) too expensive.

9.4: "The Mutants"

(Serial NNN, Six Episodes, 8th April - 13th May 1972.)

Which One is This?   The Doctor and Jo travel a thousand years into the future, only to find the Earth Empire falling and the fat colonials oppressing some tribal planetary natives in order to stop them turning into big black insect-creatures. Geoffrey Palmer once again plays a high-ranking official who dies horribly.

Firsts and Lasts   First appearance of the hexagon-based plastic "wallpaper" which became the bog-standard BBC background for every space-based series from *Blake's 7* to *Come Back Mrs. Noah* (don't ask). More pedantically, it's the first story to state the year along with the copyright notice at the end of the credits.

Six Things to Notice About "The Mutants"...

1. Theoretically a story about a violent clash of cultures on the edge of a collapsing empire, "The Mutants" is perhaps most notable for its rather... *over-excitable* dialogue. Sample quotes: 'We want our freedom and we want it now!'; 'Die, Overlord, die!'; 'Am I left with nothing but mutants?!?'; 'You will die for a cause, the cause of Varan's revenge!'. The old man in the warrior Varan's village, especially, explores whole new territories of over-acting.

2. "The Mutants" is also notable for the characters of Cotton and Stubbs, two "ordinary blokes" working for Earth's Empire, whose job seems to be to constantly chip in with "ordinary bloke" comments as the planet goes to hell around them. This is, depending on how you look at it, either an ingenious script device or very annoying. Cotton's most famous exclamation, in the middle of a life-or-death situation: 'We'll all be done for!' (And it might have worked, if he'd had the accent the writers were thinking of...)

3. There's a very odd scene in episode four, set in the cave / laboratory of Solos researcher Professor Sondergaard, which involves violent rockfalls shaking the room. To emphasise this, one of the set cameras has been rigged to distort the picture, stretching the scene to make it look as if everything's been rocked out of shape. But the director seems to have forgotten about this halfway through, and filmed some shots through the rigged camera even when the rocks *aren't*

falling, making the characters squash sideways in mid-conversation for absolutely no good reason.

4. The "off-screen" voices (radio transmissions, computer announcements, etc) are a mixed bag of accents, in an attempt to make future-Earth sound like a cultural melting-pot. Australians, Americans and Caribbeans can all be heard, in addition to the "visible" characters who are supposed to be German, Afrikaaner, Yorkshire and old Etonian... but all speaking interchangeable dialogue. Some of the off-screen ones are Jon Pertwee, once again doing funny voices to save money (see if you can guess which).

5. Pertwee also delivers one of his lines twice in his very first scene, but the camera keeps rolling anyway.

6. Everybody says it, but it's true: the opening shot of the story just is Michael Palin's "It's..." man from the start of *Monty Python's Flying Circus*.

The Continuity

The Doctor   He's incredibly resistant to radiation, being better-equipped to withstand radioactive thaesium than a man in a protective suit [alas, he forgets how to 'prepare' himself by 11.5, "Planet of the Spiders"]. Here he no longer seems to object to the Time Lords sending him on errands, believing that if they want something from him then it must be important [resignation].

• *Ethics*. He's apparently prepared to sabotage the lab equipment, and lethally, in order to stop Professor Jaeger on the Skybase. Yet earlier, he stops people shooting at mutants because they're intelligent beings.

• *Bessie*. The Doctor's making a minimum inertia superdrive for her. This defies several popular and important laws of physics [see 9.5, "The Time Monster"].

The TARDIS   Its instruments can identify the century in which the Doctor has landed, but on this occasion not the planet.

The Time Lords   The Time Lords supply the Doctor with a message pod, containing ancient Solonian tablets, for delivery to the rebel leader Ky on Solos. It materialises in the Doctor's lab without any of the usual TARDIS sound effects. [Again, it's not clear what stops the Time Lords teleporting it straight into Ky's possession. Nor is it explained where the Time Lords get the tablets, or why they want to help the Solonians anyway, and this time it doesn't seem to have anything to do with getting in the way of the Daleks. Time Lord politics is more complicated than expected.]

The container is seemingly indestructible [TARDIS material?], but it starts to open when it's in Ky's presence. The Doctor states that these things are only sent in a 'real emergency', so much so that he's reluctant to let Jo go with him to Solos.

Planet Notes

• *Solos*. A remote part of the Earth Empire, Solos has a two-thousand year elliptical orbit around its sun, and doesn't have any recognisable seasons as it doesn't tilt on its axis.

In truth its seasons are five-hundred years long, so as the planet passes from "spring" to "summer" the temperature rises and the humanoid Solonians undergo a severe metabolic change. They become "Mutts", their bodies taking on insect-like plating and their hands turning into clumsy pincers, until eventually they even have a separate thorax and abdomen. In fact this phase is only a brief one - though the atmospheric changes made by Earth's Empire triggers it too soon - and before long they take on an altogether different form.

The fully-developed Solonians are humanoid but sheathed in a multi-coloured glow, capable of killing with energy beams or causing humans to collapse with a touch. They communicate through thought transference and can float through solid walls. The Doctor considers this adaptive change to be unique in the history of the universe, but the pre-transformed Solonians are completely unaware of the process. [Because Earth has destroyed their culture, or because of the process itself? The cycle seems to have taken place many times before, so it's a mystery why the advanced Solonians don't find a way of stopping it, as it apparently causes them to revert to barbarism after another few hundred years.]

Approaching the change, Solonians find themselves drawn towards a radioactive cave system [one of many on the planet] where one particular crystal acts as a bio-catalytic agent, drawing in thaesium radiation to drive the metamorphosis. The crystal appears to be man-made, but its origin isn't explained. What the crystal has to do with the planet's orbit is anyone's guess.

The soil on Solos contains a nitrogen isotope unknown on Earth, so during the hours of daylight the ultra-violet rays create a poisonous mist, lethal to humans within an hour even though Solonians can breathe a human-friendly atmosphere with no ill effects.

Solonian society, during its humanoid phase, is tribal and has a roughly iron-age level of technology. The Empire has a Skybase in orbit, and it's obviously a segregated society. Solos used to be rich in thaesium, used by the humans as fuel for Skybase and its spaceships, but now it's been virtually mined out. The Marshal's globe of the planet suggests Earth-like oceans. [There's more on Mutts in 13.5, "The Brain of Morbius".]

History

• *Dating*. The thirtieth century, towards the end of Earth's Empire [see also **What's the Timeline of the Earth Empire?** under 10.3, "Frontier in Space".].

At this point Earth is 'politically, economically and biologically finished'. The Doctor describes it as grey, land and sea, with grey highways linking grey cities across grey deserts. Nobody lives on the ground, as the air's too poisonous, but in sky-cities [q.v. 8.4, "Colony in Space"]. Solos is one of the last planets to remain under Earth's control, the Doctor stating that humanity only moved on to the outer planets after sacking the solar system. Earth is pulling out because it simply can't afford an Empire. It still has a Bureau of Records, and seems to be run by a Council. "Earth Control" is mentioned.

Humans first arrived on Solos five-hundred years earlier. A Marshall oversees the planet, while his men - "Overlords" to the Solonians - have black-and-silver uniforms and carry energy weapons. Solonians and Overlords appear to speak the same language. The Marshal answers to an Administrator in a similar uniform, sent from Earth to oversee Solos' move towards independence. The Investigator from the Earth Council, dressed in a white robe and skullcap, arrives in a Hyperion space shuttle. His staff dress in a similar way, while his guards wear white helmets and uniforms different to those of the local imperials.

The Skybase staff get 'videos' from home. Technology on the station includes a teleport link to the surface, and a lab researching atmospheric control. Ionisation rockets are used to attempt to change the environment. The entire Skybase is due to return to Earth after the crisis, so it seems to be a "ship" rather than a fixed station.

The Analysis

Where Does This Come From? It's been read as a parable about apartheid in South Africa, or the extermination of the Native Americans. It's been read as an apology for British colonial activity in India. In Salman Rushdie's *The Satanic Verses* it's even (briefly) used as part of an extended metaphor on human transformation. And most of these things are true, but what's important to notice about "The Mutants" is the time in which it was written.

By 1972, Britain no longer had an Empire. What it had was the first generation to grow up *after* Empire, a generation whose parents still couldn't believe that Britain was no longer a world power and couldn't understand why their children thought they came from a small, parochial, frustrated little island. It's doubtful that the BBC would have produced a programme like "The Mutants" just ten years earlier, but more importantly, it's doubtful that anybody would have thought of writing it.

After World War Two - the country's last shot at global greatness - it took a quarter of a century just for the nation to work out that the Empire was something which might, possibly, be a thing to *apologise* for. This being the '70s, there's even an eco-twist here, with Empire being directly related to the abuse of the Earth... perhaps more inspired by America's treatment of the Indian territories than by the British in Asia, which was certainly Bob Baker's view of the story.

(Not, of course, that "The Mutants" was the first anti-imperial SF story. Even H. G. Wells' "The War of the Worlds", the root of all invaders-from-outer-space fiction and arguably the most influential SF story ever told, was written as a fable about colonialism; a kind of "how would *you* like it?" to the British readership. But "The War of the Worlds" was just a theoretical argument. "The Mutants" was made by people who'd actually *seen* the Empire falling, and who - thanks to the news media's expansion - were becoming increasingly aware of the consequences, especially in Africa. It's a product of an age which had already given us *Carry On Up the Khyber*, and if that's not the last word on the Empire then what is?)

All of which makes "The Mutants" sound like a great moral work, but its morality has limits. Though many of the series' other writers took a distinctly humanistic line, and frequently portrayed the villains as hurt, misguided, even *tragic*

people caught up in events they don't understand, Bob Baker and Dave Martin have no qualms about neatly bumping off the bad guys when there's no further use for them. So when Ky ascends to become a higher form of life, and supposedly metamorphoses into the most beautiful and enlightened creature in the universe... his first act is to say 'now, Marshal, you must die' and commit instant murder in order to supply a spurious sense of moral "justice". It's not pretty, and it jars unpleasantly with the message supposedly being peddled by the rest of the story.

The transformation of the "Mutts" is worth considering in itself, though. Like "The Silurians" (7.2), "The Mutants" is one of many stories to take a more biological view of SF than the rockets-and-moonbases approach of the previous generation. As we've already seen, it was a tendency borne out of the 1960s, when pop-culture began to turn towards the psychological and the anthropological *en masse*. Like all good hippies and "native" peoples, the Solonians are going to ascend to a higher plane of being (and have their consciousnesses expanded, too) as part of the great cycle of life. And just to put the capstone on it, the transformed Ky manifests himself as a wash of multi-coloured cosmic energy, far closer to something from a late '60s or early '70s album sleeve than anything previously seen in the series.

Even the radioactive cave is trippy.

Things That Don't Make Sense The complete Solonian transformation, from human to mutant to superhuman, is so severe that even Ky's clothes change. [The radiation destroys his original clothing, and his robes as a super-being are some kind of telepathic illusion... possibly].

As ever, the space-science is terrible here. After a great big hole's blown in the wall of the Skybase, the air rushes out of the station for just a few moments before the "pressure" balances and everybody in the area can shuffle out of the room as if nothing's wrong. And in a space-station a door malfunction is basically a death-sentence unless fixed right away, yet Stubbs and Cotton ignore two of these in order to play chess. Then they arrange an even more lethal power-cut.

By day, the planet's atmosphere is unbreathable to humans. Then, when Sondergaard is accompanying the Doctor - and all Jaeger's missiles are falling on this one small part of the planet - this is conveniently ignored, so it's the evil missiles which make the Professor unwell. Later,

Sondergaard and the mutants can beam up despite the macrophisor being removed for Jaeger's experiments. And why is the teleporter on Solos not near any of the mines or factories we hear about, but in the middle of nowhere?

Stubbs has been told repeatedly that the Marshal wants him in constant contact when hunting for Ky in the caves. So he instantly forgets this and starts talking to the Doctor about bringing down the Marshal, oblivious to the open mic and his audience, i.e. the fat man with the detonator and the gas grenades.

Critique It's a story with almost unprecedented scope, a planetary conflict on the edge of an empire too large to fit on screen, more a precursor to *Star Wars* than anything else done by *Doctor Who* before 1977. Which begs the question… why is the finished programme such a mess?

The answer is simply that just about every single aspect of it is botched, fumbled or downright sloppy. Much of the dialogue is unconscionably awful. A couple of the performances make you wonder if the actors actually got *paid* for this. The "native culture" of the Solonians is portrayed so badly that it looks like a racial insult even though the race in question isn't real. But apart from the Mutts themselves, what *really* kills "The Mutants" is the design. What's meant to be an epic vision of the future comes across as SF television at its cheapest, complete with wall-signs in absurdly kitsch digital writing. (Actually this foreshadows the worst of the Baker and Martin stories from the later Graham Williams era, in which there's a terrible tendency for "future" stories to take place in bland, shaky-looking installation sets.)

Paul Whitsun-Jones' performance as the Marshal has often been criticised for his tendency to chew the furniture, yet he's not the one to blame at all. He's doing his best to put in a performance as a big, angry, operatic villain, but he's doing it in an environment where nobody's even trying to generate any atmosphere - not even in the atmosphere generation lab, ironically - and on top of that he's got to deliver his lines in a costume that makes him look like a Christmas pudding. Right at the end, it looks as if the Investigator (Peter Howell, not the Radiophonic Workshop one) can barely believe he's being asked to say that Cotton (Rick James, not the "Superfreak" one) is going to be the acting governor.

Ultimately "The Mutants" *does* have many good points, including a plot with potential, a genuinely interesting backstory and a few nice *Time-Machine*-style cave scenes, but it's best if you close your eyes and imagine what it's *supposed* to be like instead of focusing on what's actually on the screen. Perhaps most tellingly, this is the one story which no-one of that generation recalls watching at the time.

The Facts

Written by Bob Baker and Dave Martin. Directed by Christopher Barry. Viewing figures: 9.1 million, 7.8 million, 7.9 million, 7.5 million, 7.9 million, 6.5 million.

Supporting Cast Paul Whitsun-Jones (Marshal), James Mellor (Varan), Garrick Hagon (Ky), Geoffrey Palmer (Administrator), Christopher Coll (Stubbs), Rick James (Cotton), George Pravda (Jaeger), John Hollis (Sondergaard), Peter Howell (Investigator).

Working Titles "Independence", "The Emergents".

Cliffhangers Escaping from the Skybase, Ky kidnaps Jo and drags her into the teleporter, just as the guards open fire on them; the Doctor and Varan both attempt to escape the Skybase at the same time, something which results in Varan grabbing the Doctor around the throat and shouting 'die, Overlord, die'; gas floods the Mutt caves, where the Doctor and company find themselves sealed in by the Marshal; the Marshal (idiotically) blasts through the hull of the Skybase, resulting in Varan being sucked out into space while Jo and her companions hang on for dear life; trapped in Skybase's refuelling lock with Jo and Ky, Cotton suddenly realises that the refuelling process is about to begin and that radiation is going to flood the area.

The Lore

• Barry Letts originally devised the idea of the Solonian life-cycle in the 1960s, but then-script-editor Gerry Davis rejected it as being too complex for the series. Letts later suggested adding it to Baker and Martin's (rather flat) story about an Earth colony on the brink of independence. After a promising first episode, Terrance Dicks wrote to the authors voicing his concerns that the storyline was becoming lost in a welter of other ideas: entire sub-plots about cloning and asylum-seekers from Earth, a Vietnam parable and Ky becoming spherical (!) were removed, and an ending included.

• The rather endearing mutant costumes were designed by James Acheson, who's since gone on to win various Oscars for costume design and who worked on the 2002 *Spider-Man* movie.

• Another gallery-only day of experimental CSO work was needed for the effects in episode six, as well as make-up tests for the ageing of Ian Collier in the next story. The location filming, mainly done at Chiselhurst Caves, included reference photos for the CSO work of the Thaesium cave in episode four. Baker and Martin had specified much more than was actually shot there, but Barry Letts opted for more controllable (and cheaper) studio model-work.

• The original script of "The Mutants" referred to the mutations as "munts" instead of "mutts", "munt" being racist Rhodesian slang for a black African. It's not hard to guess why it was changed.

9.5: "The Time Monster"

(Serial OOO, Six Episodes, 20th May - 24th June 1972.)

Which One is This? Hail, Atlantis. The Master's back, and this time it's personal; the UNIT troops get waylaid by Roundheads; two TARDISes collide; Jo finds the ancient Minoan civilisation 'groovy', while Ingrid Pitt hears 'strange music'; Benton enters his second childhood; and the Doctor meets a Greek God after slaying the Minotaur.

Firsts and Lasts "The Time Monster" isn't a story that gets an easy ride from *Doctor Who* fans, but what's surprising is just how much of the series' later mythology starts here. This is the first story which dwells on the idea of the TARDIS as a living, feeling thing, and the first time the Ship's "telepathic circuits" get mentioned, as well as the first time the Doctor acknowledges the existence of the "vortex" it travels through.

It's the first story in which the Doctor explicitly talks about his youth, and the first time he takes a step towards alien Buddhism by mentioning the old hermit who used to live on his homeworld. And perhaps most strikingly, it's the story which defines the Doctor/Master relationship as we now

like to remember it, showing them to be locked in a combat so mythic that they can't even stay out of each others' dreams. Overall "The Time Monster" has to be considered a keystone in the series' history, as well as the end of a (two-year-long) era, since it's the last story to feature both the Master and the "classic" UNIT line-up.

"The Time Monster" also sees the only appearance of the re-redesigned TARDIS console room, which was changed *again* for Season Ten as almost nobody liked it.

Six Things to Notice About "The Time Monster"...

1. Pitched as an epic, mythological battle between the Doctor and the Master (who this time gets to be *the* villain of the story instead of just an agent for invading monsters), "The Time Monster" begins with the Doctor suffering a nightmare vision of his arch-rival bringing on the apocalypse and ends with the fall of Atlantis. This is, of course, the *third* time Atlantis has fallen in the course of the series.

2. Those searching for traces of the "hippy" influence on *Doctor Who* need look no further than episode six, which starts in the New Age version of Atlantis (it looks an *awful* lot like an early '70s rock musical) and culminates in the Doctor and the Master facing each other in a rainbow-coloured void, where they both end up facing an enormous floating female god-head in mystical face-paint. Jo Grant's verdict: 'Groovy.'

3. The two "ordinary" supporting characters here - Professor Thascales' lab-assistants, Ruth and Stuart - are notable for delivering dialogue that makes the Atlanteans' prose-poetry sound believable by comparison. Ruth spends most of the story complaining about the way she keeps getting patronised by men, while Stuart gets to slouch about the place in a very '70s-sit-com fashion (and in a very '70s-sit-com moustache). His worst line: 'May God save the good ship Women's Lib, and all who sail in her.' Her worst line: 'Simmer down, Stu.'

4. Whereas the *best* line comes from the Doctor, hurriedly trying to spur the Brigadier into action after his vision of the future: 'The Master. I've just seen him.' 'The Master? Where?' 'In a dream. Not half an hour ago!' (And the Brigadier gets to deliver some more gloriously off-hand orders, when calling for back-up: 'Oh, and Yates? Shove a couple of anti-tank guns in the boot, will you?')

5. There's a very peculiar scene in episode four, in which the Doctor describes the Master as "paranoid" for wanting to take over the universe, and the Master replies 'who isn't... the only difference is, I'm a little more honest than the rest'. It's a strange, ill-fitting piece of dialogue, the first (and only) time that the series tries to bring cod-psychology to the Time Lord psyche.

6. Episode three sees the UNIT troops assaulted by various military forces from history, including a V-1 buzz-bomb. Since the BBC could hardly be expected to build a brand-new V-1 for this (short) sequence, stock footage of a V-1 is used. Unfortunately, the stock footage - unlike the rest of the episode - is in black and white.

The Continuity

The Doctor The Doctor dreams about the Master and the Crystal of Kronos shortly before the *real* Master begins tapping the Crystal's power, suggesting some kind of telepathy or precognition. [It's the first time we see the Doctor dream, unless you count the whole of 6.2, "The Mind Robber".] The nightmare-version of the Master is gloating, triumphant and larger-than-life [much like the Master's vision of the Doctor in 8.2, "The Mind of Evil"], which suggests genuine fear or insecurity on the Doctor's part. He's obsessed with - even paranoid about - finding the Master at this stage.

The Doctor claims his reactions are 'ten times faster' than Jo's, and he knows how to bullfight. When Kronos slows down time, the Doctor and the Master aren't affected as much everyone else, and the Doctor's capable of running in slow-motion when everyone else is frozen [q.v. **How Does Time Work?** under 9.1, "Day of the Daleks"]. According to the Doctor, everybody has race memories. The Master believes, understandably, that the Doctor can't stand not having the last word.

The Doctor also abandons 'hai!' in favour of 'on y va!' when hitting people.

• *Ethics.* The Doctor doesn't want anybody to suffer eternal torment, not even the Master, and even goes as far as asking Kronos for the Master's freedom. He admits to having subconscious thoughts of which he's not proud. [They sound like a Donna Summer record.]

• *Inventory.* Here the Doctor rigs up a hand-held 'time sensor' which detects disturbances in the time-field, revealing the distance and bearing of the nearest active time machine. The distance is given in Venusian feet.

The Doctor also builds a 'time flow analogue' from a wine bottle, some cutlery, two corks and a mug with tea-leaves in it, stating that 'the relationship between the different molecular bonds and the actual shapes forms a crystalline structure of ratios'. He claims that he and the Master made these at school to spoil each others' time experiments, and here the lash-up temporarily jams the Master's TOMTIT equipment. The contraption also spins around even though it doesn't have a power-source.

["Analogue" suggests that the creation's very shape mirrors the movement of time, possibly even resonating with the vortex. This might mean that the energy which makes it spin comes from the vortex itself - the Crystal of Kronos does much the same thing, and funnily enough it's a similar shape - and it certainly suggests that tapping into time is much easier than you'd expect. This could explain why Edward Waterfield is able to summon Daleks from the future using a carefully-assembled collection of mirrors (4.9, "Evil of the Daleks"), and backs up the claim made in the novels that the Time Lords built the vortex as an easy way of accessing history. In effect, contraptions like the analogue "hack" the system. This really does look a lot like magic, though.]

• *Background.* The Doctor knows the location of Atlantis, and knows about both Kronos and the Crystal. He's been outside of time before [in the vortex, or in the TARDIS?], describing it as 'a place that is no place'. [Either his memory-blocks are shifting or this is where he went in "Inferno". As he has knowledge of Chronovores, the former's more likely.]

When he was a little boy, the Doctor lived in a house 'halfway up the top of a mountain' [sic?]. Behind the house was a brittle old hermit who sat under an ancient, twisted tree [see 11.5, "Planet of the Spiders"], a 'monk' who'd ostensibly been there for half his lifetime and who'd learned the secret of life. On 'the blackest day' of the Doctor's existence - and he doesn't explain what caused this misery, although he tells Jo that he'll explain one day - the Doctor asked this hermit for help.

Up on the mountain it was cold and grey, with weeds and a few sludgy patches of snow, but the hermit pointed to a flower 'just like a daisy'. Looking at it through the hermit's eyes, the Doctor saw it glowing with life, and on the way down the

Just How Chauvinistic is Doctor Who?

This seems a good enough time to talk about the subject of Women's Lib, since in "The Time Monster" Ruth and Stuart won't shut up about it. And it's this story, with Ruth constantly complaining about male prejudice and Stuart constantly being sarcastic to her afterwards, that's often cited as a test-case for the way '70s *Doctor Who* treated the (fashionable) feminist issues of its era.

The cynical view is that Ruth represents the series trying to come to terms with the "new" feminism of the age - the subtext being, "because *Doctor Who* is a series where all the women are just ditzy assistants who scream a lot" - and forcing contrived, and rather embarrassing, pro-emancipation messages into a supporting character's mouth. Except... it's far more accurate to say that Ruth represents *Doctor Who* trying to come to terms with feminism *as a popular subject*.

The truth is, by this stage the series didn't *need* to prove it was in touch with the times. Like *The Avengers*, and like many of the other adventure serials of the late '60s, it had introduced "emancipated" female characters long before equal rights was the hot topic of conversation. In fact, ironically enough, it was only in the early '70s that the ditzy assistant (Jo Grant, although even *she's* ostensibly a highly-trained agent underneath it all) came into fashion. Right before her were Liz Shaw and Zoe Herriot, both of whom were blatantly cleverer than any of the male supporting cast and almost as clever as the know-it-all alien at the heart of the series. Even Barbara Wright, despite some occasional chauvinism from Ian Chesterton, was no shrinking violet and *that* was in 1963.

Throughout the '60s, female companions were consistently shown as intelligent, resourceful and at least as capable as the boys, with only one real "screamer" (Victoria) among them. What chauvinism there was came from male characters / writers' occasional, off-handed comments, not from any stupidity or weakness in the women themselves. It *is* hard not to wince when the soldiers in "The Invasion" (6.3) agree that Zoe is 'much prettier than a computer', even if it's exactly the kind of thing you'd expect a bunch of obnoxious squaddies to say. Yet the scene in "The Moonbase" (4.4) where the Doctor asks Polly to make the coffee - while he gets on with the *real* work - seems perfectly reasonable (although the coffee-making actually provides the missing clue which later saves everyone's lives, typically). The Doctor gives the menial jobs to humans all the time, male or female. Bear in mind, during the UNIT era it's the manly Sergeant Benton who gets the coffee-making duties, and in "The Time Monster" itself it's Stuart, rather than his female counterpart, who's asked to put the kettle on.

With hindsight, by the early '70s *Doctor Who* had made its position on feminism clear without even meaning to. Its position was definitely "pro". The trouble was that by 1972, the audience was far more conscious of feminism as a contemporary concern, as terms like "Women's Lib" became easy media catch-words. By '72 it barely mattered what the programme's track record was, or how self-willed the Doctor's female companions had been pre-Jo. What was noticeable, and what the production team must have been aware of, was that the programme had never explicitly said anything about the subject.

The point of Ruth in "The Time Monster" isn't that she's the first sign of feminism in the programme, it's that she's the first one to go on about it so much. And two years later, when Sarah Jane Smith arrived to fill Jo Grant's role as the Doctor's sidekick, the same logic applied. It's a matter of record that Barry Letts wanted a companion who was more "liberated", and in tune with the modern age, which suggests that he'd completely forgotten the programme's past history. Liz Shaw was already at *least* as "liberated" as Sarah, but never felt the need to prove her credentials. She didn't overtly mention Women's Lib in her very first story. She didn't insist on dressing like a tomboy. She didn't object to the Doctor calling her 'my dear', and there was no reason that she *should* have done, since at the same time he was being a lot more patronising to the butch, moustache-wielding Brigadier.

In effect, the "popular" feminism of the early 1970s (meaning, the media fuss about bra-burning rather than what *actual* feminists practised) did more harm to *Doctor Who* than good. It convinced the programme-makers that "feminism" meant "constantly talking about feminism", something which eventually made the women seem far more two-dimensional than they had half a decade earlier.

You could perhaps argue that this was also a result of the programme's changing style. UNIT's presence removed the need for the Doctor to have a strapping male companion like Ian or Jamie, which meant that by default the *female* character ended up asking the stupid questions instead. Again, see "The Moonbase" and Ben and Jamie's

continued on page 95...

mountain everything shone in the sunlight. [This is closer to Buddhist parable than anything we've heard from the Doctor before, and it's remarkably similar to the story of how the spirit of the Dharma was passed on to Mahakasyapa by Buddha. It's possible that it isn't supposed to be taken *entirely* literally. Note that the Doctor says 'I laughed too, when I first heard it' as if reciting a story someone else told him.]

Explaining this part of his past to Jo, the Doctor seems more open and more "human" than ever before, and there's no sense of him feeling the need to surround himself with an air of mystery. [An actual *love* for humanity comes across in this period, something which seems unique to the Third Doctor. He's always had an affection for Earth, but it's hard to picture most of his other incarnations opening up in this way. Certainly, it's impossible to imagine - say - the Fourth Doctor displaying either the frailty or the sentimentality that the Doctor demonstrates here.]

• *Bessie.* She now has a "super drive", which can accelerate her to ridiculous speeds. The brakes work by the absorption of inertia, so the Doctor can stop at high speed without the passengers flying through the windscreen. [The thing the Doctor was fitting in 9.4, "The Mutants". A device like this would make faster-than-light travel a realisable dream, but instead it's used to break various British traffic laws.] The Doctor indicates that Bessie might be in some way 'alive', in the same way the TARDIS is.

The Supporting Cast

• *Jo Grant.* She's now starting to think scientifically, at last. She may know a smattering of Greek.

• *UNIT.* There seem to be UNIT HQs all over the world, and every section of UNIT has the search for the Master written into standing orders, priority A1. Under subsection 3A of the preamble to the Seventh Enabling Act, paragraph 24G, the Brigadier can have UNIT take over from a government investigation during a crisis like the TOMTIT affair.

"Our" UNIT HQ would seem to be seventy to a hundred miles from Cambridge.

• *The Brigadier.* He's less prepared to believe the Doctor's claims than ever before. [A result of the Doctor moving away from "aliens", which he understands, and towards "unlikely ancient gods". He becomes even more cynical by the time of 10.1, "The Three Doctors", so he's no longer coping very well under the strain of the job.] He calls Yates 'Mike' twice [once in the cliffhanger to episode three, but it's not repeated in the reprise], and he knows what a V1 doodlebug sounds like.

• *Sergeant Benton.* If there's a prize for the most uses of the phrase 'the oldest trick in the book', he gets it. However, he's astute enough to outwit the Master, decisive enough to get the scientists to do something and - considering it's his day off - rather keen to investigate the possibilities of TOMTIT. He doesn't even seem to mind, when a TOMTIT effect that reverted him to infancy is undone, finding himself stark naked in front of two young women and his superior officer.

The Supporting Cast (Evil)

• *The Master.* Here he's more blasé, arrogant and power-mad than ever before, once again posing as an academic in England even though this puts him perilously close to the Doctor. [He may have chosen Wootton as his base because of the number of battles fought there, as if anticipating a chance to humiliate Mike Yates with the TOMTIT machine.] He demonstrates the ability to exactly replicate the Brigadier's voice, even if his Greek accent vanishes before long, and he's skilled at seduction. He's still smoking fat cigars.

The Master wears a TV-wristwatch which can apparently monitor outside events without the need for cameras, and which can tap in to UNIT's radio signals. He also owns a handy map of Atlantis. After exploiting the strengths of those around him, and their strongly-held beliefs [e.g. 9.3, "The Sea Devils"], the Master now returns to dominating the weak-minded: 'It's quite like old times.'

The TARDIS(es) The TARDIS has telepathic circuits, and TARDISes communicate telepathically, so when the Doctor is lost in the vortex he can use the Ship to communicate with Jo in the console room. This connection seems to be the TARDIS' idea, not the Doctor's [the Master doesn't have such a good rapport with his own Ship, which is why he's not expecting the Doctor to do this].

There's a control on the console marked "extreme emergency" which, when pulled, can retrieve the Doctor from the vortex again and make him materialise inside the Ship. The Master can use the telepathic circuits to predict the Doctor's words before he says them, and force them to come out of his mouth backwards.

Just How Chauvinistic is Doctor Who?

...continued from page 93

macho posturing when they're trying to decide who's going to get the dangerous Cyberman-killing job, deflated when Polly insists that it was her plan and that she should carry it out. The Brigadier is just as ignorant as Jo about the nature of the universe, but he simply doesn't care about the Doctor's answers, as long as he knows what to blow up. The fact that Mike Yates is also prepared to ask the Doctor for exposition - at least when he's around, and not shooting at monsters out in the field - demonstrates that supplying feed-lines is an equal opportunities job.

[Though pedant would point out that if you play the Doctor's backwards speech backwards then it still sounds like rubbish].

Both the Doctor and the Master have renovated their TARDIS console rooms, so now they look suspiciously similar, and once again the scanner is set into a roundel [and once again this only lasts for one story]. The TARDIS is, for the first time, said to be outside time when it travels. The time it takes for a journey depends on the TARDIS' 'mood', according to the Doctor. [You get the feeling there's an attempt to explain the "rules" of the TARDIS here, ready for the Doctor's numerous off-Earth travels in Season Ten.] Here he's able to land the TARDIS in the same location as the Master's, thanks to the time sensor.

When the Doctor's TARDIS and the Master's TARDIS occupy roughly the same space, the Doctor's TARDIS materialises in the Master's console room but at the same time the Master's TARDIS materialises in the Doctor's console room. The Doctor's vaguely surprised by this, so he's never tried it before. Weirdly, however, the exterior of the Master's TARDIS is also seen in his laboratory on Earth at the same time. [This might suggest that the exterior of a TARDIS is just a handy interface to the extra-dimensional interior, and *not* a real "outer shell" to the craft. The Master's TARDIS might therefore generate *two* interfaces, one on Earth for its pilot's convenience, one leading into the interior of the other TARDIS trying to co-exist alongside it. Alternatively they may be topologically inside one another, like a Klein bottle, as suggested by "Logopolis" (18.7). This would chime with the conversation the Doctor has with King Dalios about Ideal Forms, conducted a thousand years before Plato had the same idea. See **How Important are the TARDIS' Outsides?** under 21.3, "Frontios".]

While the TARDISes are linked, they can 'time-lock' so that one can't escape the other, while the Master's vehicle is capable of flinging the Doctor's off into the vortex. But it's also established that if the atoms of two TARDISes attempt to occupy *exactly* the same point in space and time, then the result is a 'time ram' in which both Ships are utterly annihilated.

According to the Master, $E=MC^3$ in the extra-temporal physics of the time vortex.

The Non-Humans

• *Kronos, the Chronovore.* Chronovores are creatures 'beyond human imagining' which live outside time [in the vortex], and Kronos is the fiercest of the lot. When Kronos first manifests himself, he appears as a roughly humanoid figure with wings and what looks like a Grecian-style helmet for a face, although he's glowing so brightly that the light blots out his features.

In this form, held captive by the Master and held back by the seal of the high priest from Atlantis, he doesn't seem capable of speech but screeches like an animal. When he attacks the Doctor, the Doctor ends up lost in the vortex, supposedly 'alive forever' in the nothingness. The Doctor believes that creation is finely-balanced, and that when the Master opens the floodgates of Kronos' power all order and structure will be swept away.

Only once free of the Master does Kronos reveal himself in a different form, claiming that shapes are meaningless and only wishing to go back outside time. Though the people of Atlantis know Kronos as a male deity, here "he" appears as a huge female face, existing on the boundary between 'your reality and mine'. Kronos is beyond human morality, as she's capable of destroying a city without remorse but also thanks the Doctor for her release. She wishes to cause the Master eternal pain for what he did, but allows him to escape after the Doctor's request for mercy. [There appear to be Chronovore codes of conduct.]

Stu knows the name of Kronos after he encounters the Chronovore, something the Doctor puts down to 'race memory'. Kronos herself recognises the Doctor 'of old', though he doesn't seem to know her personally.

• *Venusians*. Venusian feet are about three feet in length, so they're always tripping over themselves, and one Venusian mile is roughly the same as four and a half Earth miles. An old Venusian proverb goes 'if the thraskin puts his fingers in his ears, it is polite to shout', although "thraskin" is a word seldom used since the twenty-fifth dynasty and the modern equivalent is "plinge". [A word coined by Spike Milligan, so the Doctor could well be making this up as he goes along.]

Planet Notes

• *Atlantis, Earth*. Believed to be part of the Minoan civilisation, c. 1550 - 1500 BC, Atlantis bears obvious cultural similarities to classical Greece - the Doctor refers to the Atlanteans' 'cousins in Athens' - and its royalty seems to intermarry with other monarchies, since the King's wife is herself the daughter of kings. Many of those in the background appear Asian or African, and the Queen has a Persian cat.

Perhaps thanks to Kronos, there are distinctly supernatural powers at work in the city. The doomed King Dalios was there when the Temple of Poseidon was built, 537 years ago, although his great age is unique even in Atlantean terms. [The Atlanteans don't seem to *know* he's that old, so he can't have been King for long, and something must have gone wrong with the line of succession. Or is blanking their minds another of his powers...?]

Once Atlantis worshipped Kronos, and the city prospered, but the result was a decadent society and natural disasters seem to have followed. Though a high priest keeps the Crystal of Kronos in the Temple of Poseidon, the secrets of controlling the Chronovore have been lost for five-hundred years, so only the Crystal and the seal of the high priest remain. The city has been in decline ever since, and is now close to starving, apparently in need of rainfall. There's mention of a council under the King.

The Crystal of Kronos, seemingly just a trident-shaped piece of quartz, can draw power from outside time to fuel the Master's TOMTIT machine. The priests of Atlantis used the crystal to draw Kronos into time. It's not clear where the Master gets hold of the Crystal he uses, but the Doctor states that it's made the jump through interstitial time; that in the 1970s it's linked to the original Crystal, thousands of years in the past; that it is

the original; and that it's outside time, but that its appearance is here. The Atlanteans claim it's just a fraction of the whole Crystal, split from the genuine article during an attempt to destroy it. [It's hard to know where to start on this, although it's worth mentioning that the "real" Crystal seems to be exactly the same size and shape as the fragment.]

This apparently means that nobody can move it while there's energy in it, even though they can touch it. Even more strangely, there initially seems to be *another* fragment in the Temple when the Master draws the high priest through time to England, but that fragment vanishes and doesn't turn up anywhere else.

When the Master taps the power of the Crystal of Kronos, it's capable of drawing whole armies through time to the present day; slowing down local time to a stop; pushing a window-cleaner off a ladder, for some reason; turning Benton into a baby; and causing Stuart's personal time to accelerate, so that he becomes an old man in seconds. [This isn't just a case of speeding up time, since if his whole *timeline* were pushed forward then he'd end up in a different location and have fifty years' worth of extra memories. Chronovore abilities seem more like magic than science.]

The *true* crystal is hidden in the depths of Atlantis, protected by a guardian who was once human and a friend of King Dalios. While human, the guardian was an athlete who wished for the strength of the bull and a long life in which to use it, so Kronos gave the man his desire by making him half-man, half-beast. The Doctor recognises the guardian as the minotaur, though the word isn't known in Atlantis [which suggests that the Doctor has never met the "real" minotaur or the "real" Theseus at this point; see 17.5, "The Horns of Nimon"].

In the 1970s there's volcanic activity around the Thera group of islands off Greece, now known as the Santorini islands. It happens shortly before the Master begins using his fragment of the Crystal, but the significance of this is never explained. [However, the Master goes back in time later on and leaves the fragment there, which means that at the start of the story it's in two places at once. Perhaps the two versions of the splinter are "resonating" with each other and causing the disturbance.]

The city obviously isn't in the Atlantic, although strangely its inhabitants refer to it as

Atlantis anyway [the real name's being translated into the one we know for the sake of convenience].

History

• *Dating.* [Late 1973 or early 1974.] Ruth has been working on the TOMTIT device for 'months', presumably with Professor Thascales, so it must be that long since the Master's escape from prison in 10.3, "The Sea Devils." [According to Benton's jokey reference it's Michaelmas, i.e. the 29th of September, but this jars with the date in "Day of the Daleks". See What's the UNIT Timeline? under 8.5, "The Daemons", for a full account.]

Atlantis is initially said to have existed 4,000 years ago, though the Doctor later specifies 3,500 years ago. [The latter is more likely, since by the time he gives the later date he's seen the TARDIS console readings. The secrets of Kronos were lost to Atlantis five-hundred years ago, so the first date marks Atlantis at its height and the second marks its destruction. 1500 BC is, indeed, the traditional date for the fall of Atlantis and the actual date of the eruption of Santorini.]

The TOMTIT project - Transmission Of Matter Through Interstitular Time - takes place at the Newton Institute in Wootton, Cambridge, seventy to a hundred miles from UNIT HQ. It's explained that time isn't smooth but made up of bits, and that with TOMTIT it's possible to transport objects through space by breaking them down into light-waves and pushing them through the interstices between "now" and "now". The Doctor doesn't seem surprised that humans are attempting something so advanced. [He doesn't expect it to work until he finds out that the Master's involved. See **How Do You Transmit Matter?** under 6.5, "The Seeds of Death". Intriguingly, the January 2004 edition of *Scientific American* details the theory of "loop quantum gravity", which is essentially interstitial time / space as it's depicted here. Aside from unifying quantum theory and relativity, this could have all sorts of useful benefits for people writing guidebooks to science-fiction series of the 1970s. It'd be nice if theoretical physics goes '70s-retro...]

The Doctor refers to World War Two as 'the Hitler War' [how it's seen by the Time Lords?].

The Analysis

Where Does This Come From? Writing years after the fact, producer Barry Letts recalled that by 1972 he was aware of *Doctor Who* becoming a science-fiction series rather than a fantasy, and that "The Time Monster" was an attempt to restore the balance by bringing mythology back into the series. Looking back even *more* years after the fact, it seems a truly odd thing to say.

In fact, in 1972 *Doctor Who* was far more inclined towards fantasy than it had been in the late '60s. It's true that the fairy-tale "grandfather with a magic box" was a long way in the past, and that the series had completely given up historical stories in favour of monster stories. Yet nobody could truthfully say that there was more SF in the series during Jon Pertwee's run (killer toys, sub-terranean lizard-men, daemons summoned by black magic) than during Patrick Troughton's (moonbases, Martians and space-stations threatened by robot-people... 6.2, "The Mind Robber", is the only exception).

The series may have become dependent on its monsters, but more often than not they were *folklore* monsters, burrowing their way out of the Earth like hobgoblins instead of landing in space-ships like proper aliens. Would it have looked that way at the time, though? In the age of consciousness-expansion there was some debate about what actually qualified as "science" anyway. In the popular imagination the '60s had started to replace the "hard" physical sciences with the "soft" social ones, something which comes across *particularly* strongly in the literary SF of the time.

So this may be Greek mythology, but it's Greek mythology for the pop-psychologists, and Jo talks about 'all that Cretan jazz' as if it's positively trendy. Which, of course, it was. In Britain you couldn't move for (French composer) Erik Satie "gymnopedies" and pseudo-classical interior décor, thick eyeliner and elaborate hairdos straight out of the Aeschylus' Oresteia, not to mention endless documentaries - many of them for children - about the "truths" behind old legends.

Aside from the Ancient Astronaut idea of myths being half-remembered cosmic events, this was the era when Linear B (a syllabary used for writing Mycenaean) had been decoded and was confirming a lot of the ancient stories. When package holidays led to large numbers of people seeing Knossos in the flesh and when Victorian efforts to find Atlantis were being re-evaluated. The ruins of Akrotini had been discovered on the *real* Santorini just five years earlier, opening up the question of whether this was the genuine, bona fide sunken city described by Plato, especially since Akrotini seemed to have been centuries ahead of its time. Every schoolchild knew that the Labyrinth was a real place.

Checklist of "cosmic" ideas seen here: a doomed but highly-developed ancient civilisation, an astrally-projected Doctor floating around in the vortex with no body to call his own, a smidgeon of Jungian shared consciousness and the aforementioned psychedelic god-head.

Things That Don't Make Sense The doodlebug falls on Wootton in the same place that a doodlebug fell in 1944, the idea presumably being that the Crystal of Kronos draws it through time but not space. So… why does one of the locals remember the 1944 bomb going off, when transporting it to the 1970s means that it never hit the ground thirty years earlier? And if the time sensor allows the Doctor's TARDIS to materialise in (roughly) the same place as the Master's, then why doesn't the Doctor plug it straight into the console and go directly to the Master from his lab at UNIT HQ, instead of roaring around the country in Bessie telling Jo that they have to hurry?

The TOMTIT machine's effects are…whatever Barry Letts thought would be fun to do, basically. Baby Benton is purely gratuitous and baffling. Why don't Stu and Ruth suffer the same effect? Terry Walsh, playing the comedy window-cleaner who just happens to be outside during a dangerous time-experiment, falls off his ladder in slow-motion but is injured as if time had flowed at the same rate for him as for the ground he hits (which isn't the case, otherwise the camera's point-of-view would have run at the same speed). And the Master yells 'come Kronos, come!' when everything appears to be going wrong with TOMTIT, but no-one seems to notice.

It's often been pointed out that the word "Chronovore" is an ugly mix of Greek and Latin, but to be fair, *lots* of English words are ugly mixes of Greek and Latin. "Television", for a start.

Critique Barry Letts and Robert Sloman go slightly berserk in order to bring the season to a big finish. "The Time Monster" quite wilfully sets out to be an epic, the closest the series had ever come to

"*Doctor Who*: The Motion Picture". UNIT gets involved in pitched battles; the Doctor / Master relationship becomes more intense than ever; there are major revelations about the Doctor's past, as well as the nature of the TARDIS; and it all ends with the destruction of Atlantis. It relies on mythology, not only classical mythology but the mythology of *Doctor Who* itself, and it clearly wants to be legendary. Does it succeed…?

On the whole, no. Too much of it goes on for too long. Too much of the dialogue is untenable ('a real pippin of a dream!'). Several performances, to take a phrase which crops up a lot, 'stink of bad fish'. Too many of the fantasy elements just end up looking silly (on the other hand, full marks for the attempted Shakespearean costume drama of the last two episodes). But - and it's become chronically unfashionable to say this - there's so much scope here, so much potential greatness, that anyone who ends up sneering at *all* of it has probably missed the whole point of *Doctor Who* in the 1970s.

This was, above all, an attempt to make folklore for a modern generation. It's hard to stomach the endless technobabble, it's true, but it's just as hard to avoid being charmed by the performances of Delgado's Master and George Cormack's King Dalios. It's dated very, very badly, yet this doesn't change the fact that it's an attempt at something big, mythic and celebratory. And at least it bloody well *tried* to be spectacular, at a time when most other adventure serials aimed for "functional".

But perhaps the main problem with "The Time Monster" is that it devotes itself to setting up the final battle between the Doctor and the Master, planned for two years down the line, a story which - for obvious and bitterly unfair reasons - could never be made. Conversely, the story has a good claim to have inspired the whole run of ITV's effort to snatch the Doctor's crown, *The Tomorrow People* (they even poached back Paul Bernard to direct the pilot).

The Facts

Written by Robert Sloman. Directed by Paul Bernard. Viewing figures: 7.6 million, 7.4 million, 8.1 million, 7.6 million, 6.0 million, 7.6 million.

Supporting Cast Roger Delgado (The Master), Wanda Moore (Dr. Ruth Ingram), Ian Collier (Stuart Hyde), John Wyse (Dr. Percival), Terry

Walsh (Window Cleaner), Donald Eccles (Krasis), Aidan Murphy (Hippias), Marc Boyle (Kronos), George Cormack (Dalios), Ingrid Pitt (Galleia), Derek Murcott (Crito), Susan Penhaligon (Lakis), Michael Walker (Miseus), Dave Prowse (Minotaur), Ingrid Bower (Face of Kronos).

Cliffhangers At the first demonstration of the TOMTIT project, the power builds up beyond the machine's limits and the Master calls out to Kronos to manifest himself; the Master re-activates the TOMTIT device, and the priest from Atlantis materialises in the control room; the Master causes a V-1 doodlebug to appear over the UNIT convoy, and the Brigadier loses radio contact with Yates as it explodes; having condemned the Doctor to the vortex, the Master uses a control on his own TARDIS to set the Doctor's Ship adrift, with Jo still inside it; Jo finds herself locked inside the catacombs beneath Atlantis, and a horrible bellowing noise rings out along the passage.

The Lore

• The design for the Atlantis set is taken almost unchanged from the reconstruction of the Central Court or the Palace of Minos, excavated by Sir Arthur Evans in 1901 and painted from the plans by Piet de Jong. The costumes for the women derive from frescos and statuary, especially the famous snake-goddess votary (although no nipples were exposed at prime-time).

• As has been noted (see 9.1, "Day of the Daleks"), Robert Sloman's original script involved the Daleks experimenting with time and summoning "historical" opponents for UNIT, hence all the messing-about with Roundheads. This "timescoop" idea would turn up again in stories like "Invasion of the Dinosaurs" (11.2) and "The Five Doctors" (20.7).

• The minotaur in episode six is played by Dave Prowse, the man best-known for being inside Darth Vader, at least until recently. Despite the billing, however, many of the Minotaur's scenes were in fact played by Terry Walsh. Susan Penhaligon, later a big name in '70s TV, got her break as Lakis (Queen Galleia's servant) because the actress originally cast was fired for being consistently late. Weirdly, Ian Collier - who plays Stuart - ends up playing Omega in 20.1, "Arc of Infinity" (and again in the stiffly-named Big Finish audio "Omega").

• Filming was affected by a collision between the horse and the Land Rover, and only diligent paperwork avoided a tangled negligence suit. As a result the actor hired as a driver, Marc Boyle, ended up playing Kronos. This was his first on-screen credit.

• A script alteration at the last minute prevented years of dull fanzine articles: in the original version, Jo mentions that she doesn't speak ancient Greek, so the Doctor flips a switch under the console to solve the problem. How Benton could understand the Altantean priest Krasis, who allies himself with the Master, would have been a puzzle even with this *deus ex machina* left in place.

• The scenes of baby Benton were shot on film, but for some reason remounted, with a different child (perhaps the original sprog acted the rest of the cast off the screen).

• An under-running episode three was bulked out with the scene about making a time-flow analogue out of odds and ends. You can tell, somehow.

• The 'daisiest daisy' scene was written by Barry Letts, as part of his project to make the Doctor a flawed figure. Bizarrely, heroic playwright Dennis Potter said something which echoed it almost verbatim in his final interview (as if a writer of his calibre watched *Doctor Who*...).

• Ingrid Pitt (Queen Galleia) later reunited with Jon Pertwee for the film *The House That Dripped Blood*, a movie notable for being one of the very few places where you can hear Pertwee doing something like his "normal" voice instead of a funny accent. Which means that he sounds - and dresses - exactly like the Doctor. Except he's a vampire.

10.1: "The Three Doctors"

(Serial RRR, Four Episodes, 30th December 1972 - 20th January 1973.)

Which One is This? It's anniversary party time for the series, so the First and Second Doctors get invited back on board the TARDIS and there's even anti-matter-flavoured jelly. The villain is revealed as the very first Time Lord of all (who'd like to come and meet us, but…), though not before he steals UNIT HQ and drags it through a black hole.

Firsts and Lasts Nominally the story marking *Doctor Who*'s tenth birthday (as it actually broadcast shortly after its ninth), "The Three Doctors" sees multiple Doctors meeting for the first time (almost passé now, but *ludicrously* exciting in 1973), as well as revealing more than ever about Time Lord history and Time Lord politics.

Here we meet Omega, who's not only the first historical Time Lord but also the first Time Lord to receive a name rather than a title like "Doctor" or "Master" or "that Monk", and learn that the Time Lord planet has both a President and a Chancellor. Since the story's ending sees the Doctor rewarded with a new dematerialisation circuit, it's not only the end of his Earth exile - even if it isn't, in itself, the end of the UNIT age - but also the start of a whole new era in which he actually has some control over where the Ship's supposed to go. What's more the TARDIS gets yet another '70s re-fit, this one lasting for the next four years.

The Doctor, in this case the Second Doctor, carries jelly-babies for the first time. Arguably, it's also the first time he actually saves the entire universe. Plus it's the first story to credit Dick Mills with "Special Sound", a responsibility he'll hold for the next seventeen years.

Four Things to Notice About "The Three Doctors"…

1. Infamously, "The Three Doctors" sees the last appearance of William Hartnell as the First Doctor, though he was too ill to attend the studio recording sessions (he died in 1975, at the age of 67) and shot all his scenes on film. As a result the First Doctor only addresses his successors from a monitor screen in the TARDIS, and spends most of that time chiding them for missing the obvious. Conventional wisdom holds that this is a sad, tragic way for Hartnell's time on the programme to end, but really, it just makes you remember where the series came from. The First Doctor *wasn't* an action hero, and his role as oracle and peacemaker to the Other Two is pitched perfectly, even if he looks unpleasantly unwell at times. He'd be so much less interesting if he had to run up and down corridors like everyone else. (See 20.7, "The Five Doctors", for something closer to what was originally planned.)

2. Meanwhile, the sight of Patrick Troughton and Jon Pertwee squaring off against each other as the Second and Third Doctors - the sight, as with Pertwee and Delgado, of two actors who are just *built* for this kind of thing - eclipses just about everything else in the story.

3. "The Three Doctors" also sees the first real appearance of the Stupid Brigadier. Though he's increasingly found it hard to accept anything the Doctor tells him over the last three years (compare 7.1, "Spearhead from Space" with 9.5, "The Time Monster"), here he goes into a state of denial not seen on television again until the era of *Buffy the Vampire Slayer*, refusing to believe that the TARDIS interior is anything but an illusion; convincing himself that an alien world is actually a beach in Cromer; and concocting his own paranoid theory about the Second Doctor's appearance even when everybody else tells him it's wrong. The Doctor finally seems to have broken his mind (although see **The Supporting Cast** for the defence argument). The Brigadier's staff are just as unlikely. One UNIT soldier's now-notorious response to the gel-guards, as they wobble towards UNIT HQ: 'Holy Moses! What's *that*?'

4. Scientifically-minded viewers who've ever wanted to observe a singularity - the point at the exact centre of a black hole, where all physical laws break down - will be interested to learn that it looks like a hole in the floor with a BBC smoke machine inside it. See also **Why All These Black Holes?**.

The Continuity

The Doctor(s) There's immediate tension between the Second and Third Doctors when they meet, so their personalities aren't "compatible" even if they seem to have the same sense of ethics. The Second Doctor doesn't even like the new-look TARDIS console room, and frequently tricks his younger / later self into doing all the dangerous work [well, if he got killed then there'd be an enormous paradox].

When they're together the Doctors can telepathically "conference" by shutting their eyes and concentrating. [We might conclude that only iterations of the same Time Lord can do this, as none of the people on the Doctor's homeworld are ever seen to try it. But if so, then it's not clear how the Doctor *knows* he can do it when Time Lords are never supposed to meet themselves. On the other hand, Time-Lord-to-Time-Lord telepathy *does* take place in Big Finish audio adventures such as "The Apocalypse Element", which begs the question of why the Time Lords in "The Invasion of Time" (15.6) waste so much time talking to each other.]

The Doctors' force of will is stronger when they team up. Both the Second and Third Doctors defer to the First, as if the First Doctor's older *personality* grants him wisdom beyond theirs, despite the fact that they've got more experience. The President of the Time Lords describes the First Doctor as the 'earliest' Doctor, establishing for the first time that there are no prior versions which have never been revealed [but see 13.5, "The Brain of Morbius"].

Neither the First nor Second Doctors are surprised to find themselves in the Third's company, meaning that they must receive some kind of "briefing" from the Time Lords before they're dispatched. Yet it's unclear whether they retain any of their memories when they go back into their own timestreams [q.v. 20.7, "The Five Doctors"]. The Second Doctor remembers meeting Benton during the Cyberman invasion [6.3], but hasn't seen him since and has no knowledge of the Third Doctor's adventures, while the First Doctor can mysteriously identify Omega's energy-creature as a 'time-bridge' when his successors can't.

Neither the Second or Third Doctors know the lyrics of the Beatles.

• *Inventory.* The Second Doctor arrives on Earth with his recorder, although it's destroyed along with Omega's realm. [Is there a point after

Season 10 Cast/Crew

- Jon Pertwee (the Doctor)
- Katy Manning (Jo Grant)
- Nicholas Courtney
  (Brigadier Lethbridge-Stewart)
- Richard Franklin (Captain Yates)
- John Levene (Sergeant Benton)

- Barry Letts (Producer)
- Terrance Dicks (Script Editor)

"The Invasion" (6.3) when it vanishes from the Second Doctor's adventures? We never see it after "Evil of the Daleks" (4.7), although it's alluded to in "The Enemy of the World" (5.4).] The Third Doctor carries a pencil and a bunch of fake flowers, which he can produce from his jacket as a conjuring-trick, but these too get left in Omega's world.

The Second Doctor uses a small Philips screwdriver to fix the Brigadier's radio, and tosses a coin to decide which version of himself is going to do something dangerous. The Third Doctor acts as if this is a con. [The novelisation suggests that it's a two-headed Martian crown - used by Ice Warriors? - so it never comes up tails. See also 16.2, "The Pirate Planet".]

The Third Doctor's sonic screwdriver acts as an anti-matter detector that makes the same Geiger-Counter noise as anti-matter itself, but it's useless in Omega's world, for some reason.

The Supporting Cast

• *UNIT.* The Brigadier describes UNIT HQ as a 'top secret security establishment', even though there's a great big sign outside which says "MINISTRY OF DEFENCE, UNIT HEADQUARTERS". [It's already been established that UNIT's existence is common knowledge. The Brigadier presumably just means that the base runs top secret operations.] In the Brigadier's office there's a video link to the Security Council in Geneva. Dr. Tyler contacts UNIT as a matter of course when a man goes missing in the vicinity of space-technology, and was already planning a visit after seeing anomalous results from his 'cosmic ray' research.

• *The Brigadier.* Here he sees the TARDIS interior, and visits an alien world, for the first time. The shock of this may partly explain why he's less willing to accept anything the Doctor says than ever before. [Nevertheless, he adapts to somewhat bizarre circumstances better than is generally recognised. The thing which he finds hardest to accept is that the Second Doctor has somehow come back, evidently because he *really* doesn't like things to be out of place at his HQ. But he rapidly improvises a cover-story for the Security Council - the Second Doctor is the Third's 'assistant', so presumably they don't have a photo of Jo on file - and at every weird turn of events he's immediately thinking of damage-limitation. When UNIT HQ is transported somewhere, he's worried about the diplomatic repercussions if it's on foreign soil, something which few other officers would be smart enough to see so quickly. In short, his brief reaction to what he thinks might be Cromer is an anomaly, and his assumption that a Time Lord messing with a time machine has resulted in something going wrong with time isn't *wholly* unwarranted. If anything, it suggests that he just doesn't trust the Doctor much, even though the Doctor's almost invariably right. Nevertheless, it's worth noting that his next trip in the TARDIS triggers a nervous breakdown; see 20.3, "Mawdryn Undead".]

The TARDIS Redecorated, again, and the Third Doctor has "fiddled" with the controls so much that the Second Doctor has trouble using the scanner. The Time Lords ultimately reward the Doctor with a new dematerialisation circuit, and return his knowledge of time-travel law and 'dematerialisation codes'. It's possible to boost a walkie-talkie through the TARDIS' communication circuit.

Under the TARDIS console is the Ship's force-field generator, a portable device which not only creates a force-field around the Ship but also seems to have a force-field operational within itself. The Second Doctor's recorder, trapped inside this field, isn't converted into anti-matter along with the rest of the Ship when Omega draws it into his realm. The suggestion seems to be that nobody can leave the Ship until the force-field's disconnected. [So it's not a normal defensive feature of a stationary TARDIS, although "The Pirate Planet" (16.2) hints that it protects the Ship in flight]. The device is eventually destroyed along with Omega's realm [and another force-field is in use by "The Pirate Planet"].

The console room also has a ceiling and odd cylindrical "booths" to one side, much like the original design. The monitor is colour, at last, but is once again a TV set suspended from the ceiling. It can show the TARDIS itself from outside, as if from a camera placed ten feet away. It's also got sound, and can apparently transmit both sound and pictures to other places, the TARDIS crew using it as a "camera" when addressing the First Doctor [much as in 9.5, "The Time Monster"].

The Time Lords Time Lord operations appear to be run from a "control room", where robed figures observe instruments and monitor screens. The Time Lords have a Chancellor and a President, the President being deferential to the Chancellor and calling him 'excellency', although ultimately the President seems to have the final word. [After 14.3, "The Deadly Assassin", the Chancellor is subservient to the President. Possibly the power-structure remains unchanged, but custom is altered.]

When Omega drains 'cosmic energy' into his black hole, threatening the whole of space-time with collapse, the Time Lord planet seems particularly hard-hit [because it's closest to the hole?] and is so depleted of energy that it's effectively paralysed. The Doctor's TARDIS doesn't work during this period [suggesting that it takes its power directly from Time Lord central - see **What Makes TARDISes Work?** under 1.3, "The Edge of Destruction" - although the Second Doctor's arrival seems to remove this problem, so it may be the Third Doctor's memory that's at fault].

During the crisis the Time Lords feel they can't spare anyone to help the Doctor, as everyone is needed to combat the energy drain. [Meaning that they can't spare anybody capable of helping the Doctor? Most Time Lords would be useless in the outside universe.] However, they do have the ability to make the Doctor's own time-stream cross itself, even though it uses up a great deal of 'temporal energy'.

Crossing one's own time-stream and meeting one's 'other selves' expressly contravenes the First Law of Time [which has changed by the time of 14.2, "The Hand of Fear"]. This may be the first insinuation that a complete change of form is normal for Time Lords rather than being a quirk of the Doctor's. When the First Doctor is caught in a 'time eddy' he's only visible by scanner, where he's seen sitting in a triangular 'transportation unit'. [The Second Doctor doesn't have one of these when he arrives on Earth, so it probably only exists in the vortex.]

The worst thing about this crisis isn't that the Time Lords are facing destruction, but that they

Why All These Black Holes?

Perhaps the most surprising thing about "The Three Doctors" is that the science is almost exactly right. That is, as far as was known in 1972, the material about black holes was at least permitted by scientific theory. At the time, no-one had any way of knowing if such bodies even existed.

Although the original speculation about collapsing stars dates back to the Enlightenment mathematician Laplace, it was only in 1964 that physicist John Wheeler coined the term "black hole". After that, people got interested. Between 1799 and 1964, Einstein happened, and so did quantum theory. The two don't quite mesh, which is where the fun starts. Einstein says, crudely, that mass and energy are the same thing from different points of view. He also says that space and time have a similar sort of relationship. And mass distorts space (or energy distorts time, or any other combination). The amount by which mass dents space is called... gravity.

With this so far? If you get enough mass / energy in one place (e.g. a star), it noticeably affects space-time. A *seriously* large mass in a small space will become a denser mass in an even smaller space. Once gravity overcomes the far stronger forces within an atom, the matter becomes super-dense and behaves very oddly indeed (see **Why Are Elements So Weird In Space?** under 22.2, "Vengeance on Varos").

Once you've got so much mass in so small a space, it keeps getting smaller and denser until the escape velocity is beyond the speed of light. In other words, to get away from it you need to move faster than anything in the universe *can* move. So even light can't escape this "black hole", and that's nearly all we can be sure of. The *event horizon* is the point beyond which we can't know anything about the black hole at all, since there's no way for the information to get back to us, and the event horizon can be pretty big. If an entire galaxy became a black hole (and some think the whole universe is inside one), then it'd be about a third of a light-year across. The surface gravity wouldn't be that bad, but it'd be inescapable and no-one would know you were there. So far, Omega's place seems plausible.

Further in it gets more sticky. A large mass in a small area, getting denser and denser and smaller and smaller, ultimately tends to become an infinite mass in a one-dimensional point: the singularity. This will destroy *everything*, and remove it from the universe entirely. However, depending on what the original mass was doing before it became a black hole, the singularity could be a revolving torus (i.e. a doughnut) and big enough to fly through.

According to the physics, this is a nifty way to get around inconvenient space-time snags like "causality". Even though black holes can "boil off" particles and x-rays through quantum effects - what's now called Hawking Radiation, and we'll talk about *him* later - the singularity is eternal, if big enough. So a singularity created at the Big Bang (which was, after all, a large mass in a small area) should still be around, somewhere. And you should, although in the early '70s this was thought impossible, get "naked" singularities with no remaining black hole around them. If 1% of stars implode in the way that's been described here, then there should be a billion in this galaxy, and if only the top 1% of *those* are eternal then that's still 10,000... except they eat each other on contact. The "whirlpool" shape of galaxies is now thought to be a result of super-massive black holes draining everything else out of the cosmos.

To where, though? It seems to defy common sense, even *this* kind of manic space-age common sense, that all the energy / matter goes nowhere. Some of the earliest theories suggested that "white holes" spewed out matter and energy elsewhere in the cosmos. This idea helped to explain another anomaly: the theories say that anti-matter should be as plentiful as matter, but can't coexist with it. So where is it? Either in an anti-cosmos (as whimsically postulated in "The Mutants") or on the other side of space and time. The process of entering a black hole strips particles down to their charges while stretching them out into infinitely-long lines with no elapsed time - a chronosynclastic infundibularisation, or as scientists call it, "spaghettifying" - so the difference between matter and anti-matter becomes academic.

So at the point when "The Three Doctors" was written, the idea was that if you fell down a black hole - and if your angle was right - then you'd cross space and time, and either emerge as a stream of particles at the beginning of time or in an anti-matter cosmos equal and opposite to this one. (Gerry Anderson made a very lavish pilot for a series called *Into Infinity* based on this premise, and most of it was spent explaining the science to the viewers, which is probably why it remained a pilot.) Throw in quantum theory, and black holes become a one-way anti-entropic hoover: they restore energy and mass to the universe in unpredictable ways.

continued on page 105...

ABOUT TIME 1970–1974

will have failed 'those we are pledged to protect'. This is the last time that the Time Lords appear so selfless, but it doesn't seem out of keeping with anything they've said before. [The "protection" agenda may be the way they *like* to see themselves. In later stories they sanction assassination and retro-genocide, ostensibly for "the good of all".]

At the conclusion of this crisis, the destruction of Omega's realm creates a supernova out of the black hole, which the Time Lords see as being a whole new source of energy. "["The Deadly Assassin" (14.3) establishes that Time Lord society is powered by something which Rassilon took *out* of a black hole, arguably the same one created by Omega: see **Did Rassilon Know Omega?** under "The Deadly Assassin". So the black hole, "emptied" millennia ago, hasn't been of any importance to the Time Lords until now. It's odd, though, that a race which can go anywhere in space and time sees one particular supernova as an interesting new power source.]

The Time Lords don't understand how anything can exist in a black hole [because as "The Deadly Assassin" establishes, they've forgotten what ancient artefacts like the Sash of Rassilon actually do], and have difficulty believing that any force in the universe is their equal. On the other hand, the President seems to have been aware all along that Omega was alive, or at the very least he's not surprised by it. [This indicates that the version of the story Omega tells may not be a paranoid fantasy, but an accurate summary of a genuine betrayal; the first indication that Time Lord history is largely propaganda. The novelisation of "Remembrance of the Daleks", like the later New Adventures, hints that Rassilon deliberately sent Omega to his doom.]

The three high-ranking Time Lords all speak of the Doctor as a near-equal, whereas after this he's half-forgotten, or anonymous. [Given the lack of man-power available here, it's possible there are fewer Time Lords at this stage. Not for the last time, the strong hint is given that the Time Lords equate to angels, with the "fallen" playing their part in some kind of cosmic plan. Omega, as the first of the fallen and the "Light Bringer", even sounds like Milton's version of Lucifer.]

Ancient Time Lords

• *Omega.* Considered legendary by the Time Lords, and even the Doctor admits to honouring him as a hero. As a solar engineer [see 25.1,

"Remembrance of the Daleks" for more details], Omega made time-travel possible for the Time Lords by turning a star into a black hole, something which he claims happened 'thousands of years' ago. [23.4, "The Ultimate Foe", suggests millions. Either Omega has lost track of time or it just doesn't pass in the same way for him, which is scientifically unavoidable, so close to an event horizon.]

It was his duty to 'find and create' the power-source to give the Time Lords the energy they needed, but it was known to be a dangerous mission and he was lost in the supernova he created [which then turned into the black hole, apparently]. According to the Doctor he's been revered ever since. The Doctor also suggests that Omega could 'resume' a place on the High Council, meaning that the High Council pre-dates the Time Lords.

In fact Omega survived the mission, and now exists inside a realm of anti-matter inside a black hole. It's not explained how Omega's brain and body survived the black hole for long enough to allow his will to build a new world there, nor does anybody explain what anti-matter has got to do with black holes. [See also **What Does Anti-Matter Do?** under 13.2, "Planet of Evil".] Omega is incapable of leaving his realm without another mind to keep it stable, and he seems to need a Time Lord to do the job. Here he suggests that his brothers only became Time Lords *after* his sacrifice [but even before then his people must have had greater-than-normal mental powers, or he wouldn't need another of his kind to take over from him].

Omega primarily wants revenge on the Time Lords for abandoning him, believing that they should have made him a god. Constant exposure to the singularity has a corrosive effect due to the acceleration of the particles in the 'light-stream', hence the mask he wears, but in fact there's no physical substance left under his armour and his will is all that's left. The 'dark side' of his mind can telepathically wrestle the Doctor, appearing in this psychic sparring-match as something bald and hideous. [What does the Second Doctor see during all of this? Do both antagonists disappear into a dreamscape, and if so then is Omega connected to the Matrix? He might be, if "Arc of Infinity" (20.1) makes any gesture towards sense.]

He somehow recognises the two Doctors in his world as being the same individual, and knows about the High Council's Laws of Time even

Why All These Black Holes?

...continued from page 103

This defies the Second Law of Thermodynamics, which basically states that everything will eventually end up being tepid and inert (see 18.7, "Logopolis"), so something that *defies* it gives you one more reason to feel optimistic about the universe. Particles and energy can skip around the event horizon of a black hole, because according to quantum theory they're not solid "lumps" but waves of probability, and the "gap" each particle makes in the surrounding energy-state forms an anti-particle elsewhere. This may seem nigh-incomprehensible to the layperson, but the upshot is that if one half of a particle is created "inside" the horizon, then the other half could pop into being "outside". And if you think *this* is weird, ponder exactly how your watch or mobile 'phone works; this is mainstream, kosher physics and has been since about 1920.

In other words a black hole can, if treated right, become an inexhaustible supply of energy just by bunging waste matter in its direction. Hang on, though: as all SF writers know, quantum theory also suggests that the outcome of an event can be changed by someone observing it. Consciousness makes a difference to the way things work. So instead of just a "halo" of Hawking radiation, if a conscious mind were to go near a singularity then could it bias the random output and create whatever it feels like?

A couple of years after "The Three Doctors" was broadcast, Steven Hawking gave a lecture saying pretty much that. Obviously there's no way of involving a conscious observer in the process, but yes, the emissions of "fuzzy" black holes as they fizz away into nothing - leaving behind these horrible naked singularities - are so random in nature that a grand piano, the Bandril Ambassador or a book exactly like this one but with "Pertwee" changed to "puffin" every time is just as likely to emerge as heat or light. Without predictability, science might have returned to being a branch of philosophy. This isn't the place to explain exactly what happened next, but there was an apparent get-out clause in the small-print of General Relativity.

About a year later, the fat hit the fire again. The journal *Physical Review D* published a paper entitled "Rotating Singularities and the Possibility of Global Causality Violation" by Frank Tipler. In this he suggested that by a geometrical trick, you could "swap" space and time, and travel back and forth to any point *up to the creation of the singularity*. (*New Scientist* got hold of it in the summer of 1980, and ran a feature illustrated with a publicity photo from "The Masque of Mandragora". You can see the appeal.) Tipler later concluded that anyone able to do this would have done it, so obviously we must be the most advanced species in the cosmos and it's all for our benefit. He called this the "anthropic" principle and it was briefly fashionable. Also a fad of its day was Adrian Berry's pop-science book *The Iron Sun*, about building black holes as tunnels through space-time, which provided the basis for both "The Horns of Nimon" and an early draft of "The Sunmakers". (N.B. as with "The Deadly Assassin", "The Horns of Nimon" and by implication "Terror of the Vervoids", Omega's black hole is artificial in origin. In *Doctor Who* terms a "natural" black hole has yet to appear.)

In theory, crossing the beams of two powerful lasers ought to create micro-singularities, but these wouldn't last long enough to be noticeable. Much of the most exciting work in this field was later discredited, and we have only inferential evidence that Cygnus X1 is indeed a black hole. Nevertheless the simple fact that writers for *Doctor Who* had both the means and the opportunity to use something from real science before any other series, accurately and dramatically (as opposed to picking between the two as usual), makes this period of the programme special.

By the time of "The Deadly Assassin" four years later, black holes have become an all-purpose way of making space / time shenanigans seem legitimate and scary, while Rassilon's journey is told as if he were Moses climbing Mount Sinai. However, as a symbol of the Time Lords' sovereignty over time, the implication that their Eye of Harmony is *the* black hole - from the Big Bang - is very potent. Unlike the Time Lords themselves, by this stage.

though he presumably left the universe before they were devised. He also appears to know about terrestrial mythology, describing himself as the "Atlas" of his world. [Prometheus is a better parallel, stealing fire from heaven and being tortured for eternity bound to a rock; compare this with Rassilon's fate in 20.7, "The Five Doctors".]

It amuses Omega to use the Doctor as the instrument of his revenge, as if he's aware of either the Doctor's strained relations with his people or of the Doctor's future. [Again, Rassilon in "The Five Doctors" seems to have foreknowledge of both the Doctor and the Master.]

The Non-Humans

• *Gel-Guards*. [Never named on-screen.] Omega can dispatch lumps of anti-matter from his own realm into the "normal" universe, sending them along a stream of faster-than-light 'compressed light', although he states that these organisms can exist in either the world of matter or the world of anti-matter without the usual colossal explosion. The anti-matter splodge on Earth apparently has some limited intelligence, and has been scanning Earth [and we assume many other planets] for a Time Lord. It's eventually re-enforced by almost-humanoid lumps of jelly, each one with a single eye in the middle of its forehead and pincers that function as energy weapons. Omega also uses these creatures to guard his palace [simple humanoid shapes are easier for his will to maintain than proper "people"]. Distractingly, gel-guards burble as they move.

Anything targeted by the anti-matter can be transported into Omega's world, something the First Doctor calls a 'time-bridge', though when the realm is destroyed everything snaps back to its original location. Objects entering Omega's realm are converted into anti-matter [and so is the interior of the TARDIS, which is presumably in another dimension].

History

• *Dating*. [Probably early 1974. See **What's the UNIT Timeline?** under 8.5, "The Daemons"].

Dr. Tyler suggests that Britain's space research isn't as good as NASA's [but have NASA got a man on Mars?], his cosmic ray monitoring device being the most sophisticated this side of Cape Kennedy. The box is marked "Wessex University" [so it may just be the University's space research which isn't NASA-standard]. Houston has recently put up a 'space monitor', and the Cold War still seems to be on, with Tyler referring to 'Yanks and the Other Lot'.

Dr. Tyler's research balloon lands at a wildlife sanctuary at Minsbridge, England. [Where the locals have exactly the same "rustic" accent as *all* the locals in the early '70s.]

Additional Sources

Here's the story...

Bob Baker and Dave Martin's revised outline for "The Three Doctors" gave the name of the first Time Lord as "Ohm", which is an almost-obvious joke. OHM upside-down is WHO, the suggestion

being that Ohm was the Doctor's counterpart at the *beginning* of Time Lord history (and possibly that the Doctor is the end-product of the Time Lord line, although this point would be easier to argue if the word "Who" were actually used as his name in the series itself). In the final script it's changed to "Omega", the Greek letter Omega being the symbol used in physics to represent the ohm, i.e. a unit of electrical resistance. So the sort-of-joke still stands.

This all follows the lead of *The Making of Doctor Who* (1972 edition), which - as has already been mentioned - was at one time the only guide to *Doctor Who* available in the shops and therefore a comfort to a generation. And the catalogue of the Doctor's adventures in *The Making* is presented as a transcript from the Doctor's trial, in which his "name" is given as a series of Greek symbols. This trend, begun in the book and put on-screen in "The Three Doctors", eventually reaches its nadir in "The Armageddon Factor" (16.6). Terrance Dicks whisked a copy of the book to Baker and Martin, languishing in Bristol, along with his lengthy list of recommendations, suggestions and revisions (see 8.3, "The Claws of Axos"; 9.5, "The Mutants"; 12.3, "The Sontaran Experiment"; and above all 14.2, "The Hand of Fear").

Another "first" in this book is the idea that the Doctor's fate, had he been found guilty, would have been execution and removal from the records of the Time Lords. This is far more in keeping with their later, quasi-Soviet way of handling things than the usual fate in the novels of the time, to have your 'life-stream' reversed so that you never really existed.

For the record, the book gives the Doctor's full "name" as _3 _x2. How dull.

The Analysis

Where Does This Come From? It's time for messing-around-with-science again. After all the pop-mythology and consciousness expansion of Season Nine, "The Three Doctors" comes across as a wilful effort to bring big, solid SF concepts back into the series. In the course of a single story there's a black hole, a supernova, anti-matter *and* some ruminations on the possibility of super-lucent emissions. The fact that no more than two of these things seem to go together at any one time barely seems relevant. (The business about Omega engineering both a black hole and a supernova is never explained, and as for the black hole turning *into* a supernova… still, they may have seemed connected at the time; see **Why All These Black Holes?**).

There is, at least, a frisson of physics here. A suggestion that some of this might, somehow, be feasible… at least in terms of cold, hard, jargon-heavy theory.

But as ever in this era of *Doctor Who*, the fact that half the programme-makers seem to have been hooked on transcendental meditation changes the rules. If this is physics, it's the physics of *2001*, in which science is pushed to the fore but mindbending head-trips and mental revelations still accompany expeditions to the furthest reaches of space. There was a time when *Doctor Who* would have dealt with the idea of a "singularity" by putting one on Pluto and claiming that the people of the twenty-first century had built a base around it, but here, the point where natural laws break down becomes a *psychological* phenomenon. Omega can control it by his own will, and everything we see is a product of his imagination. (Again, compare this with the *Space: 1999* episode "Black Sun", in which a black hole is a philosophical event rather than a great big super-dense mass in space.)

For all its talk of collapsing stars and lightstreams, the greatest power here is the power of the mind, so the Doctors can escape a prison cell just by pretending there's a door and the face-off against Omega becomes a nigh-Buddhist confrontation with the dark side of the enemy's psyche. As in Season Nine, who needs LSD when you've got colour television?

(In fact, though the story is often cited as the ultimate example of Bob 'n' Dave's "hard science" approach, this was actually a last-minute bodge to replace a more fantasy-styled story of the Realm of the Dead. Terrance Dicks requested a more literal "Death World", citing Harry Harrison's *Deathworld* trilogy, and - crucially - recommending that the foe be 'equal and opposite' to the Time Lords. It'd be the work of moments to show how 'equal and opposite', a theme running through this story, is in keeping with certain Eastern philosophies. But Baker and Martin don't really seem to have taken this on board. More likely, Dicks and Barry Letts had been thinking along those lines anyway, and suggested it as a "solution" to the need for a workable script.)

On a more prosaic level, the plot of "The Three Doctors" has often been compared to *The Wizard of Oz*, and there's obviously something no-place-like-homey about the way the Doctors send their various human accomplices back to Earth from Omega's world. But this volume would also suggest comparing the sight which greets the Doctor on his arrival in Omega's realm - a blasted, desolate landscape, littered with broken walls and scattered furnishings from UNIT HQ - with *The Bed-Sitting Room* (1969).

And a lot of material from prior *Doctor Who* seems to have been cannibalised, too. Omega wants to escape the world he's created in much the same way as the Master of the Land of Fiction (6.2, "The Mind Robber"). Old situations are evoked when the Doctor tells Jo, 'when I tell you to run, run', and later when the Second Doctor says to Benton 'it's quite like old times'. This sense of familiarity is part of the story's problem; unless you count the final episode of "The War Games", with its retreads of old scenes and "monster shopping list", it's the first time that the programme has been its own subject. This time the threat isn't to Earth but to the Doctor himself.

Things That Don't Make Sense It's debatable whether the writers of "The Three Doctors" actually *meant* it to have the feel of a Christmas pantomime, but either way, it's a story full of characters so stupid that they seem to be asking the audience to shout 'behind you!' or 'don't pull the rope!' at them. Sergeant Benton is left on his own to guard a highly volatile mass of anti-matter, but then petulantly throws a gum-wrapper at it as soon as nobody's looking, causing the Doctor and company to rush back into the lab as if they're about to ask the audience 'did you see what happened, boys and girls?'.

And then there's Dr. Tyler, a man with no motives in life other than to do whatever's convenient for the plot. This is a character who instantly gets in touch with a UN security organisation when he thinks he's seen a yokel by the side of a river but can't find the man a few minutes later. (It turns out that Ollis has been dragged into another universe, but the man could have just gone for a pee in the bushes for all Tyler knows). A character who shows no sign of activity for an episode and a half, but - when the script underruns by a couple of minutes - changes his entire personality and makes a sudden attempt to escape from Omega's palace (where does he think he's going to go?) just so the gel-guards can chase after him for a while. A character who, despite being a high-ranking scientist with a vested interest in extreme physics and a habit of finding everything he sees absolutely fascinating, ultimately walks out of the TARDIS saying 'well, I think I've seen enough for one day, thanks' as soon as the story no longer needs him. The supporting cast of *Doctor Who* have never been exactly three-dimensional, but *really*...

Omega's captivity doesn't make a great deal of sense either, since he's capable of sending gel-guards all the way to Earth with specific instructions to find the Doctor, but has never tried sending a request for help to anybody in the whole of space and time. At the very least, couldn't he have abducted someone from the Time Lord planet millennia ago? Nor has he tried taking his hat off in several hundred years, apparently. And when the Time Lords are desperately trying to "help" the Third Doctor on Earth, it never occurs to them that the simplest, most useful and most energy-efficient thing for them to do would be to give him his memories of time-travel theory back (as they do, in the blinking of an eye, *after* the crisis is over).

Suddenly, in episode two, Tyler knows that the source of the 'space lightning' is a black hole even though he's never been told. Suddenly, in episode three, the President knows that Omega's behind all of this. Suddenly, in episode four, the First Doctor can come and go across the event horizon whenever he feels like being condescending to someone. The door to the Doctor's lab is open when it's transported away from Earth, but mysteriously locks itself once it's transferred to an alien world [the Doctor's right, natural laws really *don't* apply here]. Anti-matter draws UNIT HQ into another universe matter, but leaves behind a flat stretch of ground with no foundations. *Really* nit-picking now: how come the end credits say "BBC 1973", when the first episode was shown - and the whole thing made - in 1972?

And can anybody explain exactly *how* the Second Doctor's recorder slips into the TARDIS force-field generator like that?

Critique A story that's generally remembered as an all-time classic, thanks to the constant confrontations between Jon Pertwee and Patrick Troughton, whose scenes together go some way beyond "great" and into the realms of "*iconically* great". Sadly, though, the scenes between the Doctors are just about *all* "The Three Doctors" has

to recommend it.

Take away Troughton, and what you're left with is a dull, crass, tacky-looking piece of SF about cardboard characters being pushed through plot-loopholes big enough to swallow UNIT HQ all on their own. (Arguably, even the Doctor vs. Doctor scenes are a con. This isn't the Troughton we had for 127 episodes in the '60s, but a half-remembered mulch of gimmicks and Victoriana - 'I may call you Jo, mayn't I?' - a "potty professor" instead of the avuncular wolf-in-sheep's-clothing he'd once been. Even *this* doesn't remove anything from his performance, since by definition meeting his future self was the one thing he could never do during his "spell", so it's just another facet of an ever-changing interpretation. But in this and subsequent reunions he plays "The Second Doctor", a Time Lord dressed as a tramp, and not "the New Doctor Who" as he had in the past.)

Nor does the "revelatory" material about the Time Lords' origins excuse the banality of the plot. We may accept Omega as a *fait accompli* now, but claiming that the Doctor's once-mythic people owe their power to a trite, booming megalomaniac with the worst pulp-SF appellation imaginable - "Omega", for Heaven's sake! - is a little like being told that the Doctor's father was an interplanetary conqueror called Zaagon the Destroyer. Omega himself, a fallen angel whose will has outlasted his body, is almost a Hans Anderson character (in the style of the Scholar's Shadow); in theory, and to many of those watching at the time, it was a beautiful allegorical idea. But watching it again now, even Stephen Thorne's barnstorming and scenery-chewing is inadequate to the task of making the idea work on its budget.

The Facts

Written by Bob Baker and Dave Martin. Directed by Lennie Mayne. Viewing figures: 9.6 million, 10.8 million, 8.8 million, 11.9 million.

Supporting Cast Patrick Troughton, William Hartnell (Dr. Who), Rex Robinson (Dr. Tyler), Roy Purcell (President of the Council), Laurie Webb (Mr. Ollis), Clyde Pollitt (Chancellor), Graham Leaman (Time Lord), Denys Palmer (Corporal Palmer), Stephen Thorne (Omega).

Working Titles "The Black Hole".

Cliffhangers The Third Doctor leaves the safety of the TARDIS to face the anti-matter organism in the UNIT lab, but Jo insists on running after him, and the creature causes them both to vanish in a flash of 'kinetic energy'; the whole of UNIT HQ disappears from the landscape, and hurtles into the black hole; locked in telepathic combat in a featureless black limbo, the Doctor finds himself being strangled to death by the dark side of Omega's mind.

The Lore

• The late filming of this story, necessitated by Patrick Troughton's other work commitments, made this production more like 1960s *Doctor Who* than had been planned. Pre-filming of Troughton and Hartnell in "their own time-streams", and Hartnell's harangues to his later selves, were shot on the 6th of November with the rest of the location shoot taking place over the next three days. Studio work began on the 27th, and the first episode was broadcast on the 30th of December.

• The clip of the Second Doctor seen on the monitor screen in the Time Lord control room was shot on location, and isn't an excerpt from "The Macra Terror" as is sometimes claimed. The First Doctor's dialogue scenes were filmed at Ealing, not in William Hartnell's garage, as is *also* sometimes claimed.

• The original storyline involved the Doctors meeting in the realm of the dead, but Terrance Dicks deemed it too "scary". Note, however, that in episode two the Chancellor believes the Doctor to be dead and Jo wakes up believing the same thing (she does this a lot).

• Dicks also claims that despite numerous letters from the public suggesting this "team-up", it was a visit from an elderly gentleman he later realised was William Hartnell - and had to chase after, when he twigged that he'd accidentally snubbed the man to whom he owed his job - which led to the idea being floated. Hartnell appears to have concealed the full extent of his illness from the production team, so Dicks had to rewrite all the First Doctor's scenes in a day or so. Something very similar happened to him with "The Five Doctors" (20.7)…

• Troughton's imprecise manner with the scripts threw Pertwee off; unused to improvising, Pertwee found his predecessor's advice ('it doesn't matter what we do, they're all watching the monsters') infuriating. As a consequence, their scenes

together in "The Five Doctors" were kept to a minimum.

• The anti-matter "scout" was a fun-fur rod-puppet, subjected to grey-scale differentiation (i.e. shot in black and white with high contrast, so that the shades of grey become more distinct, on three levels instead of around twenty). Each shade was then given a false colour.

• Nicholas Courtney ad-libbed the 'I'm pretty sure that's Cromer…' line, as was his salute when leaving the Doctors behind.

• In order to preserve some sense of continuity, both designer Roger Liminton and soundmaker Dick Mills went back to the source for this story. The TARDIS set was rethought from photos of the Peter Brachaki design from 1963 (hence the return of what are sometimes said to be "transporter pads", even though they pre-dated Star Trek by three years).

• But for an over-run in filming *Emmerdale Farm*, Frazer Hines was due to make a brief appearance in episode four as Jamie, asking the second Doctor where he'd been all this time.

• Both Graham Leaman and Clyde Pollitt, seen in the control room here, had been senior Time Lords before. Pollitt (here playing the Chancellor) was present at the Doctor's trial in "The War Games", while Leaman (here just credited as "Time Lord") was one of those who sent the Doctor to interfere on Uxareius in "Colony in Space". As the idea of regeneration hadn't really taken hold in the series at this stage, except with regard to the Doctor, the re-casting *must* have been meant to indicate that these were the same people.

This has been seized upon by fans who believe that the Second Doctor had a series of "secret" Time-Lord-sponsored adventures after "The War Games" - see **Is There a Season 6B?** under 22.4, "The Two Doctors" - as the Chancellor's qualms about investigating the Doctor's time-stream seem to be out of proportion to the scale of the threat from Omega. The theory suggests that the Chancellor knows about the Second Doctor's covert missions for the Time Lords, and is trying to stop the President investigating the Doctor's timeline just so he doesn't get found out. Which is fine… as long as you can believe that he's prepared to jeopardise the future of (1) the Time Lords and (2) everyone else in the cosmos in order to keep things hushed up.

• In November 1973, Dame David Bowie - under the influence of an incredible amount of recreational pharmacology - told *Rolling Stone* the plot of his "Ziggy Stardust" stage-show. Some have seen the man's maunderings as reminiscent of the plot of "The Three Doctors", but anyone reading the popular-science journals at the time would have picked up ideas about anti-matter, black holes and the like. The bit about Ziggy meeting multiple versions of himself, however, seems to match. Almost. A bit. Bowie was in Britain when the story was broadcast, recording "Aladdin Sane" (or at least his body was physically present). But the phone box on the back of the album isn't really much of a clue, no matter what some people might claim. Now, if Hartnell had actually *said* 'let all the children boogie…'

10.2: "Carnival of Monsters"

(Serial PPP, Four Episodes, 27th January - 17th February 1973.)

Which One is This? The blurb on the Target novelisation puts it best: 'The Doctor and Jo land on a cargo ship crossing the Indian Ocean in the year 1926… *or so they think.*' Much running around inside oversized electronic circuits as everything turns out to be part of a miniaturised alien peepshow, and the Doctor talks to the (giant) hand as it snatches away his TARDIS.

Firsts and Lasts The Doctor mentions the planet of Metebelis 3 for the first time, and spends much of the next two years either trying to get there or regretting having been there. Given that for the first six years of his TV existence the Doctor had no control over the TARDIS at all (it took a stolen Dalek time machine just to get his first companions back to Earth, remember), this marks a whole new phase in the Doctor's existence: having a TARDIS that's *supposed* to work, but doesn't quite.

Ian Marter - who goes on to play Harry Sullivan in Seasons Twelve and Thirteen, and to write some of Target's best *Doctor Who* novelisations - makes his first appearance here as Handsome Young Officer Andrews on the *S. S. Bernice*. Brian Hodgson, maker of "special sounds" since the beginning, leaves to found his own company. He goes out with a bang, or rather a banshee; the Drashig scream still sends grown men scurrying for cover.

This story also sees the first use of marsh-gas as a handy distraction, a Robert Holmes speciality. (However, there's something in the air even in earlier Holmes scripts. There's an eggy smell on the Gonds' planet in "The Krotons", and the radio-telescope boffins in "Terror of the Autons" go straight from discussing tummy-trouble to talking about hydrogen. It'd be childish to point out that Holmes once submitted a storyline for *Blake's 7* which featured a planet called "Turdus" - apparently just to see if he could get it past the script editor - but see the **Lore** of 11.3, "Death to the Daleks", for more of this sort of thing.)

Four Things to Notice About "Carnival of Monsters"…

1. Robert Holmes is now often remembered as the greatest of all *Doctor Who* scriptwriters, renowned for the way he applied eccentric, even *bizarre*, characterisation to the kind of science-fiction being peddled by the BBC. He regularly created scenarios which were part space-opera and part music-hall. And "Carnival of Monsters" is the story in which the *real* Robert Holmes comes across for the first time.

His earlier scripts (from 6.4, "The Krotons" to 8.1, "Terror of the Autons") might not have been much more than by-the-book tele-fantasy fare, but here he seems to return to the series with a whole new perspective, and the result is a painfully clever story of petty bureaucracy and alien showbusiness that pre-empts Douglas Adams' best work by more than half a decade. An alien keeps miniaturised human beings inside his viewing-machine as part of an intergalactic sideshow, yet when the Doctor meets him face-to-face, the "bad guy" isn't a twisted, megalomaniacal villain but a second-rate showman in a spangled jacket who doesn't even know how to work the electronics. Prepare for post-modernism.

2. And while we're on the subject of post-modernism… "Carnival of Monsters" can be (and often has been) read as a satire on *Doctor Who* itself, with Vorg prodding his "exhibits" into jumping through viewer-friendly hoops and referring to the most vicious of the monsters in his collection as 'great favourites with the kiddies'. (Although it's probably a coincidence that when his Miniscope / TV screen shows us a Cyberman - the only time we see a Cyberman during the Pertwee years - Vorg's assistant refers to it as looking like 'a blob in a snowstorm', exactly how the

Cybermen were introduced to us in 1966. See also the Lore of 10.3, "Frontier in Space".)

3. It's a rule of thumb that *some* technical deficiency, usually the monster, has to bring down every good *Doctor Who* story. "Carnival of Monsters" gives us the Drashigs, the series' first attempt at using puppets on scaled-down sets to suggest huge, tyrannosaurus-scale alien monstrosities. With hindsight the result is... well... memorable, if not necessarily for the right reasons. Though some of the Drashig close-ups work quite well, especially when they're tearing their way into the hull of the ship, the sight of them popping up through the deck like Sooty and Sweep[3] is one of the series' most unintentionally funny moments. And yet, since this is a story *about* the need to watch monsters on television, you'll be forgiven for loving them anyway. (Certainly, the Drashigs were so popular with the viewers that they made two further appearances in hallucinations and flashbacks, and puppet-monsters were given priority in Season Eleven).

4. It's official: 'Human beings are slightly more intelligent than whelks.'

The Continuity

The Doctor Orders a large scotch on the *S. S. Bernice*, and doesn't seem to be doing it just to blend in [see 21.7, "The Twin Dilemma", for more on the Doctor and alcohol]. He's happy to be referred to as a vagabond.

Whatever mechanism translates alien languages for the Doctor's benefit, it doesn't translate carnival lingo. Or he doesn't want to admit that it does. [Similarly, either he's forgotten that the correct term is "Twenty-Three Skidoo" or he's saying "Ninety-Nine" because that's the thing doctors always tell you to say.]

• *Inventory*. The Doctor carries a string file around his neck. The sonic screwdriver can, with a simple flip of the cap, ignite pockets of marsh-gas and cause impressive explosions as a result. In the TARDIS there's a magnetic core extractor, a device not unlike the sonic screwdriver which can open the hatches inside the Miniscope.

• *Background*. He's been to Metebelis 3 before, and obviously enjoyed the experience as he's keen on taking Jo there. He knows the history of the *S. S. Bernice*, even though he seems to change it here: see **History**. He recognises a plesiosaurus on sight [q.v. 7.2, "Doctor Who and the Silurians"], and claims he took boxing lessons from John L.

Sullivan. [Sullivan was the legendary American boxer who, in 1889, became the last heavyweight champion to win his title in a bare-knuckle fight. Although it's ironic that the Doctor insists on Queensbury Rules here, since Sullivan went into a decline after Queensbury Rules were introduced. Presumably this was around the same time that the Mountain Mauler of Montana taught the Doctor wrestling; see 2.4, "The Romans".] The Doctor can't even box without shouting 'hai!' at some stage.

At some point, presumably before leaving his own world, the Doctor campaigned for the banning of the Miniscopes. This is the only known indication of the Doctor having a crusading streak before he left his own people.

The Supporting Cast

• *Jo Grant*. Carries a bunch of skeleton keys, handily. She can pass for a memsahib and improvise a story for the ship's passengers about coming aboard at Port Said. [Either she has A-Level geography or she's been abroad a lot as a child. On the other hand she hasn't even heard of '"Lateral Thinking", very odd for the early '70s, when Edward de Bono's work on the subject was second only to *The Joy of Sex* as the book that everyone was lending everyone else.]

The TARDIS The new dematerialisation circuit allows the Doctor to 'program' the Ship, at least in theory, although it obviously isn't very reliable as he ends up on completely the wrong planet here.

Time Lords Though the Time Lords don't interfere in the affairs of other cultures 'as a rule', at some point in the past the Doctor 'had a great deal to do with' the Time Lords' banning of the Miniscopes. He convinced the High Council that the machines were an offence against the dignity of sentient life, and made such a fuss that the Time Lords outlawed them. [Generations of fans have claimed that the Miniscopes were actually banned because they threatened the Time Lords' monopoly over time-travel, but that *isn't* the suggestion here. As in all stories before the 1980s, the implication is that Time Lords are non-interventionist through complacency - not out of a respect for causality - and are prepared to intervene when someone like the Doctor makes life hard for them. See **How Involved are the Time Lords?** under 15.5, "Underworld".]

All the Miniscopes were officially 'called in' and

destroyed. The Doctor indicates that when the Time Lords banned them, the one owned by Vorg somehow slipped through the net. [He doesn't consider the possibility that he might have ended up inside this one at a point *before* the Time Lords dealt with the problem, so it's possible that the Time Lords erased them from history altogether rather than just collecting them. Which might mean that this is the only one in the "current" version of the timeline.]

Here the Doctor suggests that there's an intergalactic *law* against Miniscopes, suggesting - for the first time - that the Time Lords have direct political contact with worlds outside their own. [This is also the case in 22.4, "The Two Doctors", which uses much of the same terminology as this story. If the Lurmans and the people of the Third Zone are indeed related, then the culture which connects them may be one of the few which has overt dealings with the High Council.]

The Miniscope   A 'miracle of intragalactic technology' containing miniaturised life-forms from across the history of the universe, all of which can be observed - live - on its glow-sphere screen, the Miniscope itself is apparently capable of scooping its "exhibits" from any point in space and time. The Doctor returns everything in the collection to its proper place, but only by hooking it up to the TARDIS and reversing the 'original settings'. [This means that the Miniscope must have played *some* part in collecting its specimens from history, and isn't just a receptacle for beings collected by other means, but it may not be capable of "scooping" things from elsewhere in time without some greater power source. Vorg got his Miniscope from a Wallarian, and he claims it cost 'a lot of credit-bars', though who *designed* it isn't clear. Since cultures like that of the Lurmans don't seem to have time-travel at this point - see "The Two Doctors" - we might also conclude that Vorg has no idea how valuable his doomed Miniscope really is.]

Contained within the 'scope, and eventually returned to their home eras, are… the *S. S. Bernice*, a plesiosaurus, an Ogron, a Cyberman and a colony of around twenty Drashigs.

A Miniscope's exterior plates are molectic-bonded disillom, and anything which leaves the machine's compression field returns to its normal size within a few seconds. The internal dimensions are obviously unstable, as the tiny Doctor walks for miles through the internal circuits but is

Action Man / G. I. Joe sized when he leaves. Those inside the Miniscope find themselves repeating the same actions over and over again, without knowing anything's wrong. [They're in a time-loop rather than just being hypnotised, even though they can almost-remember past loops. Otherwise they'd starve to death. Matter seems to "teleport" inside the machine's circuits, the hands of the clock on the *S. S. Bernice* resetting themselves without help, so it's not just in the passengers' minds. Even so, as outside participants the Doctor and Jo are immune.]

A simple 'aggrometer' control on the front of the Miniscope can change the subjects' levels of aggression, but the Drashigs have no intelligence centres and can't be controlled. On the other hand the plesiosaurus *does* seem to be controllable, which says a lot about the stupidity of Drashigs.

Eternity Perpetual company built the Miniscope's power generators [though apparently not the Miniscope itself] to last forever, which is why the company went bankrupt. The Miniscope came with a handbook. [So it was a mass-produced object. If this one somehow "escaped" into a version of history otherwise lacking in 'scope, then this may explain how the *S. S. Bernice* became a mystery even though returning the ship to Earth means the enigma ultimately never happens. The Miniscope *itself* is an anomaly, which messes up the way the rest of time works.]

The Non-Humans

• *Lurmans.* A space-going species from a place a long way from Earth, Lurmans appear indistinguishable from humans even if they're technologically superior. The Lurmans know of humans, but refer to them as "Tellurians" [q.v. 22.4, "The Two Doctors"]. The similarity between Lurmans and Tellurians is said to have caused some scientists to refute Voldek's theory that life in the universe is infinitely variable.

Lurmans are apparently part of a super-culture of many worlds and species, since Vorg and Shirna frequently refer to their past experiences of other planets. Shirna worked with the All-Star Dance Company, while Vorg did National Service with the Fourteenth Heavy Lasers, his battery sergeant being a crustaceoid mercenary [mentioned again in the audio play "The Paradise of Death"].

The Lurman version of the gambling game Find-the-Lady involves three magum pods and a yorrow seed. They use credit-bars as currency,

How Good Do the Effects Have to Be?

Or, "where do you draw the little blue line"?

Traditionally, there have been two schools of thought on this. One is that the effects are merely storytelling devices, to give you some idea of why the actors are doing what they're doing. The other is that by disrupting the normal rules of TV narrative you're taking the viewer "elsewhere", and should make that other place as exotic as possible.

In the first point of view, so long as everyone acts as though a dinosaur had appeared outside Marylebone Station, everything's fine and *Lamb Chop* star Shari Lewis can do the effects with sock-puppets. In the second, as long as there's a groovy electronic audio / visual effect or two as part of the narrative (instead of being bolted on as an afterthought, as in *Top of the Pops*), there's a point to watching the programme.

Both of these attitudes are left-overs from the programme's origins. By 1960s standards, *Doctor Who* was fast-paced, exhilarating and above all weird. No other programme had visual "events" like exterminations or inlay split-screen shots of people looking at alien cities. In effect, the plot of the adventure was about as important as the plot of a Fred Astaire musical: you'd hope for one, but that wasn't what you tuned in for or what you remembered afterwards. For anyone under - say - seven, the pretty pictures and crazy burbles and whooshes were a sensual pleasure (think about how every record released in that time had to have its own "sound"). *Doctor Who* wasn't a programme, it was a place you visited for twenty-five minutes, and after that gobsmacking title sequence and theme tune you knew the rules had changed.

After 1970 everything became more serious. The plots of stories were earnest little parables, culminating in "Invasion of the Dinosaurs" (11.2) and the Doctor's homily on greed (it's like Jerry Springer's "Final Thought"). CSO made whatever the writers wanted more or less possible, so the effects took on a more functional aspect. The theory was that now, you weren't supposed to notice they were effects. In many cases the plot had key moments, often at twenty-five minute intervals, when things went from montage (cutting between something normal and something odd) to mise-en-scene (the normal and the odd in the same shot). This had happened before, and memorably - Daleks on Westminster Bridge, Cybermen outside St. Paul's - but in a story like "Planet of Giants" (2.1) it was strenuously avoided, and not just for technical reasons. When it was done, it was done in mid-episode, not in a cliffhanger.

"Carnival of Monsters" is the turning point. The three cliffhangers, and indeed the plot, depend on things being seen in the same shot which belong in different realms. Moreover, as would happen a great deal from this point on, an electronic effect would be tried in *Doctor Who* and then become standard once it was shown to work. In "Carnival" it's the Eradicator effect in episode one, later applied to Alice Cooper singing "School's Out" on the aforementioned *Top of the Pops*. CSO itself became the backdrop for news bulletins. "Destiny of the Daleks" and "Meglos" were both test-beds, the producers being loaned the new Steadicam and Scene-Synch technologies, at reduced rates.

But "Carnival of Monsters" is the last time we're encouraged to "look at the pretty pictures". From this point on we're supposed to believe what we're seeing. The plesiosaurus effect is partly effective because it *looks* like an effect; it doesn't belong so it stands out. A similar shot at the end of "Terror of the Zygons" (13.1), far from being a bold, gaudy pop-art moment, is considered an embarrassment because the rest of the story is so "realistic".

People who can't handle the fact that *Doctor Who* is a series of made-up-stories - which seemed to be most of fandom, in the 1980s - were persuaded by *Star Wars* and various American SF series that a "good" effect is one which doesn't say "hey, I'm an effect". In some ways, this is understandable. *Star Wars* works because the whole project is an exercise in world-building, not just the real world with extra bits added (not something you can say about *Star Trek* in any of its recent forms), but that isn't the way *Doctor Who* works. And some of the worst excesses of modern Hollywood have been movies which are effectively just showcases for effects-work, so it's easy to see why viewers would be distrustful of anything that goes out of its way to impress. After all, we live in an age when teen-audiences are happy to go "ooh" at a computer-generated Balrog just because it's so *big*, despite the fact that the difference between a big CGI monster and a small one is just one click of an animator's mouse.

So there's nothing wrong with verisimilitude, but in much of post-'80s SF the "realistic" effects are used to suggest comfort rather than vision. Instead of telling us that the rules have changed, the standard effects shots in these programmes are the equivalent of establishing shots in cop-shows, displaying the home-base space-station as if it were a precinct building with traffic outside. It reinforces a sense of normality, even banality, with

continued on page 115...

113

have translator diodes which allow them to communicate with the people of Inter Minor and refer to spacecraft as "thrusters". Improbably, Vorg speaks the carnival lingo of Earth even though nobody knows how "Tellurians" reproduce. [It's got to be *something* to do with the way the translator diodes work].

• *Drashigs*. Huge, vicious, omnivorous-but-flesh-loving animals, like hundred-foot-long caterpillars with dragon-shaped heads and mouths big enough to swallow most dinosaurs, Drashigs are native to the swamps on one of the satellites of Grundle. They're blind, but hunt by scent and have various nobbles over their heads which appear to be sensory organs of some kind. Legend has it that when a [Lurman] battle-thruster landed on the Drashig's home-satellite, with a crew of fifty and all the latest armaments, a scout-orbiter later found the thruster eaten except for a few scraps of the reactor ventricle. In their native habitat they're only seen to come to the surface of the swamp in order to feed.

• *Wallarians*. They're notorious gamblers, and Vorg won his Miniscope during the Great Wallarian Exhibition, at which he also met a Wallarian wrestler called the Great Zarb.

• *Dinosaurs*. The plesiosaurus identified by the Doctor technically has more teeth than you'd expect from the species. [As a fish-eater, it should lack molars.] According to the Doctor, it's been extinct for 130,000,000 years [more like 140,000,000 according to fossil evidence, but then, the Doctor's actually been there].

Planet Notes

• *Inter Minor*. Obviously a highly technological planet, but also deeply insular and paranoid, Inter Minor broke all links with other worlds after the Great Space Plague a thousand years previously. It's evidently in a part of the universe which contains a number of civilised worlds, and it's nowhere near Earth, although it may be close to Metebelis 3 since that's where the Doctor's heading when the TARDIS lands there.

President Zarb, his Council and the Central Bureau have recently decided that aliens are to be re-admitted, though visas are required. The planet's Interstellar Ecology Commission forbids the transference of zoological specimens between planets, and there's a three-member Admissions Tribunal to oversee the Lurmans' arrival.

The inhabitants of Inter Minor are divided into at least two classes. The rulers of the planet are officious, bureaucratic, grey-skinned humanoids referred to as 'the official species', who have very little sense of humour and a limited understanding of the word "entertainment". The workers - "functionaries" - have the same grey skins but near-bestial features [two species descended from the same roots, so they're no longer biologically compatible].

While the rulers speak primly, referring to themselves in the third person throughout, the functionaries just grunt. Except when Shirna's getting out of her space-suit, when they make Kenneth-Conner-style 'phwoarr' noises. Functionaries seem to be treated like animals, or slaves at best, and rebellious functionaries are killed without compunction. There's currently some unrest among this underclass, which Zarb - whom we never actually see - has put down to a lack of diversion. Amusement is prohibited, but Zarb is considering lifting this restriction. Treason still carries the death penalty for the official species.

Zarb has already disbanded the army, and Inter Minor has defence pacts with all its neighbouring planets. Its only internal defence now is the "eradicator", a mounted energy weapon which destroys any organic molecules in its path. The bureaucrats carry smaller hand-held weapons which can either kill or stun. Their technology is apparently compatible with that of the Lurmans [trade routes]. Though the planet's architecture has that alien / futuristic look, much of it is also terribly functional.

There's an Inner Constellation Corrective Authority, which seems to cover this whole group of worlds, not just Inter Minor.

• *Demos*. Mentioned by Vorg, who's come to Inter Minor from there. [If it's the same Demos which used to be the homeworld of the Daemons - see 8.5 - then other species have over-run it since the Daemons' extinction. This might give us some idea of Inter Minor's location, and that of the world/s inhabited by the Lurmans, as "The Daemons" states that the planet is on the other side of Earth's galaxy. Vorg states that humans come from a 'distant galaxy', but this is part of his showman-spiel and possibly not any more reliable than anything else he says. Then again, as Earth is termed "Tellus" and humans "Tellurians", we have to assume that Greek-sounding planet names sim-

How Good Do the Effects Have to Be?

...continued from page 113

the same shot often being used in every episode. This ties in with the logic of these programmes as, in effect, soap operas set somewhere else. We revisit the same world every time. We don't need to figure out how this environment is different from ours. No conscious effort is required on the part of the viewer to relate what's happening on-screen to what's known of the world we inhabit. It's what Americans call a no-brainer.

Conversely, in *Doctor Who* - even at its slickest and most routine - the viewer is solving puzzles throughout. One of these is reconciling what we can see with what we expected to see. 'How different would the world have to be for this shot to make sense?' is a question the viewers subconsciously ask, even while they're consciously thinking 'that's a man in a foam rubber suit' or 'that dinosaur's crap'. If the tentative solutions to these puzzles chime with the way the actors are behaving, then you have a different world for very little capital outlay. If the effects tell one story and the actors another, then no amount of money, resources or buxom Vulcans in underwear can save you.

---

ply appealed to Robert Holmes. "Demos" meaning "planet of the people"...?]

• *Metebelis 3*. The famous 'blue planet of the Acteon group', according to the Doctor, who also states that the air there is 'like wine'. [By episode four Metebelis 3 has become the blue planet of the Acteon *galaxy*. "Group" seems more likely, since galaxies are very big places and most must surely have more than one blue planet. It's probably safe to say that the Doctor gets absent-minded later on, especially since he talks about the 'group' in detail. It's Jo who mentions the 'Acteon galaxy' after (mis-)hearing what the Doctor says, so her mistake probably influences him later on. In a line cut from the transmitted version, Vorg refers to the city on Inter Minor as being in the 'Acteon *system*', which apparently confirms that 'group' is closest to the mark and that the TARDIS is at least in the right area. So Metebelis 3 may or may not be in Earth's galaxy, depending on who you believe.]

History

• *Dating*. The S. S. Bernice vanished from Earth en route to Bombay from England on the 4th of June, 1926, according to the calendar in one of the cabins. [The calendar has the lay-out of a calendar for 1925, proving that days of the week really don't match the dates in the *Doctor Who* universe.] The "real" date, from Inter Minor's point of view, isn't established. [Many fan-histories have suggested that the 'Great Space Plague' which did such damage to Inter Minor is the same disease we hear about in 11.3, "Death to the Daleks". Since the plague was a thousand years ago, this would date the story to somewhere in the mid-3000s. But this is dubious, as the plague in "Death to the Daleks" seems confined to Earth's sphere of influence, whereas Inter Minor is in a completely different part of space.]

According to the Doctor, the S. S. Bernice disappeared even though the Indian Ocean was perfectly calm, a freak tidal wave being the popular explanation. This version of history is apparently changed at the end of the story, when the ship is put back in its rightful place [see **Can You Change History, Even One Line?** under 1.6, "The Aztecs"]. On board the ship, Claire mentions Fred Astaire. [In 1926 Astaire was the star of a hit show in London and Liverpool, which is where Claire must have seen him, since he didn't start making movies until 1933. Then again, the histories of showbiz personalities are clearly different in the *Doctor Who* universe. Q.v. 3.4, "The Daleks' Masterplan".]

Jo refers to 1926 as being 'about forty years' before her own time. [Suggesting that the UNIT stories aren't set in the late '70s, or she would have rounded down to "fifty". But since forty years after 1926 is 1966, at *least* half a decade out, this is damning proof that off-hand statements made by companions shouldn't be taken at face value.] The Doctor suggests that Jo was born about a thousand years too early to know the principle of anti-magnetic cohesion which holds the plates of the Miniscope in place. [This *doesn't* mean the Miniscope was built a thousand years after her time, just that human beings discovered the principle then.]

The Analysis

Where Does This Come From? Though you never would've noticed it at the time, the arrival of the "sorted-out" Robert Holmes to the series sends the programme in a whole new direction. The Doctor has always been a spanner in the works - drop him into a "serious" SF scenario, and he'll mess things up within minutes - but here we see him interacting with environments even more erratic than *he* is.

When things go wrong with the Miniscope, Vorg talks about 'bric-a-brac' caught up in the circuits instead of relying on pseudo-science. The Minorians want to get rid of the Doctor because he's a bureaucratic nightmare, not because they want to conquer the galaxy. In itself, this is a *very* different sort of adventure story to anything else in the popular media of the 1970s. (With the possible exception of *The Avengers*, which is full of devious scientific master-plans by English eccentrics, although even in *The Avengers* there's nothing as casual as a space-time-scooping-device whose user has lost the instructions.)

For one thing, "Carnival of Monsters" represents the British love of the amateurish at its most blatant. More than that, though, it's almost a form of satire. Not in the heavy-duty, political sense of the word, and its argument against keeping life-forms in captivity is a flimsy "message" at best. Yet it reflects a time when the media as a whole was becoming more aware of - and more cynical about - the institutions of both British society and the media itself. If "Day of the Daleks" suggests a world waking up to the fact that bureaucrats perhaps aren't the best people to run the world, then Inter Minor suggests that bureaucrats aren't the best people to run *anything*.

The S. S. Bernice passengers present us with a far better parody of the English imperial mentality than anything in "The Mutants", and is it *really* coincidental that the Miniscope works the way a child thinks a TV set works? The script refers to the 'scope as 'looking like a cross between a jukebox and a samovar', and this lack of awe is entirely in keeping with '50s magazine SF. (Especially Robert Sheckley and Frederik Pohl, whose "Tunnel Under the World" this resembles more than slightly... it was adapted for BBC2's *Out Of The Unknown*, the series to which Holmes submitted the story that eventually became "The Krotons".) It also suits a generation raised on war-surplus bits and bobs. Limitless potential but an awareness that if it goes wrong you thump it; welcome to the world of 1970s tech. The line about fossil fuel being stored in hygiene-chambers is a direct parody of a pre-war cliché about the working-class storing coal in the bath, and meaningless to anyone under thirty according to Barry Letts, but that alone justified it for him.

Old *Doctor Who* motifs still appear, however. The way in which the humans have been "conditioned" not to see things we can see is so reminiscent of "The War Games" (6.7) that the precise amount of rewriting done by Terrance Dicks can only be guessed at. This also applies to the existence of contiguous "zones", which only the Doctor can enter at will. Similarly, the way the characters get stuck saying the lines they've been given echoes "The Mind Robber" (6.2), although Jo never looks directly at the camera when expressing horror at the thought of people watching her misfortunes for kicks.

With hindsight, Holmes' work for the series had often hinted at the sadism of petty officialdom, starting with the ham-fisted satire of "The Krotons" (students brainwashed by teachers fight back by - ahem - dropping acid, with society shown as a machine consuming the best brains and covering up the process with euphemisms). Kalik, as actor Michael Wisher observed, got off on wielding power; 'he had his whips in the cupboard'. We'll see this taken to extremes in "The Sunmakers" (15.4) and "The Caves of Androzani" (21.6).

A word should also be said about the design. Whereas '60s *Doctor Who* stories often seemed to be the products of a society just coming to terms with the transistor - the T-Mat in "The Seeds of Death" even uses valves - by this stage the western world was obviously becoming a lot more relaxed about the existence of the micro-circuit. As a result, the Doctor and Jo find themselves scrambling around sets that resemble enormous, overly-exotic digital components, suggesting that "fascination" had finally overtaken "paranoia". Seven years later "The Horns of Nimon" would try the same trick and have the Doctor scrambling through gigantic circuit-boards all over again, but the tunnels in "The Horns of Nimon" are bland, sterile and workaday, whereas here there's a real sense of flair. The sense, in short, that there's still something terribly *exciting* about all of this new-fangled electronica.

Things That Don't Make Sense Why doesn't the plesiosaurus turn up outside the ship at any point during episodes three or four [is it scared of the Drashigs]? Why does the Doctor materialise inside the Miniscope in his characteristic lying-down position, since he was standing up when he vanished from the outside world and the device presumably isn't programmed to bend people's limbs around for no good reason? How does Orum know that the outside of the Miniscope is made from molectic-bonded disillom [unless he's a secret techno-fetishist]?

Why does the crew of the ship keep explosive in the forward hold? Why do sticks of dynamite which would only be - comparatively speaking - the size of dandruff cause so much damage to the 'scope's workings? How did the Doctor know he was going to need rubber boots that day? Why does the magical Miniscope process, which resets the clocks and rebuilds the hull after a Drashig attack, not re-seal the way out into the works? Why does "Five Foot Two, Eyes of Blue" start playing when the only people who might have a gramophone are talking in a different room? And why do the portals out of the works into the various "zones" have doors with handles? If it's for access, then why is there an iron bar across the doorway?

It takes a while for objects removed from the 'scope to grow to full size, so Kalik must be *very* dim to stand around gawping when the Drashigs get out. The story ends with Vorg being honoured for killing the Drashigs and saving Inter Minor, instead of being locked up for bringing them to the planet in the first place. Which is doubly odd when you consider that nobody *knows* Kalik released them. [Orum must have blabbed.]

Critique Often regarded by fans as a "little" event ('nothing serious, nothing political'), "Carnival of Monsters" also turns out to be the most important single story of the mid-'70s, though it's easy to overlook exactly how remarkable - how downright *inventive* - it really is.

It is, sure enough, a story on a tiny scale. There's no threat to the universe here, just small people trapped in small spaces, which thankfully means that it cares about "drama" and "comedy" far more than it cares about being "epic". Not only beautifully written but also expertly performed, with one of the best supporting casts of any *Doctor Who* story, the key to its success is its absolute lack of respect for anybody in the universe. Having ensured that all the non-humans have appalling SF names, the script sends up both the characters' own pomposity *and* the medium itself by having Kalik state that "Vorg" is a ridiculous thing for an alien to be called. The most telling line: 'One has no wish to be devoured by alien monstrosities. Even in the cause of political progress.'

Barry Letts believed this linguistic turn to be the root of the programme's (and Holmes') uniqueness. Holmes' background in political journalism, and love of the '50s "social comment" form of science fiction spearheaded by the magazine *Galaxy* - from which Douglas Adams took rather more than anyone feels comfortable admitting - was the reason that he'd initially hated *Doctor Who*. His revenge was to remake the series to his own specifications.

We mustn't forget Barry Letts' contribution. As director he gives the story a sense of place and time, with the sun moving across the desert on Inter Minor as the day progresses while the period feel of the *S. S. Bernice* is scrupulously maintained. Even composer Dudley Simpson seems to have pulled out the stops for this one. The fact that the story was cleared for DVD release ahead of more supposedly-obvious choices, and was included in the 1981 repeat season *The Five Faces of Doctor Who* alongside "big" stories like "Logopolis" and "An Unearthly Child", speaks volumes. If *Doctor Who* is - as has been stated occasionally - *Top of the Pops* with plots, then this is the Pan's People / Glam Rock story *par excellence*. Even the electronic effects leave a grin on your face.

The Facts

Written by Robert Holmes. Directed by Barry Letts. Viewing figures: 9.5 million, 9.0 million, 9.0 million, 9.2 million.

Supporting Cast Tenniel Evans (Major Daly), Ian Marter (John Andrews), Jenny McCracken (Claire Daly), Leslie Dwyer (Vorg), Cheryl Hall (Shirna), Peter Halliday (Pletrac), Michael Wisher (Kalik), Terence Lodge (Orum).

Working Titles "Peepshow".

Cliffhangers The huge hand of Vorg reaches down into the hull of the S. S. Bernice, and plucks the TARDIS out of the Miniscope in front of an astonished Doctor; in the "swamp" circuit, Jo is horrified to see the Drashigs rearing up out of the sludge; on Inter Minor, Shirna screams as a tiny, miniaturised Doctor stumbles out of the hatch at the side of the Miniscope.

The Lore

• This story was actually filmed as part of Season Nine, since "The Three Doctors" required Patrick Troughton to be free, although unlike many end-of-season stories it doesn't look particularly cheap. As a cost-cutting exercise, the original idea was for the two casts - "inside" and "outside" the machine - to be played by the same actors (Major Daly and Vorg, Claire and Shirna, and so on). This was abandoned fairly early on, but note the similarity of Lurman names to Raj terms: Sahib / Zarb, Wallarians / Wallah, etc. Note also how Orum and Major Daly say almost identical things when they're admiring the Doctor's nerve.

• Another piece of trimming: the 'scope interior set was re-used as Omega's palace in "The Three Doctors", with one piece also serving in the Time Lord control centre.

• Paddy Kingsland realised a new version of the *Doctor Who* theme for the tenth anniversary, but was considered such a failure (it is, by common consent, the worst ever arrangement of the music) that it was never broadcast in the UK. However, the "re-jigged" episodes *were* shown in Australia - as the first story of Season Ten to be completed, "Carnival of Monsters" was the only one given the new theme before the programme-makers changed their minds - and a title sequence with the alternative theme can be found on the BBC video release (as with episode five of "Frontier in Space"). The "Australian Rules" version of episode two is strange all round, since it contains extra material not featured in the British broadcast and puts the scenes in an oddly different order.

• In fact, several scenes were filmed but not originally broadcast. In the Australian edit Vorg's demonstration of the magum pod scam goes on forever, and Peter Halliday's bald wig threatens to snap off into the air. Shirna watches a monitor showing a groovy electric display and - crucially - we see Kalik being eaten by a Drashig.

• "Drashigs" is an anagram of "dishrags". Robert Holmes was quite simply doing the washing-up while he was trying to think of a name.

Like the maggots from "The Green Death" (10.5), the Drashig puppets were based on animal skulls, mainly foxes.

• Filming of this story was recorded for a documentary celebrating fifty years of the BBC, *Looking In.* From this we learn that the model spaceships were filmed upside-down, so that the rocket exhausts concealed the wires.

• Episode three originally ended differently, with the Doctor caught by the ankle inside the 'scope and dangling over a precipice as a Drashig approaches. This Drashig, which stupidly plummets to its doom in the resolution (well, they don't *have* precipices on the Drashig world), is the one the Doctor finds dead in the last episode.

• The Palare spoken by Vorg in episode four would have been pretty familiar to BBC Radio listeners. The comedy series *Round The Horne* had featured a pair of blatantly gay characters, Julian and Sandy, who used this patios to make everything sound like a double entendre. 'Varda the bonapalone' simply means 'can you see the pretty lady?' and 'nanti dinari' is 'no money'. Palare is partly Romany (originally Northern Indian), partly Italian and partly words spelled backwards, and so was used by Gypsies, carnies, showfolk, homosexuals and anyone else from a sub-culture that needed to protect itself. (See also the Virgin New Adventure *Happy Endings*, which turns Julian and Sandy into camp Silurians working as dress designers.)

• The "clue" spotted by the Doctor on the *S. S. Bernice*, that if the ship had been in the middle of the Indian Ocean then it would've been pitch dark, was added to the script when someone commented on it after the location shooting had been completed. Pertwee - who always liked to keep souvenirs from his stories - allegedly tried to take the ship's nautical compass home with him, not quite grasping the concept of "theft" in this case.

10.3: "Frontier in Space"

(Serial QQQ, Six Episodes, 24th February - 31st March 1973.)

Which One is This? *Doctor Who* finally does space opera properly, as the Doctor gets locked up in prisons all over the galaxy in order to prevent some terrible force of evil stirring up a war between humans and Draconians. Who's behind it all? You get two guesses...

Firsts and Lasts The last appearance of the original Master, prior to Roger Delgado's death in June 1973. Overall it's not a bad goodbye to the series, full of quality gloating and some elegant wit, but on the other hand our very last sight of him leaves something to be desired (see **Six Things to Notice…**).

Though previous stories have suggested that the TARDIS somehow materialises in space on its way from planet to planet, this is the first story in which we actually see the TARDIS spinning through a black void, as if it's started flying around the place like a spaceship. (Although the first of these is stated as being in hyperspace and the last has no stars.) It's also the last time the TARDIS makes the "flanged" rematerialisation noise, utilised since "The Seeds of Death" four years earlier. Things go back to normal after this.

And it's the first use of the space-gun prop which crops up again and again, most notably as the Doctor's tyrannosaurus-stunner in "Invasion of the Dinosaurs" (11.2). Oh look, it's Terry Walsh firing it.

Six Things to Notice About "Frontier in Space"…

1. Designed as an epic, galaxy-spanning piece of SF adventure (and with some politics thrown in for good measure), "Frontier in Space" has a sense of scope not seen in *Doctor Who* since "The Daleks' Masterplan" in 1966, although this time it doesn't look as if it's being made up as the writer goes along. It's a story which introduces a new setting with every episode - an Earth vessel under attack, Earth itself in the twenty-sixth century, a penal colony on the moon, a prison-ship owned by the Master, the heart of the Draconian Empire and finally the planet of the Ogrons. Yet what's *really* striking is that although the Doctor gets to see such a huge swathe of the universe, he does most of it from inside a variety of prison cells. At the very least, it's remarkable that the story creates such a sense of scale even though (true Geek fact) the Doctor spends 60% of it in captivity.

2. In fact comparisons with "The Daleks' Masterplan" (3.4) seem apt, because "Frontier in Space" is just the first half of a twelve-part saga which ultimately sees the Doctor go back to the Dalek homeworld and dispose of their army (and "The Daleks' Masterplan" was also split more or less down the middle by two writers). However, in "Frontier in Space" the Daleks only reveal themselves in episode six, the only occasion on which the Daleks' return was kept secret instead of being massively advertised by the BBC.

3. This is also the only story which does "the double" and teams the Master up with the Daleks, though as the 1999 *Comic Relief* parody "The Curse of Fatal Death" indicates, these days that's what people think he did all the time. For once the Master's allies don't try to double-cross him at the last minute, or vice versa, although he does at least get to call them 'stupid tin boxes' when they're not listening.

4. Once again, the future looks remarkably like the 1970s. The architecture of the twenty-sixth century, especially, bears an astonishing resemblance to the "ultra-modern" South Bank in London (for a very good reason). Barry Letts later argued that in the future these are listed buildings, preserved by order the way castles and Tudor cottages are today.

5. At the conclusion of the final episode, the Doctor activates one of the Master's fear-generating devices in the Ogron caves and causes all the Ogrons to scatter. Two things are noticeable here. One: the noise made by the Ogrons as they panic is much like a crowd of Gumbies from *Monty Python's Flying Circus*. (Though elsewhere in the story the Master's relationship with the Ogrons is almost exactly like Basil Fawlty and Manuel, while his response to the Daleks' orders is like Basil Fawlty and Sybil.) Two: the Master also vanishes at this point, Roger Delgado's final appearance in the series being utterly bewildering as he's simply in the middle of things one minute and gone the next. Presumably he runs off with the panicking Ogrons - bizarre in itself, since the Doctor's unconscious by this point and the Master's packing a gun - but surely we should at least be able to see which way he goes…? (See **The Lore** for the probable reason for this muddle.)

6. Best line is the Doctor's almost-concerned response, when the Master tells the Draconian Emperor that he's dedicated his life to the cause of order and peace: 'Are you feeling all right, old chap?'

The Continuity

The Doctor The Doctor feels something like a 'premonition' when Daleks are near [the same feeling he gets in 3.10, "The War Machines"]. Conversely, he can't hear the high-pitched squeak of the Master's fear-box.

• *Ethics*. He overtly states that he's acting on behalf of peace, although for only the second time in his career he's seen to use a gun, and once again he's shooting at Ogrons [q.v. 9.1, "Day of the Daleks"].

• *Inventory.* The Doctor still has his string file, but now keeps it in his boot. He has a hand-held radio direction-finder, and a small watchmaker's screwdriver apparently concealed in one of his shirt frills [honest, it's in episode six]. Reversing the polarity of the sonic screwdriver's power-source allows him to use it as an electromagnet, powerful enough to pull back huge metal bolts.

• *Background.* The Doctor claims he was once captured by the Medusoids, hairy jellyfish with claws, teeth and a leg. They put him under a mind-probe to ascertain where he was going, and he told them he was going to meet a giant rabbit, a pink elephant and a purple horse with yellow spots, technically true as all three were delegates at the Third Intergalactic Peace Conference. At least two mind-probes had nervous breakdowns as a result, and the Medusoids eventually had to let the Doctor go. Not that he's making this up or anything…

The Doctor has been to Draconia before - see **Planet Notes** - and knows its customs well. He claims that he only 'borrowed' his TARDIS, and that it was hardly the latest model at the time. Showing no surprise at the offences with which he's charged by the Master, including beating up policemen and stealing spaceships, it seems the Doctor may well have done these things at some time. Past or future.

The Supporting Cast

• *Jo Grant.* She seems to think she's being used as a general dogsbody at UNIT, or else just doing the filing. Her uncle got her the job there. When the Master's fear-machine shows Jo what she's most afraid of, she sees a Drashig, then a Mutt, then a Sea Devil. [It's working its way backwards through her monster-memories, although the Master himself is apparently no longer giving her nightmares]. By now she's learned techniques to prevent her falling for the Master's hypnosis by filling her mind with nonsense. Or more nonsense than usual.

[Note that on returning to the TARDIS at the end of the story, Jo is wielding a gun. Did the original ending have her shoot the Master? See **The Lore**.]

The Supporting Cast (Evil)

• *The Master.* Once again, the Master would apparently rather save the Doctor's life and gloat than see his rival die quickly, genuinely feeling that a long-range killing lacks 'the personal touch'. He knows some Earth poetry, specifically Tennyson. His stated part of the deal with the Daleks is to become ruler of Earth, although he's planning to make a move on the entire galaxy, somehow.

Here he's moved on from watching *The Clangers* and is seen reading Wells' *The War of the Worlds*. [Obviously there's some sense of irony here, but nonetheless, nobody is watching him read so he's not just showing off. Again, this suggests that he's at least capable of enjoying a good book; again, this suggests that he's not wholly sociopathic.]

The Master equips his Ogron underlings with portable hallucinatory hypno-sound devices, which work on the fear centres deep within the mind and make the Ogrons' victims see whatever they're most afraid of [an offshoot of the Keller process from "The Mind of Evil"?]. Even so, Jo sees the Ogron ship briefly change shape just like the Earth people do [so some of the humans' responses to the device must be programmed into its signal]. The Master himself is once again packing an energy weapon of some kind, as well as a bulky signalling device improbably concealed in his rather tight tunic. Oddly - and unlike his guise as the Adjudicator [8.4, "Colony in Space"] - he really seems to have put in some time as a high-ranking official in the government of Sirius IV, since he's using a real spaceship instead of a disguised TARDIS and his documents are good enough to fool the President. Indeed, he may well have been present at the High Court of Bassat when indictments were brought against the Doctor and Jo for supposed tax-dodging.

The TARDIS It appears in the path of the Earth vessel during its 'hyperspace transition', and the Doctor pulls off a last-minute course correction to land inside the ship 'in normal space' [see **Does the TARDIS Fly?** under 5.6, "Fury from the Deep"]. Ultimately the Doctor uses the Ship's tele-pathic circuits to send a message to the Time Lords [see the next story]. Given an accurate date, he can work out correct course co-ordinates.

What's the Timeline of the Earth Empire?

Once again, anybody who wants a detailed chronology of future-Earth should consider Lance Parkin's *History of the Universe*, which really is painfully thorough. However, what follows is an at-a-glance guide to the rise and fall of Earth's Empire, from 2100 to 3000. (For a timeline of the twenty-first century, see under 5.4, "The Enemy of the World".)

c. 2100. The end of the era in which humanity's confined to the solar system, and in which Earth keeps getting attacked from its own doorstep ("The Moonbase", "The Wheel in Space", "The Seeds of Death", etc). All the evidence from the TV series suggests that humanity starts to expand into deep space around the start of the twenty-second century, and the less canonical Missing Adventure *Killing Ground* confirms this by establishing that a massive drive towards colonisation begins in 2100 exactly, timed to mark the new century. Which makes sense.

2116: "Nightmare of Eden". Space travel is becoming more commonplace, as is exploration of the outer planets. Interstellar liners are becoming fashionable, but on the whole travel beyond the solar system is still a novelty. New laws are brought in to cover the whole of human-occupied space. There's a Space Corps by now.

c. 2140: "The Space Pirates". The Space Corps becomes increasingly important as commercial space travel opens up more and more of the galaxy. Piracy's an issue. At this time the phrase "outer planets" is being used to refer to worlds *quite* near Earth (say, eight light-years away) but beyond the solar system. The homeworld's having trouble keeping things together.

2157 - 2167: "The Dalek Invasion of Earth". Earth becomes less important in the grand scheme of things as the Daleks hit the planet with a virus, then take over wholesale. The population crashes. Until now things haven't changed much since the twentieth century, since London still has most of its landmarks. The colonies become less centralised as Earth falls, and a lot of them are probably cut off from the homeworld altogether, which would explain the kind of societies we see in stories like "The Androids of Tara" generations later.

The 2200s: More colonisation schemes across the galaxy. The Mechanoids in "The Chase" seem to

have been built around this point in time. According to "The Sensorites", by the twenty-fourth century the lower half of England has become a vast Central City, so Earth's obviously re-building and re-populating itself.

c. 2300: "Vengeance on Varos", "The Macra Terror", "The Happiness Patrol", "The Twin Dilemma". By now there are independent Earth colonies all over the galaxy, and have been for the last two centuries. The colonies still don't consider Earth to be particularly important.

2472: "Colony in Space". Earth is now not only re-populated, but horribly over-populated. A new wave of colonisations begins, this time spearheaded by non-conformists who just want to get away from a miserable, oppressive planet, but Earth is trying to keep closer checks on its colonies than ever before. The Empire has its roots in this period, with a centralised government clamping down on dissenters and planning to build floating cities for the billions.

2493: "The Rescue". More colonisation. By this point in time, the Cybermen have obviously harassed Earth and its territories (the New Adventures frequently refer to "Cyber-Wars" from the twenty-second century onwards), leading to…

2526: "Earthshock". …a conference being held on Earth, at which it's agreed that humanity should unite against the Cybermen. This obviously does a very good job of pulling the colonial powers together, and seems to be what cements the Empire, turning Earth into a single military power. What follows is the last Cyber-War, in which the resources of Voga are used to (seemingly) wipe out the Cybermen for good.

2540: "Frontier in Space". The era described by the Doctor as being the start of the Empire proper. Humans come face-to-face with the Draconians in 2520, start a war, then very nearly do it again twenty years later. The Dalek threat probably only makes the Empire stronger, though what happens to the Draconians is anyone's guess.

2700 - 2900: "Death to the Daleks", "The Sensorites", "Revenge of the Cybermen". "Death to the Daleks" takes place in the wake of the Dalek Wars, and "The Sensorites" is said to take place in

continued on page 123...

The Non-Humans

• *Draconians.* Human-like but with reptilian scales on their faces, crests on their heads and a tendency to hiss, here the Draconians are portrayed as Earth's rival power in the galaxy, the only time any other species inside human-space is shown to have a significant Empire.

They're also more than a little Japanese, with a male-dominated society that forbids females to speak in the Emperor's presence and a culture of aristocratic warrior-nobility [although rather more has been made of this Nippon-ness in fan-fiction than the author might have intended]. They claim they never lie, and the President of Earth doesn't dispute it. Their homeworld is, logically, Draconia. Like Earth, Draconia is expanding and colonising planets. The Doctor speaks of only two great empires in the Milky Way at this point.

Humans refer to Draconian ships as being 'galaxy class' and fitted with neutronic missiles. Draconians are insultingly referred to by the humans as "dragons". [Is Draconia actually in the constellation of Draco, the dragon? If so, it's a remarkable coincidence that they're reptilian. Perhaps Earth's sun is in the Draconian constellation of "the Great Ape". Draco is a long, windey constellation which contains 130 stars visible to the naked eye. There are three plausible G-class stars (like ours) within 100 parsecs: 63_ (Tyl), 14_ (Aldhibah) and 23_ (Alwaid).]

Draconians see humans as 'inscrutable'. The title of Emperor is hereditary, the Emperor being addressed as "majesty", but Emperors have been deposed before now. His son is referred to as a prince, addressed as "highness". 'My life at your command' is a typical Draconian statement of respect between people of noble rank, Draconian or otherwise. [No reason is ever given for the males forbidding the females to speak. It's presented as simple sexism, but they tolerate Jo's presence as an odd alien custom. We never see a Draconian female, let alone hear one talk. Perhaps they have sultry voices which drive their menfolk wild with desire, or perhaps they really are stupid and reared as "brood-mares".]

The fifteenth Emperor ruled five-hundred years ago [their years, but how long they are is anyone's guess], and made the Doctor an honorary noble of Draconia. There's still a legend among Draconians of a man who helped their people when they were almost overwhelmed by a 'great plague' from outer space, and the Emperor still knows the names "Doctor" and "TARDIS".

• *Ogrons.* The Doctor establishes that Ogrons are mercenaries, and that a lot of life-forms use them, not just Daleks [q.v. 9.1, "Day of the Daleks"]. The weapons carried by the Ogrons here can stun as well as kill, the Doctor believing they're 'neuronic stun-guns', but the Ogrons themselves don't get any brighter. Although they can at least fly spaceships.

• *Daleks.* For the second and last time, the commander of the Daleks is shown to be gold. Their plan here is to take over the galaxy once the human and Draconian empires have destroyed each other, but it's not clear how the Master got in touch with them. They know the Doctor at this point in their history.

Planet Notes

• *The Ogron Planet.* A 'barren and uninteresting planet' on the remote and otherwise uninhabited fringes of the galaxy, the world of the Ogrons looks like a quarry and the Ogrons themselves seem to inhabit caves, with primitive paintings on some of the walls. One of these paintings describes a large, puffy, orange "Ogron eater", a reptile the Ogrons worship out of pure fear. Though we eventually only see this creature at a distance, it appears to be something like a dinosaur-sized carnivorous air-bag. Even so, Ogrons may well be more terrified of the Daleks than of this "monster".

Galactic co-ordinates of the Ogron planet: 2349 to 6784. Earth seems to have done a survey of the world, but doesn't know much about it.

• *Sirius IV.* There's a High Court in a place called Bassat, either on Sirius III or IV. The months are long and oddly-named, with the Doctor's malfeasances supposedly committed on the 51st and 52nd of Smalk. Humans populate both III and IV, and the Sirius system, though part of the Empire was granted Dominion status - with some degree of autonomy, including the right to punish its own citizens - around the time of the last [Draconian] War. The Commissioner of Interplanetary Police from Sirius has the power to take wanted criminals from Earth's jurisdiction, the President stating that relationships with colony planets are always difficult and that if there's a war then Earth will need all the help it can get. [So the colonies are closer to Earth than they used to be, but still independent for now. This fits what we're told about Earth being a form-

This product is not authorized by the BBC. Doctor Who and TARDIS are trademarks of the BBC.

What's the Timeline of the Earth Empire?

...continued from page 121

the twenty-eighth century, so this is clearly an age of people in starchy uniforms exploring mysterious planets. "Kinda" might also be set in this epoch, and the imperials on Deva Loka talk about an over-populated homeworld. More uniforms-in-space business goes on in "Revenge of the Cybermen", which the Doctor suggests is set in the twenty-ninth century, hundreds of years after the Cyber War.

2986: "Terror of the Vervoids". The Empire would seem to be flagging by this point, since the alien Mogarians are grumbling about the way the humans have strip-mined their world and they're not just being put up against the wall and shot. If you believe the New Adventures, then a major catastrophe on Earth in 2975 heralds the fall of the Empire, which leads us to...

3000-ish: "The Mutants". The Doctor only establishes that it's 'the thirtieth century', although most fan-lore now takes it as read that it's the *late* thirtieth century. Earth is covered in endless grey sky-cities by this point, and the planet's said to be biologically and politically 'finished'. The Empire falls, and is eventually replaced by the Federation in time for "The Curse of Peladon" (c. the thirty-eighth century).

ative empire.]

The tax regime is strict, with the death penalty for non-payment of 'Planetary Income Tax' as well as vehicle landing taxes. The currency is measured in "Sc". [Presumably Sirian Credits. See 21.6, "The Caves of Androzani", for more on Sirius.]

History

• *Dating.* 2540, according to the log of the pilot, and the Doctor confirms that it's the twenty-sixth century. [The date also includes the number "72"; is it the 72nd day, i.e. the 12th of March, this being a leap-year?] The Doctor describes this period as being the beginning of Earth's Empire, and it's definitely the same Empire that he and Jo saw falling in the thirtieth century [9.4, "The Mutants"].

Earth has a world government and a single President, who seems to have a British-style Cabinet, although civil unrest is widespread across the overcrowded planet. The apparent attacks by Draconians on Earth's ships have led to demands for war from many people, with rioting reported in Tokyo, Belgrade and Peking, while the Draconian consulate in Helsinki is burned to the ground. The President is burned in effigy in Los Angeles, and certain senior officers feel a military dictatorship is required. Space travel is now commonplace, hyperspace being involved in the process.

There are references to 'battlecruisers' and luxury liners on the Mars-Venus cruise. Despite the prior claim that Earth hasn't a single blade of grass by the twenty-fifth century ["Colony in Space"], lush fields here surround the President's building, apparently for miles around. Space-port ten is nearby. Spaceships are still transporting commodities as simple as flour, and the doors of the cargo vessel are 99% durilium. [In both "Death to the Daleks" and "The Monster of Peladon" the generic outer-space-building-substance is called duralinium, which is probably related.] It only takes hours for Earth ships to get from the homeworld to the frontier.

The Arctic areas have recently been reclaimed, the Bureau of Population Control announcing that they're ready for habitation. As a special inducement to get people to live in the enclosed cities of New Glasgow and New Montreal, the 'family allowance' has been increased to two children per couple. There's evidently a Congress, with Congressman Brooke being the leader of the opposition. Earth uses mind-probes to get the truth from suspects.

Relationships with the Draconians have always been strained. Twenty years ago a Draconian ship 'arranged' to meet an Earth ship in peace, but the Earth ship was damaged by a neutron storm which also destroyed the Draconians' communications equipment. Both ships were meant to be unarmed, the Draconians sending a battle-cruiser with empty missile banks, yet on board the Earth ship General Williams made the decision to attack and destroy the alien vessel. [So the human ship wasn't unarmed, as it was supposed to be.]

The result was a war, and humanity is still anxious that there might be another. Since then a treaty between the species has established a frontier between empires which the Draconians have never violated, leading to trade treaties and cultural exchanges. The treaty also forbids espionage and subversion between species. Bizarrely nobody has ever told the General the truth about the start of the war, even though there's a Draconian embassy on Earth. Williams is, despite all this, still an adviser to the President.

In military matters the President's authority is limited, and the General takes charge. The President can only overrule him with the backing of the full Earth Senate. [There's a Senate *and* a Congress *and* a Cabinet?] The President is rather hands-on, personally supervising interrogations, negotiations with visiting police commissioners and reparations for damage caused by riots.

Many forms of dissent aren't permitted on Earth [it's much the same society we see in 8.4, "Colony in Space", only slightly worse], with the Peace Party being outlawed. Political prisoners are permanently sent to a high-security penal colony on the moon, where the influence of the peace movement's spokespeople won't spread. The Special Security Act allows prisoners to be sent there without trial. There are heavily-armoured security guards on Earth itself, carrying energy weapons. The Peace Party ostensibly has friends in the media and the government, and its sign is a very twentieth century two-fingered salute.

The Doctor knows something of this period in history, but doesn't expect the Daleks to be involved in the crisis [does the Master's involvement change known history?], and doesn't seem to believe there should be a war between humans and Draconians.

The Analysis

Where Does This Come From? Another Malcolm Hulke "…in Space" story to follow "Colony", and once again the Big Social Issues dress themselves up in futuristic shoulderpads for the family audience.

This time we can skip over the Cold War parallel of the Earth / Draconia crisis. There is a real-world resonance there, but it's not about the clash of West vs. East so much as it's about the social fall-out. Like so many other "spacey" stories of the period, this is the product of a world dwelling on Vietnam and the Arab-Israeli conflict, a world getting sick of its leadership rather than waiting for the bomb to fall. And any suggestion that the looming interplanetary war might represent a possible Third World War between Yanks and Commies is almost wholly derailed by the fact that its vision of Empire-versus-Empire is so obvi-

ously seen through the filter of James Bond. (As in "The Mind of Evil", the Master once again plays Ernst Stavro Blofeld, Bond's recurring nemesis.)

If it has *any* direct message to send to the Cold War cultures, it's that the fear of the "enemy" is a bigger problem than the "enemy" itself, with the Doctor making it quite clear - especially during his interrogation - that the whole espionage game is a pointless waste of time. And yes, there's an obvious parallel here with classic *Star Trek* 1.14, "Balance of Terror", but even *Doctor Who* at its most *Trek*-like is still notably more humanistic. There's no crude racial metaphor here, no suggestion that the Draconians should remind us of the Russians, the Chinese or any other Communist state. Occasionally we see them turning Japanese, but it's a whim on the director's part rather than an attempt at a meaningful comparison.

If anything can be said to be a "source", it's the Spanish Armada, and the President's relationship with Williams is clearly modelled on Queen Elizabeth and Sir Francis Drake (making the Draconians the Spanish, which fits their culture as well as Japan does). Fans of American TV-SF, however, will no doubt enjoy the similarities between the start of the Earth / Draconia war and the start of the Earth / Minbar war in *Babylon-5*. The Draconians, like the Minbari, approach the humans with their gunports open.

So it's not about the Cold War *per se*, but all the signs of the late '60s American / European "cultural revolution" are here. As in "Colony in Space", civil unrest on Earth once again makes it look *as though* the last five-hundred years have been one big civil rights protest, but this time we're closer to home and things become more overt. Mob violence mirrors right-wing America's backlash to the reforms of the '60s and '70s, while on the other side of the argument is the Peace Party, a group rooted in Britain's anti-nuclear movement as much as in the Vietnam protests.

Other topical points run through the story, not all of them so obvious to the modern eye. Over-population is mentioned. The President of Earth is female, not absolutely unique in SF at the time but notable nonetheless, and possibly an allusion to Israeli President Golda Meir; the Arab-Israeli conflict was heating up again that year, and her appointment of the alleged "warmonger" Moshe Dyan as defence minister was hugely controversial. The lunar compound is flagrantly Botany Bay (at the time, the increasing Australian presence in the UK meant that the British were being reminded about this every bloody day).

Oh, and the Doctor's comment to Jo in one of the story's many prison cells - 'why don't you stop pacing up and down like a perishing panda?' - was written at a time when the People's Republic of China was busy exporting pandas as goodwill gifts to the west. Anyone who'd been watching the news in late 1972 would indeed have seen a lot of panda-pacing going on, so even *that* comes across as weirdly contemporary. The President is Eastern European, Brook is almost Colonel Sanders and the newsreader is a black Jamaican, amazingly cosmopolitan at a time when Trevor MacDonald was still three years away, and therefore more futuristic than all the platform-booted guards or spherical TVs. Meanwhile small, domestic, very British items like the inversion of the term 'family allowance' - and the magnified versions of petty crimes for which the High Court at Bassat have apparently arraigned the Doctor and Jo - keep all of this within reach of our world.

"Frontier in Space" is, in short, the most 1973 of all 1973's stories (it even beats "The Green Death", which is something of an achievement). Even the spacesuits are orange.

Things That Don't Make Sense The Earth authorities lock the Doctor up in a cell *and* allow him into the President's office without even searching him for potential weapons, since he's still got the sonic screwdriver on him when he tries to escape. Nor do the Draconians search the captive Master thoroughly enough to find the gadget he uses to signal the Ogrons.

Why is the Doctor allowed his old clothes (and pocket-contents) back, while Jo gets changed into kung-fu PJs? Who's committed the greatest crime against fashion here? There's no segregation on the moon, so presumably contraceptives are in the milk-shakes. (It's a rum sort of prison that creates whole generations of dissenters, even if the life-support systems could cope).

Crucially, though, why does the prison have no CCTV? If anyone had eavesdropped on the Doctor and Jo in their various cells, then the whole story would have been different. No "objective" shots of the raid on the Heyward Gallery Detention Centre exist, in this supposedly paranoid future. Nor are any forensic tests done on the dead guards shot by obviously non-Draconian guns.

When they're chasing the Ogron ship in orbit of the planet, Williams instructs the pilot to accelerate and overtake. As any ten-year old-would have been able to tell him (with all the moonshot coverage and studio simulations on TV at the time), acceleration takes you into a *higher* orbit, so you take *longer* to go around the planet. And when spacewalking on the outside of a ship in hyperdrive, the Doctor's sent flying by a course-correction. He should have the same velocity (speed and direction) as he did when he was on the ship. So how does squirting a bit of air out of a bottle make him magically able to catch up with a vessel that's now moving away from him at several times the speed of sound, at the very least? Possibly several times the speed of light, which makes his catching-up even more impressive.

A twenty-sixth century spaceship with 1940s readouts and a control desk that looks like a music centre made by Bang and Olufsen is one thing, but the astronauts have pin-ups from *Woman's Realm* on their walls. Bill Wilde, as the Draconian pilot, persuades everyone in episode four that the aliens are called 'Triggonians' or 'Trick Onions'. The arrest warrants claim that Jo did "committt" crimes [Sirian spelling]. "Sheila", a non-speaking role, gets a credit at the end of episode three for no good reason. We can hear the Doctor's spacesuit being "secretly" zipped up while the Master's reading; is he deaf? And when the Doctor converts the sonic screwdriver into a magnet, he forgets to switch off the "physics-defying" circuit, so that when he tries to move the bolts *towards* him they move in quite the opposite direction.

One last query. The Doctor sees the monitor screen of the Earth cargo vessel when a "Draconian" appears on it to demand the humans' surrender, but he doesn't seem to see either a Draconian or an Ogron. So what *does* he see…?

Critique Given that it's the very epitome of a Doctor gets captured / Doctor escapes / Doctor gets captured story, it really is ridiculously entertaining. By rights "Frontier in Space" should be a cheap, clunky-looking piece of SF. By rights it should be hopelessly dated and virtually unwatchable (the very first line of dialogue involves a pilot telling his colleague that he'd like a cushy job on a luxury space-liner, which isn't a good sign). But here the things which date the programme - see **Where Does This Come From?** - make it work instead of weakening it, because unlike your typical space-opera B-movie, "Frontier" feels as if it's got *roots*. It's so of-its-time that watching it gives you the same buzz as watching a '70s blaxploitation pic. The chunky future-costumes and the squeezy-bottle battlecruisers might be untenable anywhere else, but since the whole story revolves around the Doctor sending up an absurdly macho galactic empire, it's not really a problem.

Katy Manning deserves a special mention here. Although she's capable of being profoundly annoying when playing up to Pertwee as if he were her sugar-daddy, for much of this story she's superb, especially in her key scenes with Delgado. Her best moment sees her talking to the Doctor's empty clothes when Jo thinks he's been cast adrift in space. Anyone watching these adventures consecutively will get a real kick out of her defiant line to the Master when he fails to hypnotise her, 'it doesn't work on me any more!', and the beginning of episode six invariably prompts yells of 'you go, girlfriend!'. Sadly she reverts to form for the next two stories, but savour the way she can switch from comedienne Joyce Grenfell to Goldie Hawn within the space of a single line.

In fact, if there's one major flaw in "Frontier in Space" it's the absence of a proper ending. Since it was designed as the first act of a two-part epic, the script feels no compunction about leaving its loose ends flapping, and lets the next story in the series bring things to a conclusion. Unfortunately, the next story is "Planet of the Daleks".

The Facts

Written by Malcolm Hulke. Directed by Paul Bernard. Viewing figures: 9.1 million, 7.8 million, 7.5 million, 7.1 million, 7.7 million, 8.9 million.

Supporting Cast Vera Fusek (President of Earth), Michael Hawkins (General Williams), Peter Birrell (Draconian Prince), Harold Goldblatt (Professor Dale), Madhav Sharma (Patel), Bill Wilde (Draconian Captain), John Woodnutt (Draconian Emperor), Stephen Thorne (First Ogron), Ramsay Williams (Congressman Brook), Michael Wisher (Dalek Voice).

Cliffhangers The Earth rescue team arrives on the cargo ship, and the crew insists that the Doctor and Jo are traitors working for the enemy; the Ogrons burst into the Doctor and Jo's cell on Earth; the Doctor and one of the peace movement supporters, Professor Dale, attempt an escape from the lunar prison, but find themselves trapped in the airlock while someone pumps out the air; held captive on the Draconian ship along with the Doctor and Jo, the Master surreptitiously activates a signalling device, and elsewhere an Ogron picks up the message; in his quarters on the Ogron planet, the Master turns his hand-held hypno-sound device on Jo.

The Lore

• Roger Delgado's final appearance as the Master was originally scheduled for the last story of Season Eleven, and therefore the last story of the Third Doctor's run (since by this stage it was already becoming clear that Jon Pertwee would probably leave the series in 1974), in which the exact nature of the "relationship" between the two Time Lords was supposedly going to be revealed once and for all. Needless to say, Delgado's premature death in a car accident prevented this, and just gave Pertwee another reason to go.

• Delgado's last film appearance was in Charlton Heston's *Antony and Cleopatra*, in which he played the soothsayer who tells Caesar to 'beware the Ides of March'. Funnily enough, Jon Pertwee once played exactly the same part... in *Carry On Cleo*. Strangely, nobody has ever taken much of an interest in comparing their performances.

• David Maloney, director of the next story, took over the reins five minutes from the end of episode six. Paul Bernard's reaction on seeing the "Ogron Testicle God" (as it's almost universally known) was to refuse to include it in the final scene, in which the Master was supposed to make his escape by using the fear-box to turn himself into one. Hence the garbled and baffling final confrontation between Pertwee and Delgado. Maloney shot a new ending as part of "Planet of the Daleks", and everyone hoped the public wouldn't see the join.

• The Draconians were a late addition to the plot, when Terry Nation refused permission for the Daleks and the Cybermen to have a big twelve-part scrap, although designs for glam-era Cyber-costumes had already been made (and the Cyberman "reminder" in "Carnival of Monsters" makes as much sense as the Ogron's cameo in the same context).

• Pertwee liked the Draconian masks, as they allowed eye-contact between actors. During filming he got chatting to one of the actors, an amateur astronomer, about ceipheid variables and globular clusters and - so he claims - forgot it was just a man in a costume.

• Effects designer Ian Scoones took a number of the models from his old job at Gerry Anderson's Century 21 studios. The shuttle's spherical nose was a lightbulb, left unpainted in one rectangular patch to make a window. The "docking" problem was solved by attaching the smaller model to the front of the camera and moving both towards the larger model, rather than faffing about with strings.

• Barry Letts and Terrance Dicks were at this time planning their "escape" from *Doctor Who* with an adult-oriented near-future series, *Moonbase 3*. Much of this story's model-work and set-design was intended as a trial run, although *Moonbase 3* has aged far less well.

• Although the Daleks' appearance in the final episode was (for once) kept secret, the following week saw a massive Dalek-based publicity campaign, centred on the *Radio Times*' "Win A Dalek" competition (ultimately won by a class of primary school children who looked less than chuffed at being photographed with it). The competition required entrants to think up a new story for the Skaroine terrors, something which Terry Nation himself hadn't done in nearly a decade. One of the authors of this present volume still insists that his entry was better than the winner's.

10.4: "Planet of the Daleks"

(Serial SSS, Six Episodes, 7th April - 12th May 1973.)

Which One is This? It's back to '60s Dalek basics, but this time in colour. Lurid green jungles, aliens in bright purple furs, Thals in pastel spacesuits and a Dalek Supreme sprayed black and gold, all on a planet with the biggest Dalek army ever assembled (apparently). Oh, and one of the Daleks is invisible.

Firsts and Lasts For a generation of schoolkids playing at being Daleks (non-British, non-old-enough readers will have to take this on trust), this story is notable for featuring the first ever use of the phrase 'my vision is impaired, I cannot see!'. Truly, a watershed.

Six Things to Notice About "Planet of the Daleks"...

1. Terry Nation returns to the series for the first time since "The Daleks' Masterplan" in 1965, a seven-and-a-half-year gap during which various other writers and production teams had been re-defined and re-created his most notable creations.

His response to this was to ignore everything that had happened while he'd been away, and go back to first Dalek principles by writing a *Flash-Gordon*-style adventure story on a jungle planet. Nation "standards" on offer here… killer plants, invisible monsters, people escaping by hiding inside Dalek casings, a bacterial weapon and a countdown to an apocalypse. And the dialogue is pure pulp SF. Sample lines: 'I'm qualified in space medicine, I'll do what I can'; 'Spiridon… one of the nastiest pieces of space-garbage in the Ninth System'; 'you've been infected by the fungoids'; and 'it's an area of huge boulders'.

2. The conclusion of the story sees tidal-waves of "molten ice" destroying an army of 10,000 Daleks deep inside their cave-system base. It was always going to be a challenge for the visual effects people, and the designers' solution is to fill a model set with an army of toy Daleks (the Louis Marx models with "Tricky Action", as used in 4.9, "Evil of the Daleks"), then throw water at them. Clifford Culley, a freelance effects designer, will return to plague the series with his false promises of cheap effects. In the years to come he'll be responsible for some terrible dinosaurs and a truly *astonishing* sequence involving a toy tank and a giant robot.

3. Almost as good as the mini-Dalek army is the scene in the darkening jungle clearing, in which the Doctor and company see the glowing eyes of predatory animals surrounding them in the undergrowth. Which basically involves several pairs of tiny electric lights being switched on all over a darkened set. The jungle's "animal noises" – the same ones used in every space jungle from "The Chase" (1965) to "Meglos" (1980) - are just as problematic, especially during the scene when Taron pours his heart out to Rebec in the middle of the wilderness. He says 'I love you', and the response is the remarkably ill-timed sound of an elephant blowing off. It happens *again* while the Doctor's giving his final, serious-minded speech about the futility of war.

4. Once again, the Thals spend the whole of the first episode avoiding the word "Dalek" in order to make the cliffhanger appearance of a Dalek seem

more surprising, even though the words "Planet of the Daleks" come up on the screen right at the start. What's odd, though, is that even the Doctor falls for it. He requests that the Time Lords send the TARDIS after the escaping Dalek spaceship; winds up on a planet where he meets some Thals, from Skaro, homeworld of the Daleks; learns that the Thals are on a military expedition to stop '...*them*'; then gasps in horror when he discovers the nature of the enemy at the end of episode one. Even given that he doesn't have the benefit of reading the *Radio Times*, who was he expecting...?

5. The full ramifications of this can be discussed in the **Continuity** section, but... this is the story in which we learn that if an air-tight seal is put over the door of the TARDIS (i.e. an unimaginably complex space-time vessel with a near-infinite interior which spends most of its time either in space or in the vortex), then the people inside will suffocate. The cause of this calamity? Spurting toadstools. Sometimes words just aren't strong enough.

6. There's an entertaining moment in episode three when the Doctor and Codal (one of the Thals), in a lift inside the Dalek city, open the doors on one of the lower levels; find a Dalek waiting for them outside; close the doors; descend for a while longer; open the doors again; and find an identical corridor outside, but this one empty. You can almost see the stage-hand giving Jon Pertwee the signal: 'It's all right, we've moved the Dalek. You can press the button again now.' (And try to watch the Doctor's rope-climb out of the ventilator shaft in episode four without imagining the Thals shouting, 'lynch him!'.)

The Continuity

The Doctor Ice begins to form on the Doctor's face after he's winged by the Master's gun and put in a coma-like state. Jo points out that he was in this state once before. [In 8.5, "The Daemons", although on that occasion there was a reason for the temperature drop and there isn't here. Can Time Lords "freeze" themselves when they're injured?]. He only has a minimal pulse, heartbeat and breathing-rate during this period, but he recovers after an hour or so. His blood is red, but the wound clears up completely in a matter of hours. Here he talks about Susan as though she were just another companion, not his "granddaughter".

• *Ethics*. The Doctor states, once and for all, that he 'abhors violence'. Just after murdering a Dalek with obvious relish [as ever, only creatures with individual personalities seem to count]. He gives a "feel the fear and do it anyway" speech, which even he terms 'a tutorial on courage', to the rather vague Thal scientist Codal.

The Supporting Cast

• *Jo Grant*. Given the chance to visit anywhere in the universe, Jo simply wants to return home to Earth. The implication is that although she likes her work with the Doctor, she doesn't like the travel [the next story suggests that she's a lot more concerned about her own planet than we thought]. Yet another effete alien falls for her here, and the way she mopes after she leaves him - despite the fact that they barely knew each other - suggests that she's already getting lonely. She veers wildly between competent guerrilla and "kooky chick", especially when she goes from planning an assault on the Daleks to saying '..and then I was rescued by this bowl...' within moments. [Notably, she loses her independent streak as soon as the Doctor shows up.]

The TARDIS When the plants on Spiridon put an air-tight seal on the TARDIS, the 'automatic oxygen supply' turns on even though the air outside is breathable, and the Doctor begins to suffocate as the supply runs out... suggesting that the Ship takes in air from the outside. The warning "Automatic Oxygen Supply Exhausted" appears on the screen when the air is getting thin, in '70s sci-fi art-nouveau computer-lettering. [This is so overwhelmingly stupid that it's almost impossible to get a grip on. The TARDIS' passengers *can't* seriously depend on external oxygen, since the TARDIS travels through the vortex and often lands in places with no atmosphere. You could argue that the Ship stores air when it's in an air-rich environment, and that the supply is simply depleted here, but this seems hard to swallow. If the Ship is as vast on the inside as we've always been led to believe, then it shouldn't take the Doctor just a couple of hours to exhaust the reserves once the doors get sealed. Besides, why should the crack in the doors be the means of drawing in air, when the TARDIS is supposed to be able to change shape? And if the door isn't normally air-tight, then what stops air leaking out into the vortex while the Ship's in flight? If this is going to make any sense at all, then it *has* to be assumed that the TARDIS' life-support systems are currently experiencing some kind of technical fault and that the door seal is almost incidental, despite the Doctor's claim that all the circuits are in order.]

Luckily, the Doctor keeps an emergency supply of oxygen canisters in the console room, inside a cabinet on casters that we've never seen before.

The picture on the scanner is initially in black-and-white [more proof of a systems fault], but it seems to fix itself by the end of the story. On one side of the console room there's a couch which slides out of the wall, and Jo already seems to know how it works. A hand-held 'log', basically a tape recorder, is found in a locker just above it. Curiously, Jo knows a single switch on the TARDIS console which can put an image of Earth up on the scanner, and various other worlds - Skaro included - also appear on the screen. [The Doctor has Earth programmed into the controls as a standard destination, but this suggests that the scanner has a "memory" for places the TARDIS has already been. Something similar is seen in 1.3, "The Edge of Destruction".] Here, decorative panels on one wall of the console room display a peculiar pattern never seen before [which looks an awful lot like a frame from the title sequence]. There are cupboards in the room which also look new. It's all horribly G-Plan.

The Time Lords When the Doctor sends them a telepathic message for help, the Time Lords guide the Ship to the planet where the Dalek army's been assembled, apparently by remote-control. [Two things are striking here. One: the Doctor is prepared to ask them for help, the only time he does this other than the Omega crisis in "The Three Doctors" (10.1) and of course his fateful decision in "The War Games" (6.7). It seems odd that he does it now, but never tries it again, not even when - for example - the entire universe is threatened (18.7, "Logopolis"). Since this can't *wholly* be a matter of pride, he may feel that he can still ask for favours after saving the Time Lords from Omega, or alternatively he may just feel that the Master's intervention in Dalek history will startle them into action. And that's the second notable point, the fact that the Time Lords are so willing to help. Once again, Dalek influence seems to be a major concern for them.]

The Non-Humans

• *Daleks*. The Dalek army assembled on Spiridon, ready for the conquest of 'all solar planets' and thereafter the galaxy, is 10,000 strong. The Doctor calls this 'the mightiest Dalek army there's ever been'. They're interested in this particular planet because of the invisibility of its natives, but its army is in suspended animation, so the planet's subterranean low temperatures are also useful [indicating that these Daleks have been here for some time, waiting for the invasion]. Some Daleks have indeed been made invisible, but the process requires large amounts of power and they can only remain unseen for around 'two work-cycles', in addition to which the process seems to be making them break down.

Here Dalek operations are run from a "Central Control" area in their base, and there's at least one section leader, although it's revealed that they have a Supreme Command somewhere off-planet. The Dalek Supreme - part of the Supreme Council - arrives in a smooth, featureless, dumbbell-like vessel, and is revealed to have a subtly different body-shape to the rest of the Dalek line, with black-and-gold livery and oversized "light-bulbs" on the dome. [The *real* reason for this is that it's actually a Dalek salvaged from the 1965 / 1966 Dalek cinema films, given a new paint-job, but it does look significantly different to the normal Dalek form.]

It's implied that the Supreme's ship is the same ship which left the Ogron planet [in "Frontier in Space", though there was no Dalek Supreme on show there], as the Doctor asks the Time Lords to take the TARDIS to the ship's destination. The Supreme recognises the section leader on sight, even though the leader's casing is the same colour as all the other Daleks. The Supreme Council exterminates subordinates who fail in their duty.

The vertical panels around a Dalek's middle are 'sensor-plates', according to the Doctor. He also states that most Daleks have an automatic defence call, a transmitter which may keep functioning even after the Dalek's deactivated and which is apparently triggered when the dome is lifted. [There's no indication of how he knows this. There doesn't seem to be any such transmitter at work in 1.2, "The Daleks".]

He also knows that Daleks are susceptible to low temperatures, the creatures inside instantly dying of shock when their casings are exposed to sub-zero levels of cold.

Their internal guidance systems function by high-frequency radio impulses, so positive feedback can jam them and give them temporary seizures. Dalek guns are still capable of disabling instead of killing - the last time they're ever seen to do this - and two Dalek guns in unison are powerful enough to make an entire Thal spaceship go up in smoke. Dalek sucker-arms can lift non-Dalek-designed objects, while one Dalek is seen with no sucker on its arm and a heat-based cutting-tool in its place [so their weapons are enough to blow up spaceships, but not to blast open metal doors?]. Dalek guns can make other Daleks explode, which is good to know. One Dalek uses an 'anti-gravitational disc', a *very* slow floating platform just big enough for a single unit.

Inside their city, the Daleks are experimenting with blood-destroying bacteria which can decimate the planet within a day, Daleks included [so Daleks have blood]. However, they and their servants can be given immunity. Victims die within an hour of exposure to infected air.

Faced with death, the Daleks palpably display fear.

• *Thals*. The other inhabitants of the Daleks' home planet have only recently developed [deep] space flight, and state that they come straight from Skaro. Nobody has ever travelled this far before. There are apparently Daleks still on or around Skaro, since the Thals know something of the Daleks' plans. [Even though this story is set after the era of "The Daleks", when the Skaro-based Daleks are wiped out. The space-travelling Daleks must have moved back to the old homeworld. See **What's the Timeline of the Daleks?** under 2.8, "The Chase".]

• As ever, the Thals are all pretty-faced humanoids with blonde hair, but they have a more pro-active attitude than before. The Doctor clearly has concerns about them becoming overly militaristic, even though they're still a bit pathetic as warriors go. They carry stubby little energy-weapons, and have a sizeable military, with Codal speaking of a 'division' of over 600 people in which he's a scientist. Some of those on Spiridon have seen action before.

The Thals know of Earth, but it's just a name in their old legends. Likewise, they've heard of the Doctor and consider him mythical after his help in defeating the Daleks 'generations ago'. This era in Skaro's history [i.e. the events of "The Daleks"] is known as the Dalek War, and the Doctor claims

they're famous as one of the most peace-loving peoples in the galaxy. [Both the Doctor and the Thals use the term 'Dalek War' even though it isn't used in "The Daleks", so the Doctor must have done some checking-up on Thal history since then. See 12.1, "Robot", for more on the Doctor's potential off-screen meetings with the Thals.] They don't shake hands on Skaro.

• *Spiridons*. The natives of Spiridon are humanoid, but invisible thanks to an 'anti-reflecting light wave', though they can be seen by the huge, purple, furry pelts they wear. They become visible on death, revealing themselves to be humanoids with lumpy faces. Though wholly sentient, only one of the Spiridons we meet here is remotely civilised, their artefacts appearing rather stone-aged despite having a fully-developed language and "natural" cures for the local killer fungus. There are ruined statues and ancient-looking buildings in the jungle. [We might conclude that, like the Exxilons in the *next* Dalek story, they're survivors of a fallen civilisation. If so then their invisibility may have been artificially generated at some point in the past, since evolutionarily speaking it seems... unlikely. Wester, the benevolent Spiridon, seems to imply that the Daleks destroyed his culture.]

Planet Notes

• *Spiridon*. A planet seemingly covered in jungle and teeming with life, Spiridon is nonetheless unique as it has a core of molten ice; "molten ice" meaning a cold, gooey 'allotrope' of ice rather than just water. The ice occasionally erupts through ice volcanoes. The planet is tropical in the day, sub-freezing at night, and after dark there are boulders which give off heat absorbed during daylight hours. These tend to be popular with the local animals, which include large, unseen predators with glowing eyes [the big, furry, purple things the Spiridons skin?] and huge - but equally unseen - flying animals.

Spiridon's plant life includes large flower-like 'fungoids' which spit sickly yellow slime at their victims [different from the fungoids seen in 2.8, "The Chase", even though they're from the pen of the same writer]. The spores in this slime spread across the flesh of anyone "infected" until it engulfs them. There are also eye-plants, which amusingly turn to stare at anyone who passes, visible or otherwise; and a tentacle that sneaks through the undergrowth and grapples things.

 This product is not authorized by the BBC. Doctor Who and TARDIS are trademarks of the BBC.

Skaro is 'many systems' away, and the Thals refer to Spiridon as being in the 'Ninth System'. The Dalek city on Spiridon is either a Dalek pre-fab base that's been constructed inside the shell of the native Spiridon architecture, or a Spiridon city that's just been re-fitted.

History

• *Dating*. Presumably 2540 [following directly on from "Frontier in Space"].

Once the army's buried in the molten ice of Spiridon, the Doctor believes it'll take centuries to melt the Daleks out. [Presumably the Earth Empire later deals with them, unless these Daleks end up being used during the next invasion attempt on Earth in 3.4, "The Daleks' Masterplan".]

The Analysis

Where Does This Come From? Up until now, even the simplest or the oddest-looking *Doctor Who* story of the Pertwee run has smacked of the modern, the fashionable or the outright topical. That ends here. "Planet of the Daleks" is, above all else, a story about re-cycling the writer's old back-catalogue. It's not clear whether Terry Nation had actually bothered watching any *Doctor Who* since 1966, but the evidence suggests not, since "Planet" ignores virtually every change that had been made to the programme (bar the use of colour, which is admittedly extraordinary).

Yet even early *Doctor Who* often seemed more advanced than this. Typical of a *Boys' Own* adventure, episode four sees the two male leads - the Doctor and Taron - chide their female companions for being vaguely independent within minutes of each other. Ostensibly the story's theme is "the meaning of bravery", with various members of the Thal group overcoming fear, letting concern about others jeopardise their mission and indulging in acts of impatient and / or suicidal stupidity. The Doctor for his part gives lectures on both the nature of courage and the importance of not glamorising warfare. But these feel like trivial, lightweight ideas, which might be covered in just a single scene of any other story. Besides, the rules we "learn" about bravery here only seem to apply to characters in gung-ho adventure stories (usually starring Dana Andrews and set in the Philippines), and it's difficult to see any real-world relevance in them. A far cry from the first half of this supposed epic, "Frontier in Space".

If you wanted to make an in-depth analysis of Nation's work, you might at least note the use of imagery that suggests his future output as well as his '60s material. Though the city-in-the-jungle motif comes via the original Dalek story from *Tarzan*, Alex Raymond's work on *Flash Gordon* and ultimately the adventure stories of Rider Haggard, its use here to suggest "fallen civilisation" hints at the *Chariots of the Gods* style of the later "Death to the Daleks" (11.3), and also hints at Nation's plans for his later series *Survivors*. And while we're on that subject, it's worth mentioning that the Spiridon named Wester - the one gentle alien among a species of vicious, superstitious thugs - is just Bellal ("Death to the Daleks") in furs.

Things That Don't Make Sense Odd things to do between recovering from a near-death coma and collapsing from hypoxia: (1) Decide to rethink your outfit. (2) After changing into a natty purple ensemble (because purple is obviously "in" on Spiridon), *now* you decide to repair the Ship's systems.

Even apart from the stuff about the TARDIS air supply, a small amount of goo from the local plant-life is apparently strong enough to seal the doors shut despite the fact that they're powered by great big motors and open inwards. 10,000 Daleks is supposed to be a shockingly huge number and enough to conquer the galaxy, even though 10,000 is just a tiny fraction of (say) the 350,000 troops who were evacuated at Dunkirk (once again, Terry Nation doesn't seem to grasp quite how large the galaxy is). The Daleks "search" the body of Marat (a Thal) remarkably efficiently, considering that they can't even bend down to roll him over. Nice idea though it is, the escape using heat and a tarpaulin to rise up the shaft isn't really workable; if it's so much colder a mile down than at the surface - which is, you recall, a jungle - then there ought to be a massive downdraft. When the Doctor opens the hatch that overlooks the Dalek army, it's fitted with two little round handles. Is all Dalek furniture built this way?

Invisible Spiridons only leave footprints in the ground when there's an ominous close-up involved. Assuming that the Spiridons are natives of Spiridon (and the name is a bit of a clue), why did no other animals develop this handy knack of not-being-seen? How do they find mates? What does a Spiridon man look for in a woman? In evolutionary terms this is a non-starter, and if it's technological then why don't they have any other advanced science, and why couldn't the Daleks have developed it unaided? Do they *know* that they're invisible to other species? Most other invisible creatures at least hint at a possible cause and lifestyle, even if it's only 'a galaxy accident' in "The Ark" (3.6). Worse, as it takes the Daleks so much energy to achieve, how come the Spiridons don't have to eat all the time?

The Thal spaceship, which seems to be a flat-pack DIY kit, is full of loose objects like fire-extinguishers and trimphones; helpful if the gravity systems fail or they go into a tight spin. It's as if they expected invisible heavy-breathing aliens to reveal their presence by picking things up menacingly. And presumably their base of operations really needs the cobwebbed corpse of the pilot stuck in a chair on the off-chance that some visitors need scaring.

Their space-suits don't seem terribly airtight, either. Maybe gloves would have been a good idea. Especially if once per episode you're going to stick your fingers in liquid supposed to be -100°c. Speaking of which, an allotrope of ice at significantly low temperature bubbles to the surface on a tropical, steamy, sultry planet and yet none of the local wildlife has adapted. You'd expect mist, at least. And why will it need a thousand years to dig the Dalek popsicles out? A few days with a stirrup-pump should be all that's needed (compare with 12.4, "Genesis of the Daleks").

If the Daleks are based on Skaro, and the Thals are based on Skaro, then how come the Daleks can conquer entire star-systems but leave a continent on their own world free to develop weapons, space-travel and an anti-Dalek army? And the Thals return home in a stolen Dalek ship, so let's hope the Thal anti-aircraft guns are as efficient as their crap pistols.

Critique You've got to *try* to be positive, but in the case of "Planet of the Daleks"… well, it's not just that there aren't many positive things you can say, it's that there's so little to even comment on. It's a plot which by today's standards would barely fill an hour of television, with a near-total lack of new ideas, and even the subplot about invisible Daleks (which might, at least, make things interesting from a child's point of view) gets forgotten after the first two episodes. If you happened to be nine in 1973 then the sight of the Dalek ship landing in episode six must have been fantastic, and that's about all you can say.

But perhaps the greatest flaw in "Planet" is that it misunderstands the whole nature of *Doctor Who* as a programme. At its best, the series overcomes cheap SF, whereas this just wants to *be* cheap SF. The fact that it's meant to follow on from "Frontier in Space" only highlights the problem, since "Frontier" deliberately has the Doctor set out to subvert the clunky future-world around him, whereas here he just wanders through one bad set-piece after another and becomes a willing participant in each and every one. Nation obviously wants the Thals to be key players in the story, rather than just the Doctor's sidekicks, but they're all so wooden that you don't care even when they die in agony.

Even the Daleks are unimpressive. Gone are the days of expressionistic sets and experimental camera angles, now they're just randomly shoved in front of the camera and the director doesn't even bother re-shooting when they wobble (some have argued that episode three looks a lot spookier without colour, all moody shadows and slow pans). A story so weak that Jo ends up getting knocked unconscious by a foam-rubber rock just to keep up the tension when things get slow, "Planet of the Daleks" is on the whole dull beyond redemption. "Death to the Daleks" isn't very good either, but at least it has the good grace to only be four episodes long.

The Facts

Written by Terry Nation. Directed by David Maloney. Viewing figures: 11.0 million, 10.7 million, 10.1 million, 8.3 million, 9.7 million, 8.5 million. Overall, a sharp rise over the preceding stories thanks to the big Dalek publicity splash (what was it P. T. Barnum said…?).

Episode three only exists in the BBC archives in black-and-white.

Supporting Cast Bernard Horsfall (Taron), Prentis Hancock (Vaber), Tim Preece (Codal), Jane Howe (Rebec), Roy Skelton (Wester, Dalek Voice), Michael Wisher (Dalek Voice), Hilary Minster (Marat), Alan Tucker (Latep).

Working Titles "Destination: Daleks!". No, honestly.

Cliffhangers The Doctor and the Thals trap an invisible opponent on Spiridon, and sprayed with 'liquid colour-spray' it's revealed to be a Dalek; after another Thal ship crashes in the jungle, one of the survivors tells the Thals that there are 10,000 Daleks on the planet with them; in the lower levels of the Dalek city, the Doctor's escape-plan seems to be failing as the Daleks burn their way into the room where he and the Thals are trapped; Vaber, a Thal, heads through the jungle on a solo mission to sabotage the Dalek city, but Spiridons ambush him on the way; the Doctor and company sneak into the Dalek headquarters dressed in Spiridon furs, but one of the Daleks sounds the alarm after noticing their shoes.

The Lore

• The voice of Wester, the token "nice" Spiridon, is provided by long-term voice artist (also responsible for numerous Daleks and early Cybermen) Roy Skelton. British viewers may know that Skelton also provided the voices for the children's series *Rainbow*, which is why Wester sounds like Zippy.

• Those who lived through the '60s will recognise the Dalek "anti-gravitational discs" as the flying devices the Daleks used in the 1964 *Dalek Book*, not to mention various subsequent comic-strips. There, Daleks used them to rain down terror from the skies. Here, they use one to get up a chimney.

• As mentioned previously, the Dalek Supreme was a prop from the first Peter Cushing film, hence the jam-jar head-lights (and, yes, that's really what they are). Incidental music composer Dudley Simpson quotes the music from the movies, just to rub it in.

• The BBC, keen to cross-promote, got a Dalek to menace TV personality Jimmy Savile on the first edition of his new show *Clunk-Click*. Unfortunately this aired just after part one of the following story (see 22.3, "The Mark of the Rani", 3.10, "The War Machines" and 8.4, "Colony in Space" for more on Savile). The early '70s saw Saturday evenings on BBC1 dominated by white-haired men with big noses and frilly shirts surrounding themselves with mini-skirted dolly-birds. At times Savile, Pertwee and Bruce Forsythe[4] seemed almost interchangeable.

• Latep was originally called "Patel", but the production team realised that it'd already had one of those in the previous story (not that it stopped

them putting a "Ransome" in both "The War Games" and "Spearhead From Space", but there you go). Terry Nation decided that changing the name by swapping the vowels and putting stress on the second syllable would be a good idea, until someone showed him "Petal" written down.

• This is the only '70s story to have been repeated in prime-time on BBC1 (the "main-stream" channel) in the 1990s. It was shown on Friday nights, as part of the programme's 30th anniversary not-really-celebrations, immediately before a revived *Bruce Forsythe's Generation Game*. Each episode was preceded by a five minute film, especially made for the occasion, about some aspect of the series. The feature on "missing episodes" before part three looked like nothing so much as an apology for the fact that one-sixth of the story was in black-and-white.

10.5: "The Green Death"

(Serial TTT, Six Episodes, 19th May - 23rd June 1973.)

Which One is This? Giant maggots.

Firsts and Lasts Jo Grant's last appearance in the series, and for once the companion gets a send-off that's at least reasonably dignified (this is, without doubt, Jo and her future husband's story more than it is the Doctor's). There's even an epilogue showing a lonely, reflective Doctor slipping out of the engagement celebrations early and driving off into the night, complete with a slow fade into the end credits. "The Green Death" also sees the last appearance of the Pertwee "brainwaves" title sequence - which is, weirdly, shown upside-down at the end of the final episode - and the last appearance of the early '70s logo, at least until its surprise comeback for the 1996 TV Movie.

For the first time, the TARDIS is told to head for a specific non-Earth planet and gets there unaided. And for the first time since "The Highlanders" (2.4), the Doctor gets into drag, with Jon Pertwee expanding his repertoire of comedy voices by disguising himself as a cleaning-woman. It's not a pretty sight. (He also poses as a randy old Welsh milkman, and gets to indulge his love of fast-moving vehicles by driving a milk-float through a barricade at high speed.)

First appearance of the new-look, souped-up Bessie, with improved transmission and gearbox, since the old one packed up during "The Three

Doctors". The bonnet's noticeably longer now. The Doctor finally calls Captain Yates 'Mike' in episode five.

Six Things to Notice About "The Green Death"...

1. Despite only appearing in a single story (and then only briefly), the giant maggots are perhaps *the* best-remembered monsters of the 1970s, so much so that the first question non-fans tend to ask about *Doctor Who* is 'oh, which was the one with the giant maggots?'. Though some of the scenes in the maggot-infested mineshaft are shot on location, some of them are done with remarkably bad CSO. So while the maggot props used for close-ups are superbly nasty, the "group shots" of huge maggot-herds tend to be achieved by superimposing actors over miniaturised sets covered in real larvae. The crowning glory is the long-shot in which a tiny toy model of Bessie is pulled on a wire across a maggot-covered patch of soil, all shot on film for that authentic "outdoors" look.

2. All of which gets in the way of the deliberate eco-parable that's being told here. For years, fan-lore held that "The Green Death" was one of the very few *Doctor Who* stories that had a deliberate "topical" point to make. Though analysis of most of the rest of the Pertwee run proves this to be wrong, what's different about "The Green Death" is that Barry Letts went out of his way to commission a story based on environmental issues rather than letting Nature take its course. The result? A story about a hip young Welsh biologist / eco-campaigner who's fighting an evil chemical company that's producing enormous insects with toxic waste. And he lives in a hippy science-commune with a big psychedelic sign outside. Nice work.

3. Unless you're from Wales and *not* a university graduate, that is, since the script treats all the working-class people of the Welsh mining village in much the same way that you'd expect the Imperial English to treat coolies in India. Listen out particularly for the moment when Jo refers to Bert, the miner who's just been putrefied to death while trying to save her life, as a 'funny little Welshman'. The BBC's Professional Welshmen of the era - Mostyn Evans, Roy Evans and Talfryn Thomas - are all present and correct.

4. Aside from the maggots, the star of the show here is John Dearth as the voice of BOSS, the unhinged computer who runs Global Chemicals. A world away from the usual "does-not-compute" type of mad machine, BOSS mumbles when it's

embarrassed, quotes Oscar Wilde and hums Beethoven while it prepares to take over the world. Even HAL wasn't this good.

5. Like the B-movies of old, this is one of those SF stories in which (a) a perfectly ordinary substance turns out to be lethal to the monsters and (b) this discovery is made by accident when somebody spills something onto a laboratory slide. In this case the maggot-killer is a type of edible fungus being produced by the eco-people, which leads to some odd-looking scenes as the Doctor drives through a maggot-infested landscape while Sergeant Benton sits in the back seat throwing vegetarian food to the enemy.

6. It's a good time for bizarre and unwieldy dialogue. Cliff Jones' opening gambit with Jo is 'you'll contaminate my spores!', while later on Jo has to say 'I'm up on a slag heap with the Professor' and make it sound urgent. Extra marks, too, for the Brigadier's summary of the first corpse found at the polluted mine: 'This fellow's bright green, apparently. And dead!' (And everyone, even BOSS, loves mixed metaphors...)

The Continuity

The Doctor Here he graduates from using Venusian karate to using Venusian aikido. [If it's anything like Earth aikido then it should work by avoiding being hit by one's opponent unless they'd hurt themselves more in the process, but instead it mainly involves shouting 'hai!' and making them turn somersaults.] The Doctor actively enjoys this, and comes as close as he ever does to saying 'come and have a go if you think you're hard enough' to Hinks, the doomed guard.

Proving once again that he has a closer relationship with Jo than with most of his companions, the Doctor's obviously devastated when she leaves him, but earlier he's hurt even when she refuses to take a ride with him in the TARDIS. His reaction to Professor Jones is much like that of an over-protective father who's eyeing up the competition. He's sharp enough to see what's happening between Jo and Jones before anyone else, and briefly tries to stop them getting any closer before he accepts the inevitable. [His description of Jo as a 'fledgling' suggests that he sees himself as her mentor, something that's not particularly true of his relationships with any of his previous companions. The suggestion here is that Jo's been growing up under his supervision.]

 This product is not authorized by the BBC. Doctor Who and TARDIS are trademarks of the BBC.

Now the TARDIS is in working order, the Doctor initially refuses to investigate the colliery at the Brigadier's behest, even though he really should be interested in what's happening there. [Petulance.] He is, of course, immune to BOSS' brainwashing.

• *Inventory.* As well as displaying its usual ability to open all electronic locks, here the sonic screwdriver can emit a high-pitched shriek that alarms maggots. The Doctor acquires, then parts with, and will later wish he'd never set eyes on, a blue sapphire from Metebelis 3.

• *Background.* The Doctor's read Professor Jones' paper on DNA synthesis. He considers it 'quite remarkable' for the era.

The Supporting Cast

• *Jo Grant.* She's interested in the work of Professor Jones even before she goes to Llanfairfach on UNIT business, so much so that she refuses the Doctor's offer of a trip to Metebelis 3. She's prepared to defy UNIT in order to join the protest against Global Chemicals. [Again, Earth means a lot more to her than alien sight-seeing. It's odd that someone with such a tenuous grip on science is so concerned about ecology, so either the Doctor's really getting through to her or she's just being trendy. She has the same kind of zeal for the environment that she had for the Age of Aquarius in 8.5, "The Daemons".] Jo overtly states that the Professor's a lot like the Doctor, but then again that's before she meets him. By the end of her final "case" with UNIT, she's ostensibly a more capable and educated person than she was at the beginning, though no less headstrong or liable to knock things over. She doesn't seem to object to Professor Jones constantly patronising her.

Jo and Cliff plan to marry, then do the usual romantic thing of going to the upper reaches of the Amazon to search for a legendary super-nutritious giant toadstool. She takes the sapphire from Metebelis 3 with her as a wedding present from the Doctor [it's sent back in 11.5, "Planet of the Spiders"]. She also gets her uncle at the UN to have the Nut Hutch declared a 'United Nations priority one research complex', stating that it's only the second time she's asked him for anything. The Doctor's hope that she 'might turn into some kind of scientist' seems vindicated, as she can fix a radio with a screwdriver that she carries around in her afghan jacket. It's her turn to have the UNIT call-sign "Trap One".

• *UNIT.* The Brigadier speaks to the minister who helped draft the Third Enabling Act [see 9.5, "The Time Monster"], now the Minister of Ecology. They seem to have spoken before. He also claims to be able to 'bring influence to bear at Cabinet level' [the same minister, or does everyone in this story have a pet Secretary of State?]. The Brigadier tries to quote article 17 of the Enabling Act, but the minister overrules him with article 18, paragraph 3. This states that in matters of domestic concern, UNIT will place itself at the disposal of the host nation in all respects.

The HQ is about three hours' drive - or twenty minutes in Bessie - from South Wales. The Doctor has a computer record at UNIT.

• *The Brigadier.* Visibly flustered when the Prime Minister gives him orders. He was once stationed in Aldgate [but then, given how often UNIT changes its HQ, he must have been stationed virtually everywhere]. He drives a two-seater Mercedes, and seems enthusiastic about giving Global Chemicals military protection from cheesecloth-wearing hippy scientists, until Stevens tries to tell him how to do his job.

Despite some apparent jealousy when Cliff acts like Jo's keeper, this is the most relaxed we ever see Lethbridge-Stewart until his retirement [26.1, "Battlefield"].

• *Captain Yates.* Not strong enough to fight BOSS' mental conditioning, he's surely left emotionally damaged by events here. [Ah yes. See 11.2, "Invasion of the Dinosaurs".]

The TARDIS The Doctor no longer has any problems with the dematerialisation circuit, and believes he has total control over the Ship, but the space-time co-ordinate programmer is nearly worn out and he states that the TARDIS is 'getting on a bit'. He gets to Metebelis 3 by wiring the co-ordinates into the programmer rather than just feeding them into the console.

The Non-Humans

• *Giant Maggots.* The lethal, luminous, stinking green slime being pumped into the mine at Llanfairfach apparently causes an 'atavistic mutation' in the insect life there, causing eggs to grow to abnormal sizes and hatch out into vicious, bullet-proof maggots around two feet long. [The goo apparently converts the DNA of human cells into maggot cells, so the maggot DNA might somehow have got into the slime itself. The thing the maggots turn into isn't exactly a giant fly, which means the effects on insect genes aren't just size-related.]

Eventually, a maggot will enter its chrysalis state and emerge as a glistening dragonfly-like creature, capable of spitting slime. However, the fungus-based meat substitute eaten by the eco-researchers at the Nut Hutch conveniently kills the maggots when they try to consume it.

• *BOSS.* The Bimorphic Organisational Systems Supervisor, a sentient computer that runs Global Chemicals from the top floor of the building. [Note: sources differ on whether it's "Bimorphic" or "Biomorphic". Actor John Dearth, the voice of BOSS, seems to say the former, and the novelisation agrees. "Bimorphic" suggests two shapes, as in analogue and digital, or organic and electronic. "Biomorphic" suggests "life-shaped", which it isn't, really.]

Named BOSS by its designers, it's 'the only computer ever to be linked to a human brain': Stevens, the nominal head of the company, from whom it learned that the secret of human creativity is inefficiency. It's now self-controlling. BOSS is in constant contact with its agents, "agents" meaning the human beings it brainwashes with sonic signals delivered via headphones. Its aims: efficiency, productivity, profits for Global Chemicals and world domination.

BOSS isn't permanently trapped by the Doctor's hoary logical paradox. [It's the Epeminides Paradox, beloved of comic annual puzzle-pages. C.f. the Riddle of the Osirans in 13.3, "Pyramids of Mars".] But it *is* briefly confused, which might suggest that its brain is analogue rather than wholly digital; it looks at overall patterns, the way a human mind does, instead of going through programs step-by-step. [Since there was at least one sentient computer in Britain as early as 1966 - 3.10, "The War Machines" - it's not surprising that there are others, and BOSS seems to be a more complex machine than WOTAN. Perhaps some of the technology came from the Dalek battle computer in Radcliffe's shed (25.1, "Remembrance of the Daleks") or from Tobias Vaughn (6.3, "The Invasion"). It's not clear how BOSS got to be in charge of Global Chemicals, but it probably wasn't *meant* to be.]

Planet Notes

• *Metebelis 3.* Though the Doctor has fond memories of the place, on returning he discovers that it's a nightmare-world full of howling blizzards, nasty-looking snakes, aggressive giant birds

and shrieking things which throw rocks and spears at him. Metebelis 3 is blue all over, and described as having a blue sun [but see it again in 11.5, "Planet of the Spiders"]. He takes one of the planet's famous blue sapphires from a bird's nest, a 'crystal' that can break BOSS' brainwashing when someone stares into it. It seems to glow when it does this, and even mesmerises the Brigadier. It'll come back to haunt the Doctor in future.

• *Venus.* In addition to the aikido, the Doctor tells a story ending with the moral 'never trust a Venusian shanghorn with a perigosto stick'. Everyone apparently finds this funny.

History

• *Dating.* [Early 1974, probably April. See **What's the UNIT Timeline?** under 8.5, "The Daemons", for the evidence.]

Global Chemicals has its headquarters near Llanfairfach colliery, South Wales, the National Coal Board having closed the pit a year earlier. Newport is the nearest large town [so it's in Gwent, probably, around the Rhondda valley]. Britain is still obsessed with energy, and 'the Ministry' grants Global Chemicals the authority to restrain people under the Emergency Powers Act, with UNIT once again called on to protect the project. Professor Jones, meanwhile, indicates that he's won a Nobel Prize. There are computers all over the world by now, and BOSS plans to extend its power by connecting to 'seven other complexes', including Moscow and Zurich.

The Prime Minister at this point is called Jeremy. [Someone else is in charge by the time of 13.1, "Terror of the Zygons". See **Who's Running The Country?**.]

Additional Sources The Target novelisation of "The Green Death" (by Malcolm Hulke) changes the name of the company from Global Chemicals to Panorama Chemicals, since a real company called Global Chemicals objected to the original TV transmission on the grounds that it had never knowingly made giant insects.

Interestingly, the book also plays up the link between the company and Nazism (very '70s... the corporation is evil, and thus obviously run by fascists). The TV story begins with the company's representative addressing the Welsh villagers with a parody of Chamberlain's 'I have in my hand a piece of paper' speech, and has BOSS mention

Who's Running the Country?

On the face of it, the attempt at a strangled sort of "realism" in the UNIT stories means that we can assume the existence of a governmental system almost identical to that of the "real" Britain at the time. If we can accept the dramatic licence and the "names changed to protect the innocent" clause, then you can see how the political fall-out from various invasions, plagues and freak daffodil fatalities would accumulate during the UNIT years.

For the benefit of children and foreigners, a crash-course in real-world early '70s politics follows.

Around the time that "Inferno" (1970) was broadcast, Labour PM Harold Wilson narrowly lost the election, an election caused by economic instability after his Chancellor's decision to uncouple the pound from the Gold Standard. This election was too close to call until polling day, the decision to give the vote to eighteen-year-olds conferring the Labour Party with an advantage almost outweighed by the sense that it was time for a change.

Two days before the election, England was knocked out of the 1970 World Cup after an ill-judged penalty. Dissent rose accordingly, and so the Conservatives - led by confirmed bachelor Edward Heath - formed a government with a slender majority. Jeremy Thorpe, leader of the Liberal Party, didn't trust either of the two leading parties but was more inclined to support Labour's policies. Nevertheless the Tories (a traditional name for the Conservatives, an Irish word for "bandit") were officially the Conservative and Unionist Party of Great Britain and Northern Ireland. As the violence in Northern Ireland escalated, Heath looked safe.

Except that Heath was finished by February 1974. To list all the things that went wrong would take a book as big as this, so here are the headlines. Chancellor Reginald Maudling had managed to defy the laws of classical economics and get inflation *and* unemployment rising exponentially. He was later sent to prison, but for fraud, not for devastating the economy. Trade and Industry Secretary Peter Walker narrowly avoided being jailed along with his business partner.

Relations with the unions were deliberately confrontational. In order to be seen to be strong, both sides became intransigent, causing power-cuts, rail-strikes and "The Monster of Peladon". Heath was simultaneously pro-Europe in an era when Europe didn't want Britain, and pro-America when anyone could see that Nixon was a crook. Nixon's intervention in the Arab-Israeli conflict resulted in the Yom Kippur War and subsequent oil

price-rise. Heath was forced to introduce petrol rationing and a three-day working week. Before this forced an election, there was also a series of hilarious sex-scandals, notably Lord Lambton (a senior defence minister) and Norma Levy (who ran "cream-cake" parties).

There are any number of points at which things could have gone differently. Remarkably, Heath himself was never involved in any breath of scandal. Most of the worst threats to his administration were apparently small to outside observers, and the more damaging material from the Cabinet papers (generally released thirty years later, and so just beginning to filter though in 2004) was unknown to the public. It's still not widely known, for instance, that various prominent right-wing politicians planned a military coup in 1976 as inflation reached 25% and the International Monetary Fund was called in. Everyone in the *Doctor Who* universe behaves as if politicians are still in fear of being voted out, though, so the coup apparently didn't happen there either.

But if power-cuts could cause an election, then how might the repeated crises at Wenley Moor, Nuton and Project Inferno have affected ministerial careers? Unlike our world, most generating companies seem to have abandoned oil and coal some time before UNIT was formed. In "The Green Death" there's a well-established Ministry of Ecology, run by someone with prior Cabinet experience either in Defence or the Foreign Office who drafted UNIT's charter. If an Ecology Minister is among the twenty-two Cabinet posts, and not amalgamated with - say - the Department of the Environment (which also handles house-building, county boundaries, local council regulation and so on), then it must have been a priority distinct from other ministerial duties.

Certainly the World Ecology Bureau from "The Seeds of Doom" (13.6) seems to be run from London, not Brasilia or Athens. The government in "The Green Death" has been in power for a while. If other data on UNIT dates are valid, then the election either took place during the "gap" year between "Terror of the Autons" and "Mind of Evil" or not at all. This means that the deaths of three Permanent Under Secretaries and a Minister must be explained to the public as deaths by "natural causes". In the case of Sir James Quinlan, this is only possible if the supposedly live global telecast never went further than the studio (7.3, "The Ambassadors of Death"). The alternative is a by-

continued on page 139...

both Nietzsche and Wagner. The book goes one step further by pointing out a direct parallel between BOSS' 'one world, one people, one BOSS' philosophy and Hitler's 'ein Reich, ein Volk, ein Fuhrer'.

In addition, the book gives the miners far more dignity and individuality than the televised version, and shows Malcolm Hulke - who later criticises "The Green Death" implicitly in 11.2, "Invasion of the Dinosaurs" - tackling difficulties which the original script papers over. Anyone who owns an original copy of the book might also like to consider the illustration on page 58, which appears to show a giant security guard playing with a Jon Pertwee action figure.

The Analysis

Where Does This Come From?   Oh, bless them. The eco-concerns of "The Green Death" are genuine, but they're also so tangled up in the dressings of the era that you can virtually smell the orange-and-brown curtains.

Since the story hails from a time when environmental data was even less well-understood by the public than it is now, and when popular culture didn't even have *nicknames* for the world's ecological problems, what's striking about Cliff Jones and his friends at the Nut Hutch isn't so much that they're naïve as that they see things in terms of overall, global, *revolutionary* solutions. Not surprising, given that this generation had seen at least a limited form of social revolution over the previous decade. If this story were made today, then Nut Hutch would be organising small-scale relief programmes in obscure West African villages. Here in 1973, Cliff's planning an expedition to find a mythical fungus and change the whole world overnight.

Notably, a mad computer causes the threat to this eco-paradise. Possibly the suggestion is that the "system" itself is insane, corrupt and inefficient, but actually it has the reverse effect, making something non-human the cause of all the trouble instead of pure capitalist recklessness. Broadcast as the storm over Watergate was brewing, this is the nastiest conspiracy theory tale of the lot, at least on Earth. The implication that Cabinet members are either taking bungs or under hypnosis by a mad computer made more sense at the time.

And there's a definite attempt to give a *sheen* of reality to events here. Though the script frequent-

ly patronises the Welsh, the village setting at least has some depth, unlike the many UNIT stories which seem to take place in a field somewhere in an unspecified part of southern England. In longshot, the glimpses we see of a community on the edge of closedown aren't that far away from *Panorama*. Many of the throwaway comments could come straight from *Under Milk Wood*, especially the Doctor as the randy old milkman and Jones the Milk talking about 'Tom the Sea Captain'. Strange, though, that the producer would be so keen to commission an eco-story at a time when *Doomwatch* had already done the mutants-made-from-pollution idea to death. (*Doomwatch* had even done its own "poisonous bug" story, in a script by former *Doctor Who* script editor Gerry Davis called - wait for it - "The Web of Fear".)

When it comes to *Doctor Who* predicting the future, it should be noted that there's a fungus-based meat-substitute being served up at the Nut Hutch, and that Quorn didn't go on sale until 1986.

Things That Don't Make Sense   The gem from Metebelis 3 is referred to as a 'blue sapphire', presumably to differentiate it from all the pink and brown sapphires in the universe. The roster of words that Jon Pertwee can't pronounce now includes "chitinous" (famously, the production team later received a letter which read "the reason I'm writin' / is how to say kitin"). Jo knows all about Professor Jones from the newspapers, but there's apparently never been a photograph of him in print as she doesn't recognise him on sight. Oxyacetylene cutting equipment has to be fetched from Cardiff, but a cherry-picker lorry from the South Wales Electricity Board is on hand as soon as it's needed.

There's a surveillance camera in the waste-pipe at Global Chemicals, handy as it lets plant manager Elgin know that the Doctor and Jo are there, but it's probably less useful on the 364 days of the year when there aren't intruders in the pipe and it's just full of sludge. All the miners are stupid enough to want to touch the glowing green slime even after they've seen people die of it. Jo's uncle arranges funding for the Wholeweal commune, which Cliff interprets as 'work for the Valleys'; is Jones the Milk going to become Jones the Mycoprotein? And why is everyone over thirty ill in this village?

Who's Running the Country?

...continued from page 137

election every week and a rapid turn-over of Cabinet ministers even by Tony Blair's standards.

Which is as good a time as any to recall that, unlike today's media feeding-frenzy for ministerial scalps, gentlemen's agreements *not* to mention particular things covered pre-Watergate British politics. Certainly, no-one ever speculated about Ted Heath being 'not the marrying kind'. A stately home blowing up on the *Nine O'Clock News* was tomorrow's chip-papers, and official cover-ups for ships being sunk in the Channel were par for the course. (Don't believe it? 2,000 people died *in one night* in 1952 due to a "London Particular" smog - the kind that American *Murder She Wrote* viewers think are still common, like music-halls - and coroners' offices were instructed to make the cause of death seem natural. The Housing Minister responsible was future Prime Minister Harold MacMillan.)

Let's assume, therefore, that the most sensible timeline has Jeremy Thorpe in Number Ten from spring 1972; Thorpe, of course, is obviously supposed to be the "Jeremy" mentioned in "The Green Death". Looking back on it now, Thorpe as a Prime Minister seems unlikely, but then again no-one in that period knew all his secrets. After the 1960s, the Liberals were the Third Party of British politics, unlikely to win a general election in their own right but occasionally finding themselves in a position to tip the balance between Labour and the Conservatives.

Thorpe, a thin, quiet-looking man who himself could easily have been one of *Doctor Who*'s ministerial supporting characters, was leader of the Liberals from 1967. He'd also been a well-known figure in Soho's then-illegal gay bars, and had socialised with people like *The Beatles*' manager Brian Epstein. There's a photo of him on stage with the Jimi Hendrix Experience. In the two panicked elections of 1974, Thorpe looked like a kingmaker, travelling to the hustings by hovercraft and helicopter.

But while his flair for PR was making him a plausible Leader of the Opposition, one of his ex-lovers - a rather soppy male model by the name of Norman Scott - was saying far too many things to far too many people. Thorpe and his friends thought it'd be nice if Scott shut his mouth for good, and what followed was a case which at the very least highlights the corner-shop nature of British scandal. In America, political assassinations are supposed to involve CIA mind-control experiments and ex-marine sharpshooters hired by the Mafia. In Britain, the affair which sank Jeremy Thorpe involved the world's least competent hitman shooting Norman Scott's dog and then completely failing to hit his target. (If it gives you some idea of how ludicrous this whole affair was, then picture this: at a time when the leader of the nation's third largest political party was suspected of engineering an attempted murder, the UK press was presented with an old letter from Thorpe to Scott bearing the words "bunnies can and will go to France". This message has never been satisfactorily deciphered.)

Ultimately Thorpe and three others were found not guilty of conspiracy to commit murder, after a trial widely regarded as a complete farce. Nonetheless, his career was finished.

But had an election been called in 1972, the Liberals would have had the advantage that no-one on their front bench was associated with any of the catastrophic decisions which the other two parties had made. As a coalition with Labour, they could have called on the broadly sympathetic but more experienced second-string figures of the Wilson government (Tom Driberg, Richard Crossman, Shirley Williams…). Britain has a female PM by the time of "Terror of the Zygons", c. 1976; assuming, of course, that when the Brigadier calls the person on the other end of the hotline "Madam" he's actually talking to a woman and not just taking the piss out of Jeremy Thorpe's sexuality. In his New Adventure *No Future*, Paul Cornell suggests that this PM is Shirley Williams, which makes *at least* as much sense as the assumption that it has to be Margaret Thatcher.

Mapping other known public figures onto the various ministers who crop up in the series is a trickier manouvre, and most of them apparently aren't minister for anything in particular. However, just as an Ecology Ministry is more plausible in a Thorpe government than any other, so the "big science" energy-generating projects of Season Seven and "The Claws of Axos" make more sense if Labour's technophiliac socialist Anthony Wedgewood-Benn had centralised all power production and gone for big, shiny prestige projects (as with, say, Concorde or the Post Office Tower). Think Tank (in 12.1, "Robot") has many of the hallmarks of his pet projects, making its infiltration by fascist nerds more ironic. However, as Professor Kettlewell (also in "Robot") sees himself as a voice in the wilderness of renewable energy, it may be that the Ministry of Ecology was disbanded after

continued on page 141...

When one of the doomed Welshmen makes a telephone call from the mine in the first episode, a mysterious hand appears in the tunnel to give him his cue. (This ghostly limb will make an even more spectacular appearance in 13.3, "Pyramids of Mars".)

Critique It begins with birdsong, location filming from a helicopter and a little green man. It ends with a bug-eyed monster, the hero riding off into the sunset and the titles running upside-down. *Doctor Who* ends its tenth year as it began, by showing how far we've all come and how much remains constant.

If you remember that the authors of this piece were capable of writing a story about Atlantis - which shows that they've at least read Plato - then the oddities fit into place. This is a world where corruption breeds pestilence, where all things in nature have their counterpart (maggots have fungus, BOSS has the crystal) and where balance is the key to happiness. In their "knit-your-own-yoghurt" sort of way, the Nut Hutch scientists are really the heroes of this story, and Cliff 'n' Jo become a young-couple-in-trouble as in many a one-off serial. The problem is giving the Doctor something to do, so he picks fights with security guards, goes to other planets when the Brigadier needs to 'phone him and reverts to his "Dalek Invasion of Earth" tactics when Jo looks like dumping him for Cliff and the planet. (It's another plot with a "dummy" monster, too, since the giant maggots are the chief threat for the first five episodes but then give way to the subplot about BOSS taking over the world at the start of episode six.)

It has to be said, though, that it was all getting a little familiar. The premise of the tale is exactly that of "The Invasion" (6.3), garnished with the mutagenic goo from "Inferno" (7.4), comedy rustics from "The Daemons" (8.5) and Whitehall shenanigans from most of Season Seven. Even the brainwashing is off-the-shelf. You find yourself wondering if there was ever a version of this script in which the Doctor realises that "BOSS" is a slang term for "Master".

But week by week this story built up from something we could have seen on the news to something clearly asking us to take a stand. Stevens isn't a villain; his face when BOSS makes his conscience-filled colleague Fell 'self-destruct', in a moment that's offset with more birdsong, is

that of a man trapped. In the final debate / contest, the same face is a battlefield between the orange-tinted oscilloscope trace of BOSS and the blue-tinted burnt-in effect of the Metabelis crystal. That the conflict is depicted entirely through the psychedelic effects of *Top of the Pops* is part of the story's appeal. That's what people remember, the dayglo green goo of the title and the tangible threat of giant maggots in a coal-mine.

The Facts

Written by Robert Sloman. Directed by Michael Briant. Viewing figures: 9.2 million, 7.2 million, 7.8 million, 6.8 million, 8.3 million, 7.0 million.

The omnibus repeat, two days after Christmas, scored 10.4 million.

Supporting Cast Jerome Willis (Stevens), Stewart Bevan (Clifford Jones), Tony Adams (Elgin), Ben Howard (Hinks), Mostyn Evans (Dai Evans), Talfryn Thomas (Dave), Roy Evans (Bert), Mitzi McKenzie (Nancy), John Scott Martin (Hughes), John Rolfe (Fell), John Dearth (BOSS' Voice), Terry Walsh (Guard), Roy Skelton (James).

Cliffhangers Jo and Bert-the-funny-little-Welshman go down into the mine, but the lift mechanism's been sabotaged and makes them plummet towards the bottom of the pit; a mine tunnel collapses in front of the Doctor and Jo, and they get their first good look at the maggots when a handful crawl out of the rubble to hiss at them; Jo, on her own in the Nut Hutch living-room, fails to notice that there's a maggot shuffling across the parquet towards her; the Doctor discovers the true nature of BOSS on the top floor of the company building; a sonic pulse kills James – a Global Chemicals employee freed from BOSS' influence – in the Global Chemicals offices, and Captain Yates turns round to find Stevens and the security guards standing in the doorway.

The Lore

• Episodes one to four feature Tony Adams as Elgin, Stevens' right-hand man (or PR man, according to the novel) at Global Chemicals. In episode five he suddenly disappears, to be replaced by *another* right-hand man who fills exactly the same space in the plot, played by regular Dalek / Zippy voice-artist Roy Skelton. Almost as if somebody got sick and dropped out

Who's Running the Country?

...continued from page 139

the Llanfairfach incident. It's certainly not doing its job if "Invasion of the Dinosaurs" (11.2) is to be believed, as the eco-cult Operation Golden Age has no shortage of support. With a dynamic Science and Energy Ministry outgunning him at every turn, no wonder the Minister for Ecology is so vulnerable to overtures from Global Chemicals.

This may be the time to note that Northern Ireland is just about the only contemporary "issue" never touched on in '70s *Doctor Who*, at least not on-screen. Though the zealot-wars of "Frontier in Space" and "Genesis of the Daleks" are certainly suggestive, only the novelisations give any explicit suggestion of the Irish issue (the IRA gets a mention in *Doctor Who and the Cave-Monsters*). Aliens aside, is this the big "political" difference between the UNIT world and our own? Are we to conclude that the key divergence in history is the absence of religious demagogues and politicised gangsters exploiting a divisive issue? Alternatively, could it be the apparent decline in America's influence (see 4.5, "The Moonbase")? Or is it simply Geoff Astell's fateful kick in Mexico '70?

---

of filming halfway through…

• The bombs dropped from the helicopter were lavatory ballcocks. The maggots in some of the long-shots were inflated condoms.

• Stewart Bevan (Clifford Jones) was Katy Manning's real-life fiancé, and director Michael Briant resisted everyone's suggestions that he was perfect for the part of Cliff until meeting him under different circumstances; some versions say that Briant didn't know who Bevan was, and asked him to audition. Many fans and some BBC novelists have taken the hint from off-screen life that Jo and Cliff eventually parted company (see also 11.5, "The Monster of Peladon"). In reality, Katy Manning presented a hippy-ish crafts programme called *Serendipity*; played several small roles, including a junkie in a well-received episode of *Target*; and moved to Australia. She's become involved in *Doctor-Who*-related works again, but not as Jo, instead playing the time-travelling Iris Wildthyme in the Big Finish audios. Her most recent memorable TV appearance was alongside an "exuberant" Liza Minnelli in an edition of *Ruby Wax Meets*. (Manning and Minnelli are old friends. Their joint TV appearance involved both of them turning up late for an interview in a hotel room, in a state that was politely described in the media as "the worse for wear", and pretending to be dogs in front of an unusually speechless Ruby Wax. It really was quite wonderful to behold.)

• The scene in which Jo and Cliff meet for the first time was a last-minute rewrite. A character called "Face" had been removed from the story, and his lines given to Jones' colleague Nancy (Mitzi McKenzie, who as Mitzi Webster appeared in "Colony In Space"). However, she was otherwise engaged come the day of the shoot, so no-one else was around at Wholeweal and the scene we all know was created.

• The company was originally to be called Universal Chemicals, but there really was one of those. It later turned out that there was a Global Chemicals, too, but not in the UK. One of the chief scientists at ICI was called Bell, so the character "Bell" became "Fell". It's worth pointing out that "Jocelyn Stevens" was also the name of Robert Sloman's ultimate boss, the editor of the *Sunday Times*.

• The book Barry Letts names as the source for his thoughts on ecology, *A Blueprint For Survival* by Edward Goldsmith, seems a pretty good match for the fictional *Last Chance For Man*: the book Sir Charles Grover wrote before the events of "Invasion of the Dinosaurs" (11.2). However, the publishers of this present volume would like to acknowledge that Edward Goldsmith never attempted retro-genocide against the entire human species.

• This story's Terry Walsh moment sees him playing a jobsworth security guard at Global Chemicals. In terms of lines and screen-time he does better than Jones the Milk, but his main contribution is the fight in episode two, for which he gets a credit and is more obviously playing the Doctor than ever before (again, see 11.5, "The Monster of Peladon").

• The Monday after the transmission of episode five was the day Roger Delgado died. It was national news, and the elegiac feel of episode six was heightened, although obviously none of the cast or crew could have known this when filming.

11.1: "The Time Warrior"

(Serial UUU, Four Episodes, 15th December 1973 - 5th January 1974.)

Which One is This? The Doctor gets medieval, as a Humpty-Dumpty man from beyond the stars crash-lands in the Middle Ages and starts abducting scientists from the present / future. Loud men in period costume shout 'by my sword!', while Sarah Jane Smith tries to give the serving-wenches a lesson in female emancipation.

Firsts and Lasts As with "Carnival of Monsters", Robert Holmes once again writes a watershed story without really meaning to. Though "The Time Warrior" isn't the first pseudo-historical story (i.e. a historical story with alien interference other than that of the Doctor; the first was 2.9, "The Time Meddler"), its perfect balance of aliens and period costumes sets the tone for virtually all the "past" stories of the late '70s and '80s. So much so that it's sometimes hard to believe it wasn't always part of the programme's brief.

Other things, people and ideas making their debut here are Sarah Jane Smith, the Doctor's new companion and only link to humanity for much of the next three-and-a-half years; the Sontarans, destined to become one of the series' Big Five Monsters, immediately making an impression here as the angry goblin-dwarves of the universe; the new "time tunnel" opening sequence (they haven't quite got it right yet, with the cut-out Doctor looking especially naff); the diamond-shaped *Doctor Who* logo, which will come to represent the series more than any other piece of design; and, for the first time ever, the Doctor names his home planet as "Gallifrey".

Yet despite this "fresh start" approach for Season Eleven, this was actually the last story to be made as part of Season Ten.

Four Things to Notice About "The Time Warrior"...

1. Another Robert Holmes comedy-adventure script full of excessive character parts, "The Time Warrior" gives us Irongron (dim-witted Middle Ages warlord who shouts a lot) and Bloodaxe (the even more dim-witted second-in-command), who get most of the good comedy moments while the Doctor and the warmongering alien are busy bickering about Earth's future. Best line: Irongron's description of the Doctor as 'a long-shanked rascal with a mighty nose' (the first time the Pertwee "beak" has taken a direct hit in the series, but not the last; see 12.1, "Robot"). Meanwhile the Doctor makes the best effort yet to sum up the programme's ethos in a single sentence, when Sarah asks him if he's serious about being a Time Lord with a cosmic police box: 'About what I do, yes. Not necessarily the way I do it.'

2. Perhaps it's just the influence of the bawdy Middle Ages, but "The Time Warrior" seems distinctly ruder than any other *Doctor Who* story of the period. All the women are 'wenches', and all the guards are 'lusty'. Irongron refers to Sarah's 'taille', quite clearly meaning her bottom, while Linx the Sontaran inspects her differently-shaped thorax. And when it comes to the Doctor's relationship with his companion, Professor Ruebish becomes the first character to speak the mind of the audience with his 'I should've thought he was a bit old for that sort of thing' comment. (Ironic, though, that he says this in the first story *after* Katy Manning leaves the series...) Even Lady Eleanor is commented on, and she's Dot Cotton in a wimple.

3. One scene in episode three, in which the Doctor and Sarah dress up as monks in order to get into Irongron's castle, is notable not only for the atrocious period acting of the two guards but for This Week's Funny Accent from Jon Pertwee. It's his comedy "Postman" voice from the radio sit-com *Waterlogged Spa*... and the same one he'll use for *Worzel Gummidge*, half a decade later.

4. The opening scene sees the Sontaran ship crash-land on Earth like a "falling star", but Irongron's men are too scared to ride out and examine it until dawn. Which is handy, because it removes the need for expensive night-time location filming.

The Continuity

The Doctor Still seems to see Earth as a base of operations, even though his TARDIS is in full working order and with Jo gone there's presumably nothing keeping him here. [The Third Doctor still feels an affectionate attachment to UNIT, though this changes after he regenerates at the end of the season. Since we last saw him he may have spent some time working on the "Whomobile", which turns up in the next story, and he seems to be looking for things to occupy his time on Earth. See also the IRIS experiments in 11.5, "Planet of the Spiders".] He says he's not much of an artist, and would like to study under one of the great masters, preferably Rembrandt.

The Doctor seems to like Sarah Jane Smith on their first meeting, but principally because he enjoys annoying her. Here he's deliberately sexist in her presence [just to see the look on her face].

• *Ethics.* The Doctor believes that if Linx gives the secret of firearms to the people of the Middle Ages, then humanity will have nuclear weapons by the seventeenth century, before they're 'civilised' enough to handle the technology. [This is exactly the same point he made when the Monk tried to re-fit human history in 2.9, "The Time Meddler", this story's direct ancestor. But the Doctor's vendetta with the Monk came across as a matter of personal pride rather than an attempt to save history, whereas here he finally acts like a Time Lord by defending the timeline. His implication that twentieth century humans *are* civilised enough for nuclear weapons is quite touching.] When dining with the nobility, he demonstrates a willingness to follow their customs. [Even though Charles Laughton, playing Henry VIII, invented the custom of throwing a chicken-bone over one's shoulder.]

• *Inventory.* The Doctor uses a pen-torch to break Linx's hypnosis. [He's had one of these ever since the early days. See 1.1, "An Unearthly Child".]

• *Background.* The Doctor recognises Linx as a Sontaran, and knows the Sontarans' history. [It could be argued that he remembers them from the events of 22.4, "The Two Doctors", but this seems unlikely as the implication of "The Two Doctors" is that history's being changed. At this point in time, that particular past hasn't happened yet. Besides, in "The Two Doctors" even the Second Doctor seems to know of the Sontarans, suggesting an encounter very early on in the Doctor's life as a traveller.]

He's familiar with the work of Sarah's aunt Lavinia, having read her work on the teleological response of the virus, published at least a decade and a half ago [once again, he's taking an interest in "modern" human science]. He hints that he's a member of the Royal Society.

Season 11 Cast/Crew

- • Jon Pertwee (the Doctor)
- • Elisabeth Sladen (Sarah Jane Smith)
- • Nicholas Courtney
  (Brigadier Lethbridge-Stewart)
- • Richard Franklin (Captain Yates)
- • John Levene (Sergeant Benton)

- • Barry Letts (Producer)
- • Terrance Dicks (Script Editor)
- • Robert Holmes (uncredited,
  Script Editor with Terrance on 11.2, 11.3)

The Supporting Cast

• *Sarah Jane Smith.* A young, smart, resourceful but much-too-determined journalist, Sarah quickly becomes the Doctor's new sidekick even though - unusually - she initially regards him with distrust. She's not only prepared to consider him the prime mover in an evil plot, but critically she also takes command of a guerrilla unit to capture him. In many ways she's portrayed here as the embodiment of mid-'70s leather-jacket-wearing feminism, and she's just gagging to be described as "spunky". [Her character is vastly different in this story to her later appearances. After Season Twelve she becomes a lot more playful, almost child-like in her relationship with the Fourth Doctor, yet here she's constantly determined to show how tough she is. She'll always be pro-active, but here it's at her own behest. She adopts the persona of serving-girl-pretending-to-be-noble very convincingly, improvising in character in ways that no companion since Barbara Wright has done.]

She loudly objects to being patronised and struggles like a trooper when man-handled. A bond is obviously beginning to form between her and the Doctor by the time they leave the Middle Ages together.

Sarah has an aunt, Lavinia Smith, who's a renowned virologist and currently on a lecture tour in America [see 18.7a, *K9 and Company*: "A Girl's Best Friend"].

• *UNIT.* Unsurprisingly, Sarah's heard of it. Surprisingly, she doesn't know it's involved in investigating missing government scientists and doesn't seem to recognise Lethbridge-Stewart from all his TV appearances.

• *The Brigadier.* The Doctor has apparently told the Brigadier all about Metebelis 3. The Brigadier's either humouring him or starting to believe it.

ABOUT TIME 1970–1974

The TARDIS There's coffee-making equipment inside the Ship, as well as a reflective fan - looking like a sort of discoid venetian blind - that can block a Sontaran hypno-weapon. The Doctor summons up the equipment to build a rondium sensor which detects the delta-particles involved in Sontaran time-projection. There's also a "black light" box that reveals the ghost-image of Linx at the research centre, apparently highlighting the point where the Sontaran materialised in the twentieth century, and the Doctor uses it to track down the source of the matter transmission. It's a good day for gadgets.

The Time Lords The Doctor's homeworld is Gallifrey, and the Doctor states that the Time Lords are keen on stamping out unlicensed time-travel, telling Sarah to think of them as 'galactic ticket inspectors'. [The first time this is ever established, but it's key to the way they're portrayed in later stories. "Unlicensed" suggests that they license certain people to travel in time, which sounds unlikely, but see 24.3, "Delta and the Bannermen" and 22.4, "The Two Doctors".]

The Doctor indicates that Time Lords are no longer young once they're over 200.

The Non-Humans *Sontarans*. Squat, powerful beings with dome-shaped heads and no visible necks, the Sontarans have leering gargoyle-like faces and look more like creatures from folklore than conventional aliens. The species is cloned, and has no females, its culture being utterly obsessed by war. The suggestion here is that while creatures like the Daleks and Cybermen are ruthlessly determined to conquer the universe, the Sontarans just want a good fight.

At the Sontaran academy, a million cadets are hatched at each muster parade. The gravity on the Sontaran planet is many times that of Earth, and Linx is said to weigh 'several tons' there, so Sontarans are physically strong but designed for load-bearing rather than leverage. Conveniently, this makes them easy to tie up.

Rather than eating, a Sontaran "recharges" through a probic vent at the back of the neck, but the vent is vulnerable and a blow to it easily fells Linx. [The armour leaves it uncovered, so it must be important to keep the vent ventilated.] Sontaran spin likes to see this weakness as a strength, since it means they always have to meet the enemy face-to-face.

The Sontarans have been at war with the Rutans for millennia [see 15.1, "Horror of Fang Rock"], and Linx claims [wrongly] that there isn't a galaxy in the universe which his species hasn't subjugated. Linx is on a reconnaissance mission, though he states that Earth is of no strategic importance [this changes in time for 15.1, "Horror of Fang Rock"]. Like many military imperialists, he sees the war as a struggle for 'freedom'. Anything without a military function is an irrelevance to him. He's Commander of the Fifth Army Space Fleet in the Sontaran Army Space Corps, and he has his own 'squadron'.

The flag of the Sontaran Empire is white, and marked with what looks like a little "S". [Perhaps it's being translated into an Earth-based alphabet for our benefit, q.v. the "H" in 9.2, "The Curse of Peladon". But it *might* be a spiral galaxy, as on close inspection the "S" looks more like two crescents with a bulbous join. In the novelisation, the sound the flag makes as it pops open is said to be the Sontaran National Anthem.]

Linx knows of Gallifrey and the Time Lords, but Sontaran intelligence believes them to lack the morale to face a determined assault.

His spacecraft is an egg-like metal pod, only big enough for one soldier, but like its owner it's 'tremendously powerful' for its size and the technology on board is evidently impressive. Linx adjusts his ship's 'frequency modulator' to project himself several hundred years into the future and take scientists back to his own time. The ship's 'osmic projector' is an important part of this process. [It seems incredible that the Sontarans have this sort of technology, let alone that such a small vessel is equipped with it. Compare this with 15.6, "The Invasion of Time", in which the Sontarans want the time-travel secrets of the Time Lords.]

Linx also has the resources to build a robot "knight", unkillable even when beheaded but possessing only rudimentary intelligence. Sontaran 'space-armour' consists of a silver-black body-suit and an imposing domed helmet, while Linx carries a wand-like firearm that can kill, stun, burn metal, make weapons fly out of people's hands or hypnotise human captives with its light. There's a translator-box on his belt.

On this occasion, Sontarans have two fingers and a thumb on each hand. Linx's skin is brown rather than grey [q.v. 12.3, "The Sontaran Experiment"]. The Doctor seems to indicate that

What Caused the Sontaran-Rutan War?

In "The Two Doctors", it's as good as admitted that the war between the cosmic Roundheads (11.1, "The Time Warrior") and the Devil's jellyfish (15.1, "Horror of Fang Rock") goes beyond the confines of normal history. The Doctor believes the Sontarans and the Rutans to have been fighting for so long that they've forgotten why. The war, in Earth terms, lasts from several millennia before the Normans to a time at least 10,000 years after solar flares destroy most life on Earth. At least, that's how it seems.

However, at least one side has time-travel facilities, and it's hard to credit that a war in which only *one* side has time-technology could go on for so long without the other side suffering an absolute defeat. The Sontarans have the ability to pull things from the future even in Linx's era (and he knows about Gallifrey), so we have to conclude that the Rutans must at least know a thing or two about time-travel. Especially if you consider the supporting evidence from the New / Missing Adventures, which establish that Rutan shape-changers *have* infiltrated the Sontaran army and must surely have taken a close look at Sontaran technology.

Later Sontaran ruses involve bootlegging the Time Lord DNA sections involved in full control of time, and launching an assault on Gallifrey itself. For this to be even conceivable they must at least be on a par with the early Gallifreyans in Rassilon's era. Thus linear chronology might be a red herring. It might turn out that a pre-emptive strike by time-commandos actually started the war in the first place. This is the sort of twist that's in keeping with both the Sontarans and their real-world creator, who was more proprietorial about them than he was about (say) the Drashigs or the Autons, and who wrote out a history for Bob Baker and Dave Martin before one word of "The Sontaran Experiment" was written. We'll never know.

What we *can* say with certainty is that a cloned species can't just evolve. The Sontarans seem to be a warrior caste of another species, so if they were "adapted", then from whom? Moreover, by whom? Styre ("The Sontaran Experiment") speaks of 'liberation', and Lynx talks about a struggle for 'freedom'. Is it feasible that the Rutans created the Sontarans as slaves? This has been proposed a number of times, and it's appealing. Not only do the adaptations which make them warriors *sans puer et sans reproche* work equally well for slaves, but they're built for a high gravity environment. When we finally see a Rutan, the jelly-blob has difficulty with Earth's pull, and has a crystalline spaceship. Both species have the ability to absorb energy directly. It's unlikely that the technology of the Sontarans was developed by such a maladroit species unaided. Why else bring human scientists to Linx's lab, or test humans for their resilience? Certainly, the Sontarans have no qualms about "diluting" racial purity in order to secure a victory ("The Two Doctors"). Neither, if the Doctor's comments are to be believed, did the Rutans who made themselves shape-changers.

But does it have to have been the Rutans? Many other races claim to have conquered half the cosmos. The Dominators (6.1) test indigenous species to find out if they form a threat or a potential workforce, as do the Sontarans. The Dominators' servants, the Quarks, are later described by the Doctor as 'machine-creatures' and re-charge themselves the way Sontarans do. Even the hunched, dome-like profile of a Sontaran seems hauntingly familiar if you look at a Dominator side-on.

Many other theories have been proposed over the years. FASA's *Doctor Who Role-Playing Game* claimed, with absolutely no supporting evidence, that the Sontarans emerged from a naturally-occurring humanoid species when "General Sontar" staged a military coup and started replacing everyone with clones. In the Missing Adventure *Lords of the Storm*, the Doctor believes that nobody in the universe knows how the war started (has he never been tempted to go back and look?), but there's a theory that the Sontarans were deliberately created just to slow down the Rutan Host's nigh-unstoppable expansion. However, even the Doctor doesn't believe a word of it.

But whichever culture created them, if the Sontarans were made to fight and found an opponent that didn't give in then the fight would go on indefinitely, regardless of whether their makers survived. For all their intelligence, they see themselves as walking weapons, not as people. Conversely, whilst the Rutans were apeing Gallifreyan techniques in 1901 ("Horror of Fang Rock"), they weren't exactly made for combat. Symbolically, though, the point of them being clones and the point of the war lasting forever are the same: they're knocking lumps out of each other, unchangingly, for all of time. The fact that the war seems to have no reason beyond itself is part of what they represent. The Sontarans, with their bullet-heads, almost-moustaches and wasp-waists, are Teutonic officers lacking only monocles *unt tcherrrmen exhents*. They live for war, and that's all we're supposed to know.

not all Sontarans are built for combat, since he instantly recognises Linx's species but needs confirmation that he's a Sontaran *warrior*. [It's likely that there's a differentiation between Sontaran warriors, tacticians, weapons research experts, military engineers... and so on. Linx has no problem with the word "scientist".]

• *Rutans*. Though not seen here, they have squadrons of fighters.

History

• *Dating*. [On UNIT's timeline, mid-to-late 1974 seems likely. See **What's the UNIT Timeline?** under 8.5, "The Daemons".] Linx crash-lands on Earth during the early Middle Ages, in the region of Wessex at a time when all the troops are fighting 'interminable wars' abroad. ['Interminable wars' is usually taken to mean the Crusades, which would make the most likely date somewhere between 1190 - 1220. It's probable that Robert Holmes had this in mind, since every British schoolchild is supposed to know about Richard the Lionheart and the Crusader era is one of those historical backgrounds that TV scriptwriters used to take for granted. When a generic "man from history" is accidentally brought to the twentieth century in "Invasion of the Dinosaurs" (11.2), he too insists on talking about Good King Richard.

[In "The Sontaran Experiment" Sarah states that Linx died in the thirteenth century, but then again she's panicking at the time. It could equally be the time of King Steven (1135-54), and the conflict over the right of Queen Matilda / Maud to rule the land despite having her genitals on the inside, which would make the "votes for women" comments in episode four especially apt. This period was suddenly remembered in the '70s, unsurprising as it involved an attempted coup, runaway inflation and Womens' Rights (see **Who's Running the Country?** under 10.5, "The Green Death"). Technically Wessex ceased to exist a decade or so after the Norman conquest of 1066, but the only character who uses the name here is the Norman-hating Irongron, so perhaps he's pining for the good old Anglo-Saxon days. In itself, the use of the word "Norman" would suggest the 1100s and not the 1200s.]

Meanwhile, in the present... the British have a high-security top-secret research facility full of scientists, working on space hardware and 'new alloys'. Professor Ruebish states that the loop theory of time has been 'arrogantly dismissed by Crabshaw and his cronies', though we're not told any more about the affair than that. [Compare this with time-travel research in 11.2, "Invasion of the Dinosaurs".]

The Analysis

Where Does This Come From?   Producers and BBC accountants like historical romps; viewers and writers don't. The compromise, aliens jeopardising the "correct" run of Earth history, is possible by this point simply because the public are in on the gag.

In "The Time Meddler", half of episode four is spent explaining why it's a bad idea to rewrite the past. Here, half of episode two is spent with Sarah being the butt of the audience's ridicule for *not* twigging that she's been whisked eight centuries back in time in a dimensionally transcendental police box. As in 1965, the big joke is that our technology is as good as it will ever get. This ultimately dates back to the first use of time-travel for laughs, Mark Twain's *A Connecticut Yankee in King Arthur's Court*.

Linx is stranded on a backward planet and becomes unpaid scientific advisor to a local military leader. Sound familiar? This "fish out of water" set-up is something Robert Holmes would revisit to better effect in "The Talons of Weng-Chiang" (14.6). Holmes' original plot breakdown for "The Time Warrior" played on the idea of the Japanese soldier refusing to believe that the war was over and that Japan didn't win. Combining this with the source quoted by the Doctor - Thomas Hobbes' *Leviathan*, written soon after Charles I was beheaded, in which monarchy is the only bulwark against 'a war of all against all' - Holmes had a laboratory ready-made for his thought-experiment.

It's a cliché to have advanced aliens seeing humans as "primitive", but what if one crash-landed at a time when we really were? And what if the alien, for all his technology, was in favour of all the things we like to think technology will cure us of? Can we really say we're so much better than Saxon warlords if we've invented the Winchester 67 and the atom bomb? Just because it's an alien in the twelfth century who's collected all these scientists to build weapons, is that any worse than Her Majesty's Government and UNIT doing the same?

Once again, Holmes is using SF as a satirical distorting mirror. (And once again *Galaxy* magazine in the 1950s routinely did this sort of story, notably Poul Anderson's *The High Crusade*, in which English villagers over-run a galactic empire by hijacking a spaceship which crashes as they're about to sack - sorry, liberate - the Holy Land.) Hubris, in various forms, is present in every story this year. Human achievements are belittled and human dignity is compromised.

In the end, though, "The Time Warrior" marks another turning-point for the series. Since the advent of the colour / Pertwee era, *Doctor Who* has been a mixture of pseudo-topical Earth-bound stories and tales set on dystopian quarry-planets, but this looks like a series that wants to try something a lot more lush and a lot less restrained by the "local" concerns of the 1970s. It shouldn't be forgotten that the Middle Ages were a common subject for historical serials; BBC drama producers ran out of Tudors fairly fast. The availability of sets and costumes from stock, plus the fact that the glossier US series couldn't do this sort of thing, must have made it irresistible. There are also notable similarities to Robert Holmes' next pseudo-historical, "Pyramids of Mars" (13.3), including a trapped alien mastermind, a big bang at the end and an unlikely attempt by the Doctor to disguise himself as a servitor robot.

Things That Don't Make Sense Let's get the obvious point out of the way first: there are potatoes in Middle Ages England. They're plainly on display, and even the script refers to them. Neither Robert Holmes nor Terrance Dicks was ever allowed to forget this.

Isn't it a bit odd that when Linx makes weapons for Irongron, he starts by making guns which look exactly like human firearms from later centuries instead of weapons based on Sontaran technology? [Does he just snatch the guns from the future, along with the potatoes? If so, then why are the scientists apparently hard at work making them? If Linx travelled back in time before he crash-landed, then it's at least possible that he's trying to wreck the planet's history in order to get his compatriots to come and look for him in the past. It's a reckless sort of distress beacon, but this is a Sontaran we're talking about.]

The story concludes with Linx's spaceship exploding and Irongron's castle going up in smoke along with it, and in line with the usual morality of TV drama, the Doctor makes sure that everyone

gets out of the cataclysm except for the two principle villains. The trouble is that nobody stops to think about the wenches in the kitchen, all of whom presumably get blasted into pieces.

Irongron is eating and drinking when 'it wants but an hour til dawn', making you wonder how late these medieval party animals stay up. Or did they all say Matins? Irongron later tries to read Edward's message, but claims not to be able to understand 'Norman scribbles'. Why would a letter be in Norman and not Latin? How could anyone who can read at all read Anglo-Saxon but not Norman?

Critique The shape of the series to come, a chunky, pocket-sized story rather than one of the extended UNIT campaigns of the early colour seasons, with its show-pieces based on character acting instead of big stunts. This is, above all, *Catweazle*[5] for grown-ups.

There's also a deliberate attempt to widen the programme's scope here. This was the first time the audience had seen any "real" historical background in the programme since "The Abominable Snowmen" in 1967 (Miniscopes, alien World War One reconstructions and Atlantis don't count), and the difference is immediately obvious. Like most of Robert Holmes' best work it's a *personal* sort of affair, a series of one-on-one confrontations between the characters which let all the cast-members put in tight performances, and in addition there's even a top-flight monster that sets the tone for the cavalcade of aliens in the years ahead.

It is, on the whole, like watching the first story of the Tom Baker era. As with the bulk of the stories Holmes later script-edited, a lone alien "spokesman" heads a larger force of "grunts" (here, Irongron's men) instead of a big Sea-Devil-style alien invasion force. With hindsight only episode three seems to drag, mainly because its set-up - the Doctor uses stinkbombs and scientific trickery to stop a gang of stupid ruffians attacking an undefended castle - feels so much like a product of children's television, as opposed to the "serious" version of *Doctor Who* we now like to believe in.

In fact, with *real* hindsight the story's worst offence is the introduction of the word "Gallifrey", so familiar to us now that we never think to question it. In the letters page of *TV Action* in 1974, Barry Letts anonymously answered a query about the name of the Doctor's world, and it raised eyebrows. On-screen confirmation was mildly shock-

ABOUT TIME 1970-1974

ing at the time. When "The War Games" (6.7) coined the term "Time Lord", the Doctor's people were still shown to be nigh-god-like, removed from the rough-and-tumble of everyday galactic affairs. They may have lost some of their mystery, but even so they remained *mythic*, not just another bunch of aliens with great big spaceships and ray-guns.

However, by giving the Doctor's near-legendary homeworld a name - and let's face it, a rather stupid-sounding SF name, more suited to one of Robert Holmes' comedy planets than the home of the highest civilisation - all of that changes, and the Time Lords become *just* another hi-tech species. If it had been a deliberate attempt to redefine the way the *Doctor Who* universe works (as "The War Games" was), then it might have meant something, but here the Doctor casually name-checks Gallifrey just to keep his conversation with Linx going. At the very least, isn't it odd that he's never allowed the name of his homeworld to pass his lips before, but now seems ready to blurt it out in front of a brutal alien warmonger...?

The Facts

Written by Robert Holmes. Directed by Alan Bromly. Viewing figures: 8.7 million, 7.0 million, 6.6 million, 10.6 million.

Supporting Cast: Kevin Lindsay (Linx), Donald Pelmear (Professor Rubeish), David Daker (Irongron), John J. Carney (Bloodaxe), June Brown (Eleanor), Alan Rowe (Edward of Wessex), Jeremy Bulloch (Hal), Sheila Fay (Meg).

Working Titles "The Time Fugitive", "The Time Survivor". (It's been claimed that at one stage the story was called "Automata", but contrary to what's been written elsewhere, "Automata" was a completely different story which Holmes proposed and would far rather have written.)

Cliffhangers Watching from the cover of some barrels in Irongron's courtyard, the Doctor sees Linx take off his helmet, and we're exposed to the face of a Sontaran for the first time; Irongron raises his sword to behead the Doctor; in the castle cellar, Linx replies to the Doctor's offer of help by raising his gun and firing.

The Lore

• Famously, Robert Holmes' original plot synopsis for "The Time Warrior" was sent to script editor Terrance Dicks in the form of a Sontaran military communique, written by officer Hol Mes and addressed to the Earth-bound agent Terran Cedicks. Holmes was dubious about his brief to write a historical story, and Dicks later spoke of him being 'bodily dragged into the Middle Ages'. (Holmes eventually got his own back with 15.1, "Horror of Fang Rock".)

• Designer James Acheson claims he had an idea about an alien which removed its space-helmet to reveal a space-helmet-shaped head. This seems to have been part of the inspiration for this story (cliffhanger first, then justification; that's professionalism for you). The original plot breakdown also featured the toad-like alien hiding inside a suit of armour, and note how the Doctor describes Linx's "ghost" in the finished version.

• Holmes had a go at writing the Target novelisation of "The Time Warrior" himself, but got bogged down. The prologue of the finished version is Holmes, the remainder Terrance Dicks, although the prologue - unlike any televised *Doctor Who* story - names the Sontaran homeworld (it's Sontara) and gives the Sontarans first names (it's "Commander Jingo Linx", if you were wondering).

• The technique used to make the "time tunnel" in the title sequence was a variation on the slit-scan technique used by Douglas Trumbull in *2001: A Space Odyssey*, but the source for the "smear" was a polarised light shot of a polythene carrier bag from a supermarket. The diamond logo - most fans now think of it as the "proper" *Doctor Who* logo, although some would argue that without the nostalgia value it's quite a clumsy, awkward-looking piece of design - is very similar to the logo introduced for that year's series of *Bruce Forsythe's Generation Game* (see 10.4, "Planet of the Daleks", for more on the Forsythe / Savile / Pertwee axis of evil).

• The name "Gallifrey" is apparently based on "Gallimaufry", an old French-derived word meaning a mess or a hodge-podge, perfect for the Doctor but strangely ill-fitting for the rest of his people. Some have wondered if it's supposed to echo "Galilee", but it also sounds enough like "Galfredus" - the alternative name for Geoffrey of Monmouth - to be interesting. (Galfredus is the main source for a lot of what was thought to be historical "fact" in the late middle ages, such as the life of King Arthur, the founding of "Troynovaunt" / London by the grandson of Aeneas, and the giants Gog and Magog. If the Doctor knew Bede and Shakespeare, he probably knew Geoffrey...) Then again, the Daleks identified the Doctor as "Dr. Galloway" in "Evil of the Daleks" (4.7) before anybody had even established that he was a Time Lord, let alone where he came from. Things like this look to the uninitiated like clever planning.

• Hal the Archer is played by Jeremy Bulloch, later to play Boba Fett (N.B. he doesn't look like a Maori). Lady Eleanor is, of course, actress June Brown from *EastEnders*.

• The line 'nasty, brutish and short' is a quotation from Thomas Hobbes' *Leviathan*, the ever-popular seventeenth-century political work which advocated the "body politic", or an organic state with the King as the head. The line actually refers to the lives of people in earlier times, before a strong monarch over-ruled local warlords.

• The casting of Sarah was even more haphazard than that of Jo. Elisabeth Sladen had been selected by the 18th of April, 1973, and had visited rehearsals for "The Green Death". Yet contracts weren't signed until the 3rd of May, four days before the location shoot. Meanwhile, someone else was apparently cast as Sarah. Whoever this was, it was Sladen - unaware that Sarah was a regular character - who'd been brought to meet Pertwee (and, legend has it, who'd got a "thumbs up" from the star to Barry Letts behind her back). What happened in that fortnight? And who was the mystery actress...?

11.2: "Invasion of the Dinosaurs"

(Serial WWW, Six Episodes, 12th January - 16th February 1974.)

Which One is This? With the logic of a *Scooby Doo* villain, someone's making dinosaurs appear in central London to scare off the population. Meanwhile Sarah gets stuck on a supposed spaceship taking the supposed elite of *Earth* to a supposed new Eden, but what on Earth has that got to do with prehistoric monsters...?

Firsts and Lasts First of two appearances by the "Whomobile", the road-legal car / hovercraft /

spaceship built by a custom car designer to Jon Pertwee's own specifications. (Pertwee just called it "the Alien". Now he's got a special "mobile" that bears his name, it's almost as if the Doctor's finally qualified as a true action hero, just in time for Pertwee to leave the series. Fortunately he never gets a utility belt to go with it.)

The Third Doctor gurns for the last time during episode two, while in episode six Sarah gets her first chance to escape through a ventilation shaft. This is the first story directed by a woman, Paddy Russell, who'd been on hand since "The Massacre" (3.6) and had been a BBC staff floor manager since the *Quatermass* era in the mid-1950s.

Six Things to Notice About "Invasion of the Dinosaurs"...

1. Some *Doctor Who* stories are officially-classified as "legendary", guaranteed to be burned on the memories of those who watched them as children. But others are just "notorious", and "Invasion of the Dinosaurs" is one of the latter. The reason is simple: the dinosaurs. Pleased by the way the Drashigs had turned out in "Carnival of Monsters" (don't mock, these were simpler times), Barry Letts saw the possibilities of using puppets to fill the screen with large-scale monsters, and specifically commissioned a story about dinosaurs from Malcolm Hulke. This has to be considered a shocking error of judgement. Though the triceratops and the stegosaurus aren't bad - perhaps because they barely have to move - the tyrannosaurus fight at the start of episode six is perhaps the worst special effect in the history of the programme, a mess of latex and CSO so badly-executed that at times it's hard to believe the story was ever broadcast.

2. Or rather... in *long-shot* the tyrannosaurus may be the worst special effect in the history of the programme. The close-up shots of it, filmed using a larger and more detailed dinosaur prop, are actually quite acceptable (the *Kong*-like scenes in the hangar, when a doped tyrannosaurus suddenly wakes up and breaks free of its chains, work rather well until the monster has to stand up). Even in close-up, though, the sound of its roar is clearly just somebody going 'raaah' into a microphone.

3. Sergeant Benton gets some of his greatest-ever moments, especially when he's putting pins into UNIT's operations map to mark the sightings of prehistoric animals and obviously taking a child-like joy in it: 'We're using red pins for tyran-

nosaurus, blue for triceratops, green for the stegosaurus and pink for yer actual pterodactyl...' (He also volunteers to let the Doctor knock him out in episode five, see **The Supporting Cast**, which is just lovely.)

4. Throughout the UNIT era, the organisation's been beset by traitors in the British government, unsympathetic "allies" in the military and staff who've been brainwashed or replaced by alien duplicates. But "Invasion of the Dinosaurs" sets the all-time record for treachery, since the general in charge of the dinosaur crisis *and* the Minister with Special Powers *and* the country's foremost authority on time-travel *and* Captain Yates all turn out to be working for the enemy. With hindsight this looks like nothing so much as the *Doctor Who* version of 24, even down to the fact that the Doctor's female companion gets kidnapped in an attempt to stop him interfering. And since the story ends with the villains using their machine to slow down time, this could well be the longest day of *everyone's* life.

5. In order to turn the appearance of the dinosaurs into some kind of surprise twist, the title sequence of episode one refers to the story just as "Invasion" (or at least, it does now... see **The Facts**). It's odd, then, that the first (limp) pterodacytl turns up ten minutes into the episode instead of waiting for the cliffhanger.

6. The secret underground base in episode four is the very definition of "cardboard set". See the Doctor try to escape this maze of wobbling walls and flimsy security doors...

The Continuity

The Doctor When Professor Whitaker stops time, the Doctor can still think and act, albeit slowly. Sarah suggests that this is because he's a Time Lord, and the Doctor agrees. [Again, Time Lords seem to exist outside the normal flow of history. See **How Does Time Work?** under 9.2, "Day of the Daleks".]

The Doctor's 'Venusian ooja' - as Benton calls it - can knock someone unconscious with a pinch to the neck or a finger to the ribcage [the first real Mr. Spock influence in the Doctor's character, sadly]. He takes multiple sugars in his tea.

• *Ethics.* The Doctor recognises Sir Charles Grover as one of the founders of the Save Planet Earth society, and author of the book *Last Chance for Man*, so once again he's up to date with con-

temporary human concerns. The Brigadier believes him to be 'keen' on the whole anti-pollution movement. Strangely, though, he's never heard of Professor Whitaker and doesn't know about local research into time-travel.

• *Inventory.* He has a watch on a chain [utterly useless for a space-time traveller, unless you're planning on hypnotising something, but the Doctor still plays with it impatiently while waiting for a bus].

• *Background.* The Doctor states that the Vandals were 'quite decent chaps', and says it as if he knew them personally. When he describes a 'time eddy' caused by Operation Golden Age, in which time briefly runs backwards, he likewise speaks as if he's seen one before.

• *The Whomobile.* [Never named on-screen. The programme-makers coined the term "Whomobile", and it's doubtful that the Doctor would ever use it, though the other members of UNIT might.] The Doctor's new car - and 'car' is the only word he uses to describe it – has been brought to London from UNIT HQ. A machine with no visible wheels and a sleek UFO-like shell, it's his vehicle of choice when he wants to get somewhere in a hurry [odd, since it doesn't move as fast as the turbo-charged Bessie]. The number-plate reads WVO 2M. [This means that the car was registered between August 1973 and July 1974, and the Doctor describes it as "new", again suggesting an early-to-mid-'70s date for the UNIT stories. As it happens, M-registration gels perfectly with the timeline used elsewhere in this book.]

The Supporting Cast

• *Sarah Jane Smith.* Here the Doctor formally acknowledges her as his 'assistant', but even before that, the Brigadier doesn't seem bothered by the fact that there's a journalist around the place. Sarah likes cities rather than quiet places, and once interviewed Lady Cullingford – now a member of the People - about a private members bill involving the pollution of rivers. She recognises most of the other people on the alleged spaceship as well. Her qualifications for taking over from Jo Grant are established when she's knocked unconscious by a falling piece of masonry.

• *The Brigadier.* By now he's starting to regard the Doctor's eccentricities with some affection. His inability to listen to the Doctor is worse than ever, though, since he finds the existence of a secret government bunker under London 'difficult to

When Did the Doctor Get His Driving Licence?

The Doctor's lack of formal ID has long been a problem, so we can conclude that if there *is* a driver's licence (perhaps with his photo on it, assuming it has the right face) then he never carries it. He's seen to carry UK currency for various ages, including pre- and post-decimal coins, but never any paperwork until he joins UNIT. Even this has him down as "Dr. John Smith", so anything from his first two embodiments is going to be inconsistent (see 5.7, "The Wheel in Space" for the first use of this name, and it's Jamie who picks it). If he decided to get formal "proof" of his existence in the two weeks between destroying WOTAN and leaving Earth, the chances are that the name "Who" would be on the documents; see **Is His Name Really Who?** under 3.10, "The War Machines".

There is, of course, a problem straight away. Under UK law, no-one can drive over the age of seventy without regular testing. In applying to the DVLA (Driver Vehicle Licensing Authority, based in Swansea these days), he'd need to give a date of birth, a permanent address and so on. A medical might be required, and certainly a rudimentary eye-test forms part of the basic driving exam. The First Doctor might not have submitted to such humiliation, and almost definitely wouldn't lie about his age. Assuming he was sure what it was. There's the casual mention of 'every time I come back to London' at the start of "The War Machines", so there may have been other visits before we even met him, but this is shaky ground.

The first time we see the Doctor drive anything one might normally drive is in "The Invasion" (6.3), when he uses a UNIT jeep that's somehow kept inside a Hercules transporter plane. However, up to this point we've seen him fly a helicopter in "Fury from the Deep" (5.6). He learned this by watching Astrid Ferrier in "Enemy of the World" (5.4), so it's entirely possible that the Doctor's driving skills were similarly acquired.

The only other time we see contemporary transport with the early Doctor as a passenger is the taxi in "The War Machines" (3.10). There may not have been any formal lessons, and the idea that the Doctor learned everything he knows about driving from a London cabbie might at least explain some of the Third Doctor's behaviour behind the wheel.

However, the Austin Metropolitan - the classic "black cab" - is diesel-powered and has totally different gearing to most vehicles. Had he tried to drive a jeep like a taxi-driver, he would've broken down. (Fortunately the Automobile Association has a call-out service, and roadside boxes to ring for assistance. They look remarkably like police boxes, so the Doctor may have joined for a laugh.) Thus, when the Doctor's driving around London he's breaking several laws. Then, of course, there's photo ID. The Driving Licence has only recently required this, so if we assume that the rest of Britain stayed much the same when Jeremy Thorpe's government was sending men to Mars and funding time-travel experiments, it may not have mattered that the person driving Bessie in "Robot" (12.1) didn't in any way resemble her owner.

The assumption has always been that the licence came as part of the process of being formally "identified" for UNIT purposes. He must have had a licence to buy Bessie, unless the Brigadier did it for him. However, this isn't as certain as one might think. The bureaucrat Chinn, in "The Claws of Axos" (8.3), indicates that the Doctor's file is empty and that no official record of his existence can be traced (and if there is a year's gap between "Terror of the Autons" and "The Mind of Evil", then this is very remiss). Whenever asked for ID he provides a UNIT pass, which Jo carries for him on most occasions. When arrested in "Invasion of the Dinosaurs", he has nothing to prove that he is who he says he is. Perhaps Jo took his pass to Peru with her.

And there's a lot more to consider here than just this Doctor's love of cars. Although he seems puzzled by the offer of a salary, and later describes himself as UNIT's 'unpaid' adviser, the Doctor isn't always short of the readies. If the country acknowledges his existence then he pays tax, pays national insurance and must legally be defined as either a British Subject or not. If not, his access to naval bases and all the government research facilities in Season Seven must be a matter for diplomatic staff. If he's been granted citizenship, he technically would have had to undergo the same checks as immigrants and all UN personnel. As the Brigadier often points out, the Doctor is "attached" to UNIT, not a full member. Outside UK territory, he has no more legal status than he had when the TARDIS dumped him in Oxley Wood at the start of his exile. Officially, then, he might not exist.

Perhaps this is just as well. Bessie's "superdrive" and inertial damping brake enable him to break all accepted speed-limits in the UK, especially since those limits were considerably lowered during the fuel crisis (see **Who's Running the Country?** under 10.5, "The Green Death"). At certain points in "Day of the Daleks" (9.1) and at the end of "The

continued on page 153...

believe' even though he's spent the last few weeks chasing dinosaurs.

• *Sergeant Benton.* Despite the constant friction between the Doctor and UNIT, it's a sign of the men's trust in their scientific advisor that when General Finch orders Benton to arrest the Doctor as a traitor, Benton offers to let the Doctor knock him unconscious as soon as they're left alone. Benton seems to enjoy beating up a General once the man turns out to be a traitor.

• *Captain Yates.* He's just got back from leave after the events at Llanfairfach [10.5, "The Green Death"]. When he unexpectedly turns out to be a traitor working for Operation Golden Age, Yates is obviously confused, not wanting to harm any of his UNIT friends even though the scheme will erase them from history altogether. He also believes that the Doctor might side with them, proving that he doesn't understand the Doctor as well as the more "lowly" ranks of UNIT. [It's long been held that Mike Yates' defection to Operation Golden Age is a result of temporary madness, triggered by his brainwashing in "The Green Death", though this is never explicitly stated here. It makes sense, though, that he'd turn to a rabidly pro-environmental "cult" after what BOSS and Global Chemicals did to him. If the brainwashing isn't directly responsible for him changing sides, then at the very least stress must be getting to the Captain, as he shows definite lapses of judgement here. Evidently he's only an efficient soldier when he's fighting for the good guys.]

Ultimately the Brigadier arranges for Yates to have a few weeks' sick leave and the chance to resign quietly [see 11.5, "Planet of the Spiders", for his next move].

The TARDIS Obviously its navigation isn't perfect yet, as the Doctor gets back to London rather than UNIT HQ and turns up some weeks after he left. He states the space-time co-ordinates are 'a bit out'.

The Non-Humans

• *Dinosaurs.* Brontosaurs, tyrannosaurs, triceratopses, stegosauruses and pterodactyls are all in evidence here. This time the Doctor positively identifies a tyrannosaurus [q.v. 7.2, "The Silurians"], even though its hands are the wrong shape and it's powerful enough to knock down whole buildings. The Doctor describes it as 'the largest and fiercest predator of all time'.

[Assuming that he means *land-based* predator, and *on Earth* rather than anywhere in the universe... he's apparently never heard of the giganotosaurus, discovered in 1995, so his dinosaur-knowledge isn't complete and may be informed by Earth's received wisdom c. 1974. Here the tyrannosaurus is an active predator, not just a scavenger as some palaeontologists now claim.] He states that it's been extinct for 65,000,000 years, and he also pedantically points out that a brontosaurus should properly be called an apatosaurus. The triceratops faced by the Brigadier, meanwhile, is a truly huge specimen of its type.

Planet Notes

• *Florana.* Probably one of the most beautiful planets in the universe, according to the Doctor [see 11.3, "Death to the Daleks"]. It's always carpeted with perfumed flowers, the seas are like warm milk, the sands are as soft as swan's down, the streams flow with water clearer than the clearest crystal... and so on.

History

• *Dating.* At least a few weeks after the Doctor and Sarah left Earth. [See **What's the UNIT Timeline?** under 8.5, "The Daemons". The map of the London Underground seen here is a mid-'70s one. It has to be pre-1979 because the London *Evening News* is still being published.] The rental shops are promoting colour television sets as a new, exciting thing.

8,000,000 people have been evacuated from London in the wake of the dinosaur appearances, with the government relocating to Harrogate. The city's under martial law in accordance with the Emergency Powers Act. [In reality the population of London was only 7,000,000 in the mid-'70s, and hadn't even reached 8,000,000 by the end of the century, unless the meaning here is "Greater London". The evacuated zone seems confined to north of the Thames, but extends to Chiswick and - from the map - Cockfosters and Enfield, outside the North Circular Road. But see 8.3, "The Claws of Axos", for at least one good reason why a baby-boom in Britain might have occurred over the last two years.]

In the vicinity of Whitehall there's an underground bunker with a nuclear reactor, built 'back in the Cold War days', twenty years before. [It seems massively unlikely that the entire Cold War has ended by this point, since the stories made /

When Did the Doctor Get His Driving Licence?

...continued from page 151

Green Death", he also would have risked prosecution for driving under the influence of alcohol; maybe that super-charged alien metabolism saves him from failing breathalyser tests. By "Planet of the Spiders" he's happily stealing hovercraft, so not having a valid licence for either of his improbable cars is a minor infraction. There doesn't seem to be any protection under law for UNIT personnel, any more than for policemen who injure the public in the course of their duties (although, as has been noted before, UNIT troops appear to be licensed to kill and don't need to caution suspects before opening fire).

The Doctor is also capable of piloting more complex vehicles, including spaceships (10.3, "Frontier in Space"; 6.5, "The Seeds of Death"; 7.3, "The Ambassadors of Death"; 1.7, "The Sensorites"; 21.6, "The Caves of Androzani" and so on). Did he qualify for these? Did he pick it up as he went along? Most importantly, does he - as is hinted in "Robot" - carry all of these documents around but *not* his UK Driving Licence?

set in the 1980s seem to suggest a world where there's still a schism between the US and USSR. See especially 19.7, "Time-Flight". Given that the mid-'70s was a period of détente between East and West, Grover probably means that the shelter was built in the worst days of the Cold War. That a small enough nuclear reactor could have been built in the mid-'50s is believable in a world where time-travel and space-fleets are accepted by novelists and journalists.]

The athlete John Crichton successfully performed a [high] jump of 2.362 metres at the last Olympics [clearly supposed to suggest a world record, which it would have been]. Eco-concern is so great that all manner of generals, politicians and scientists are prepared to work together on Operation Golden Age in an attempt to erase humanity from the face of the Earth. The "colonists" selected to re-populate the prehistoric world believe they're being taken to another planet on a spaceship. [Unlike most "cult" members they're not entirely stupid, so for this to be feasible there must at least be some talk of space-colonisation in this period.]

Human research into time-travel is unexpectedly advanced here, with Professor Whitaker not only developing the technology to snatch dinosaurs and medieval peasants from their own time but also planning to wind back the whole of the Earth to the prehistoric era [to the age of the dinosaurs, or just to the pre-human epoch?].

Whitaker applied for a government grant and was refused, since nobody believed his theory of time-travel would work. He was an outsider, always getting into arguments with other scientists. [Compare with 11.1, "The Time Warrior". Was Whitaker a victim of 'Crabshaw and his cronies'? Some of the science used here may come

from alien sources like the Master, whose TOMTIT project in "The Time Monster" must have made *some* impression on the academic community. At least one scientist was aiming at time-travel in 8.3, "The Claws of Axos", and the same kind of technology we see here is put into effect again in 17.2, "City of Death". Whitaker's theories were dismissed as nonsense by government advisors, and TOMTIT also appeared to be nonsense to most researchers on Earth. But by far the most likely "suspect" for this anachronistic technology is Dr. Fendelman: see 15.3, "Image of the Fendahl".]

The end of the story sees Grover and Whitaker sent hurtling back to the "Golden Age" on their own, and their fate remains unknown [but if anyone can settle the argument about the age of the Silurians then it's them]. Many of the people on the fake spaceship used in Operation Golden Age appear to be in suspended animation, and it's not clear whether this "sleep" is real or part of the fraud.

[Some have proposed the theory that when Whitaker's machine is activated at the end of the story, time is rolled back by several weeks before the Doctor can switch it off, so that the dinosaur crisis never happened and nobody outside the room remembers it. But that's not the implication of the script, which seems to suggest that the machine's just warming up when the Doctor gets to it. This "forget the dinosaurs!" theory also creates a number of horrible paradoxes that aren't even worth mentioning in a volume as pedantic as *this* one.]

At some point a Chinese scientist called Chung Sen will experiment with time-travel, but according to the Doctor he hasn't been born yet.

The Analysis

Where Does This Come From? The moccasin's on the other foot now. After years of providing us with pro-environmental stories (some of them also written by Malcolm Hulke), the programme unexpectedly presents us with a coda in which it turns out that not *everybody* who wants a greener, cleaner world can be trusted. A sudden burst of cynicism, as the Pertwee / Letts years drew to a close? Possibly, but there's no suggestion here that the series has actually changed its stance, since the Doctor insists that he sympathises with Operation Golden Age before adding a serious 'but'. It'd be going too far to say that this injects a sense of realism into the eco-argument after "The Green Death", since realism seems less at home here among the rubber dinosaurs than it did among the giant maggots, yet there is a sense of *Doctor Who* reining in its optimism.

You got that a lot in the mid-seventies. Nixon cancelled the Apollo programme to pay for Vietnam, a war he kept going to get re-elected. While America was losing faith in its leaders, in Britain a crippling economic crisis or two (see 10.6, "The Green Death") confirmed that the wheels had come off. The Club of Rome, a German-based global think tank, warned everyone about a population timebomb, and the idea of oil running out was no longer a thing that might happen "one day" but "next month". On the surface, the message of "Invasion of the Dinosaurs" is that there's no going back and we have to make what we can of the future. *Below* the surface, the message is that however you feel about the state of the Earth, you can't really trust anybody. Before now, threats to the modern world have come from non-humans (most notably BOSS in "The Green Death") or from greedy / reckless / inept individuals (just about any politician shown in the series between 1970 and 1974), yet here the villain of the piece is an entire social movement. No, more specifically; the villain is a *cult*.

It makes sense. Politics post-baby-boom was never going to be easy to follow. '60s hippy liberalism seemed to go hand-in-hand with the environmental movement, as demonstrated by Cliff Jones and his Nut Hutch, but at the same time the more suspicious, less open-minded groups were bound to use the fear of an over-technological, over-populated Earth as ammunition. The boundaries of "left" and "right" are hazy, and in "The

Green Death" even Professor Jones himself regards the conservative work-ethic doctrine of "a day's food for a day's work" to be ethically correct.

Nowhere is this political fuzziness more overt than in the "cults" of the era. Charles Manson obviously springs to mind as the prime icon of '60s come-down (with a "family" that decked itself out in the symbols of flower-power, but wanted to exterminate the Black Man just as much as any right-wing zealot), although Manson's only memorable thanks to the celebrity body-count. You could point to any number of other "revolutionary" groups who seemed to share the hippy ideal of a peaceful, harmonious planet but believed that brainwashing and forced labour were all part of the process.

That eco-campaigners like Grover and Lady Culingford are involved in Operation Golden Age, along with several high-profile idealists, might seem odd to anyone who doesn't remember Bhagwan Shree Rajneesh. The cultists heading for a new Eden in "Invasion of the Dinosaurs" call themselves *the People*, suggesting the language of the Jesus-Freaks - whose manifestation in Britain, the Festival of Light, included singer Cliff Richard and that well-known critic of *Doctor Who*, Mary Whitehouse - and they see 'permissiveness' as one of the problems facing humanity. 'Usury', too, which suggests a lot since the word's often used as racist shorthand for "Jewishness". If this marks the end of pure idealism in the series, then it's only following the lead of the entire Love Generation.

While we should note in passing that the plot here is almost fingerprint-identical to the ersatz-Bond machinations of Salamander in "The Enemy of the World" (5.4), this is quite unmistakably the first post-Watergate story. Everyone is part of a conspiracy. The plucky journalist who 'follows the money' can't trust anyone. As this story was broadcast, the election campaign - well, one of them - rolled on, with every politician emphasising the fact that you couldn't trust the other lot.

Another thing to mention in passing is even more obvious: that the technology of time-travel is the technology of television. Even the term 'rollback', used by Whitaker at every opportunity, is the same as the 'rollback and mix' that makes the TARDIS appear and disappear. The scoop has a scanner, somehow, and peeps in on the dinosaurs (like the then-recent Saturday morning kids' show *Outa Space*, for which many of the dinosaurs here were originally made). CCTV, the big "threat" in

"Day of the Daleks" and "The Green Death", is routine in this story.

Of course, the dinosaurs themselves are almost a side-issue, and rightly so. In episode four you get twenty seconds of pterodactyl action, and that's about it. It should be noted that in the mid-1970s, popular culture was going through one of its "dinosaur phases", as it does from time to time. While the children of the '90s had *Jurassic Park*, the children of the '70s had *The Land that Time Forgot* and - later - the seminal B-movie *At the Earth's Core*. Comparing these films to "Invasion of the Dinosaurs", however, you have to feel a sense of regret that the production team went for puppets rather than men in chunky costumes. It's also worth mentioning that the scenes of a deserted London in episode one - scenes more than a little reminiscent of *The Avengers* 6.18, "The Morning After" (1969) - are not only shot on the same filmstock that the BBC used for location news reports at the time, but are also filmed in a remarkably similar style, full of montages and slow pans. This gives the whole affair a real smack of *actual* Britain circa 1973, at least until the monsters turn up.

Things That Don't Make Sense   Mike talks to Sarah about 'that business in Wales with the giant maggots' as if he's expecting her to know what he's talking about [did she investigate it?]. Sarah herself is so anal that she can remember the world high jump record to three decimal places, despite never showing any enthusiasm for sport even in her capacity as a journalist. The Doctor's stun-gun uses a technique as yet undeveloped on Earth, yet Whitaker - without even seeing it - devises a gizmo to deactivate it. And the Brigadier hired Liz Shaw…?

Happily for children everywhere, five types of dinosaur are snatched from the past by Operation Golden Age and they just happen to be the five most famous dinosaur species. Many of them weren't even native to prehistoric Britain, so Whitaker's technology must be able to reach a long way through space as well as time, which doesn't seem a very efficient way of doing things. Besides, if he can grab objects from any time *and* any place then he could kidnap the Doctor whenever he liked just by setting the machine to "UNIT base-camp, a few seconds ago".

Likewise, the conspirators are relying on a nuclear reactor under Marylebone Station. Couldn't that on its own be used to evacuate London, without faffing about with hyp-

silophodons or ankylosauri? It's almost as if the original plan was just Whitaker's way of saying 'I told you so' to the people who rejected his proposals, before the Eco-Nazis contacted him with an offer of support. But then, these are people who think that the best way of dealing with a nosy reporter like Sarah is to put her on the fake spaceship with their stooges and let her unravel the least reliable part of their plan, so efficiency can't be their forte. They also decide to take Sarah back in time with them after re-capturing her, just so she can cause *more* trouble for them in the prehistoric era.

Nobody addresses the obvious paradox of Operation Golden Age, in which the conspirators believe they can wind back time and live on prehistoric Earth even though they're planning to make sure their ancestors never existed. And if Whitaker's time-field would rewind history on Earth but not anywhere else in the universe, then what would happen to the Doctor? Presumably he'd vanish from the planet at the beginning of "Spearhead from Space", as his exile ran backwards, but where would he go after that?

If London's so polluted, how can the dinosaurs breathe? Why don't they suffer from more recently-evolved diseases (unless that's what killed them, given that they vanish back to their own era after a while)? And as with every other life-form in *Doctor Who*, why don't they leave dung? Or does that *also* get sucked back into the cretaceous?

And why was the story about dinosaurs given to the writer who couldn't even name Silurians properly?

Critique   Once cited by *Doctor Who Magazine* as one of the ten worst stories ever made, "Invasion of the Dinosaurs" is nowhere near as bad as its reputation. It isn't even the worst story of Season Eleven, and the criticism it receives is largely aimed at the tyrannosaurus rather than the story.

Hideous puppets aside, its problem is that it's too long, too padded and too unsure of itself. The bulk of episode five is given over to UNIT being ordered to hunt down the Doctor in an extended car chase around deserted London's green spaces, a chase so bland that most people can't even remember it five minutes after it's over. (UNIT being asked to hunt down the Doctor is potentially rather poignant, but here it's a sign that the script has run out of things to do between T-Rex manifestations and the Doctor saying 'good gwief!' at the end of each episode.) The sense of exhaustion with this sort of story is inescapable. The programme-makers know they've done everything possible with UNIT and monsters-in-London. Copying *The Lost World* so obviously is an admission of defeat, much like the "Whomobile".

In its defence, it's got to be said that most six-parters are shamelessly padded, and at the very least this is a story with some half-decent conceits behind it. The juxtaposition of a city full of dinosaurs and a fake spaceship full of Hampstead Radicals is weird, but strangely pleasing. Much of it may seem tired, but for the most part it still remains watchable, perhaps because it knows exactly what it is. It knows that although there are "issues" being addressed here, at the end of the day it's a rollicking family adventure story, *not* serious drama. As a result it wisely lets the anti-establishment figure of the Doctor carry the show instead of dwelling on the "political thriller" elements, and it never quite sinks to the level of a bad dinosaur B-movie, mainly because the characters get to say 'wow, look, dinosaurs!' along with all the children in the audience.

The Facts

Written by Malcolm Hulke. Directed by Paddy Russell. Viewing figures: 11.0 million, 10.1 million, 11.0 million, 9.0 million, 9.0 million, 7.5 million.

The original colour version of episode one no longer exists in the BBC archives, and the story behind this is confusing. Fan-lore has always claimed that since episode one was titled "Invasion" rather than "Invasion of the Dinosaurs", it was accidentally wiped at the same time as the 1968 Patrick Troughton story "The Invasion". Which sounds logical... except that "The Invasion" was wiped three years before "Dinosaurs" was even made. To make things more complicated, all the evidence now suggests that it was only re-titled "Invasion" for export to Australia, and that the original British transmission kept the full title. It seems likely that the story was caught up in the next round of "wipes" in 1979, although this is a long and complicated story. Luckily, episode one was tele-recorded from an unknown source, so at least a low-grade black-and-white copy is still in existence.

Supporting Cast John Bennett (General Finch), Terry Walsh (Warehouse Looter), Noel Johnson (Charles Grover M.P.), Peter Miles (Professor Whitaker), Martin Jarvis (Butler), Terence Wilton (Mark), Carmen Silvera (Ruth), Brian Badcoe (Adam).

Working Titles "Timescoop" (a word which eventually finds its way into the programme nearly a decade later, for 20.7, "The Five Doctors").

Cliffhangers A tyrannosaurus ('raaah!') stops the military vehicle that's transporting the Doctor and Sarah to a detention camp; the Doctor's stun-gun fails to work on an apatosaurus after Yates' sabotage, which isn't a problem until *another* tyrannosaurus appears (and after the Doctor has already said 'mind you, I wouldn't want to try it on a tyrannosaurus', too); having been rendered unconscious by the Operation Golden Age conspirators, Sarah wakes up on what appears to be a spaceship and is told by "Mark" that she left Earth three months ago; the Doctor arrives at the hangar just as a stegosaurus materialises, giving General Finch a chance to arrest him on suspicion of being the monster-maker; the Doctor hurries across London but once *again* finds a tyrannosaurus appearing in his way. The last episode ends with the Doctor offering to take Sarah to Florana, the planet they're aiming for at the start of the next story.

The Lore

• Jon Pertwee's departure from *Doctor Who* was officially announced between episodes four and five of "Invasion of the Dinosaurs". Pertwee left partly because he was afraid of being typecast, partly because the rest of the show's "family" was moving on, although technically he was sacked rather than resigning. Feeling the need for a change, he asked the BBC for more money on the grounds that he had nothing to lose, and was formally dismissed as a result. His response was, so to speak, to shrug and say 'thought so'.

• Paddy Russell recalls that by this stage Pertwee was spending longer with the costumiers, deciding what to wear, than in rehearsals or learning scripts. She also mentions her annoyance at the way the Whomobile was presented to her as a *fait accompli*.

• The Whomobile is (or was) actually a road-worthy vehicle, though its "wings" had to be removed for it to comply with British traffic laws, with a TV, telephone and stereo all fitted in the interior. It was formally registered as an "invalid trike".

• The scene in episode one, in which everyone has to find chairs to sit on instead of huddling on the floor, may have been connected with Pertwee's increasing lumbar inflammation. A stunt seems to have aggravated his old injury; spotting exactly which one is hard, but something from "The Time Warrior" seems most likely.

• Many of the paintings on the classroom wall were competition entries for a *Blue Peter* contest, possibly the "Car of the Future" one from circa "Frontier in Space".

• Richard Franklin, whose character in "Invasion of the Dinosaurs" joins a lunatic organisation that wants to turn back time to a mythical golden age of "green and pleasant lands", stood as a candidate in the 2001 British general election on behalf of the UK Independence Party. Non-British readers probably won't see the funny side of this.

• The villainous scientist who cracks the secrets of time-travel years ahead of anyone else is called "Whitaker", a name he shares with *Doctor Who's* original script editor. The same script editor who complained so much when Malcolm Hulke re-wrote "The Ambassadors of Death". The same script editor who was in charge during 1963-64, when Hulke's submissions "Beyond the Sun" and "Doctor Who and the Clock" were both dumped in ways that made Hulke feel badly mistreated. The same script editor who wrote "The Enemy of the World", to which the plot of "Invasion of the Dinosaurs" owes a remarkable amount. Coincidence…?

• Martin Jarvis - now a household name - was quite insistent when telling his friends that he was playing a character *called* Butler, not *a* butler. He was never really ashamed of his work in *Doctor Who* (2.5, "The Web Planet"; 22.2, "Vengeance on Varos"; 18.7, "Logopolis", sort of), but his street-cred wasn't so high in 1973.

• Clifford Culley - see 10.5, "Planet of the Daleks" and 12.1, "Robot" - worked at a small effects company near Pinewood Studios (Westbury Design and Optical), and touted for the job of making the dinosaurs. He then read the scripts more carefully and found that many of the things he was being asked to do were tricky with rod-puppets. By now he was committed, and all things considered the worst thing is how nearly he got away with it.

• A final point of cultural critique here. The first edition of the novelisation (*Doctor Who and the Dinosaur Invasion*, with an ending that connects Von Daniken, the visions of Ezekiel and Operation Golden Age, so evocative of the era) had what at the time seemed like the greatest cover of any book ever published. A still of the pterodactyl attacking the Doctor had been alchemically transformed into something exciting; the Roy Lichtenstein-style graphic K-KLACK!! from its beak deserved a range of t-shirts all on its own; and the tyrannosaurus looked thoroughly terrifying even though it wasn't *completely* dissimilar to the BBC TV version. Target Books disagreed, and Chris Achilleos - who made the early books so enticing - was fired. The world seemed much duller after that.

11.3: "Death to the Daleks"

(Serial XXX, Four Episodes, 23rd February - 16th March 1974.)

Which One is This? Humans and Daleks have to live together in less-than-perfect harmony, on a planet whose living city eats so much energy that even Dalek-guns don't work. The Doctor saves the day by playing *Tomb Raider* in an ancient monument full of brain-teasers.

Firsts and Lasts Though this isn't the first time that an ominous alien force drags the TARDIS off-course and forces it to crash-materialise on a strange planet, it is the first time that it's happened since the Doctor got the Ship's dematerialisation circuit working. In other words, we're now entering the era of the programme in which "ominous alien force" is a plot device designed to get the Doctor to go to interesting places. "Death to the Daleks" can also be considered the last "proper" Dalek story, since from 1975 onwards their limelight's going to be stolen by Davros.

Sarah gets to say 'what is it, Doctor?' for the first time, and to wear a swimsuit, though if anything this just proves that she's not the dolly-bird type. It's the first story script-edited by Robert Holmes, as Terrance Dicks was busy rushing "The Monster of Peladon" through. (Holmes becomes the long-term script editor in Season Twelve, and the programme becomes a much more horror-driven affair at the same time, partly because Holmes wanted to pitch the series at an older audience. This might explain why "Death to the Daleks" is a much more brutal-looking story than those around it, and why the attempted ritual sacrifice of Sarah seems so much more sordid than Jo Grant's "altar-piece" in 8.5, "The Daemons".)

Four Things to Notice About "Death to the Daleks"...

1. Principally remembered as "the one where the Daleks aren't in charge all the time", the most iconic moment of "Death to the Daleks" comes in episode two, when a pack of primitives makes one of the Daleks blow up in the middle of a quarry and then dances around it like a totem-pole. Many regarded the sight of the burning Dalek-casing as the Best Dalek Death of the series until 1984 (when one got dramatically pushed out of a window for 21.4, "Resurrection of the Daleks"). The Daleks here pretend that there are only four of their kind on the planet, in order to lull the humans into a false sense of security, which is handy considering that the BBC didn't have more than four of the newly-repainted Dalek "costumes".

2. As in "Planet of the Daleks", Terry Nation's script glosses over the idea of the TARDIS being an unimaginably complex interdimensional organism and instead portrays the Ship as a box with some engines in it. Whereas in "Planet" the Ship doesn't even have its own working air supply, in "Death to the Daleks" the Doctor has to open its doors with a crank-handle when some of the power gets drained.

3. The Daleks, ostensibly the most ruthless and unflappable beings in the universe, use a small toy police box as their target when they're testing their new weapons. Since the Daleks we see here only have a small ship and probably aren't equipped with moulds for die-cast model-making, we can only conclude that they routinely *carry little models of the TARDIS around with them*. The Doctor really has made an impression on their culture.

4. As ever in a Terry Nation script, the human supporting cast really is astonishingly wet, the Marine Space Corps being made up of upper-middle class people in blue jumpsuits called "Jill" and "Richard". Breaking the mould is Galloway, the big gruff Scotsman, but *he* turns out to be violent and treacherous. Guess who's going to carry out the suicidal act of redemption? And this being a Nation production, Jill's surname is "Tarrant". Even the Space Corps badge looks like the Federation insignia from *Blake's 7*, while at the

start of episode three the Doctor mutates into Vila Restal. He makes lame jokes ('the root won... Daleks, nil'), lets Sarah pull him to safety, exhibits comic cowardice and starts calling everyone 'my friend'.

The Continuity

The Doctor

• *Ethics.* His usual belief in the sanctity of intelligent life obviously doesn't apply to Daleks, as he takes a great deal of pleasure in seeing the Exxilon City blow them up. [Note that he has no qualms about killing the City, either. As ever in stories like this, he states his pragmatism thus: 'why not, when the only alternative to living is dying...']

• *Inventory.* In the City he loses a five-piastre coin, which he says he probably won't need [he's been to either post-war Egypt or the Lebanon]. The sonic screwdriver can be used as a "mine-detector" to find explosive charges in the floor of the City.

• *Background.* The Doctor has been to the planet Florana several times, and each time he comes back feeling a hundred years younger. [This seems odd, since he's only just managed to get his TARDIS under control. Does the TARDIS keep going back there of its own accord, or did the Doctor spend much longer travelling before "An Unearthly Child" (1.1) than is often believed? See **How Old is the Doctor?** under 16.5, "The Power of Kroll".] He's seen a temple in Peru which was allegedly too impressive to have been built by primitive man.

The Supporting Cast

• *Sarah Jane Smith.* Whisked out of her own time and off into space, she's already starting to lose some of her self-will and become reliant on the Doctor, often sounding like a little girl looking for reassurance. [This peculiar new environment is stripping away her independence. She gets some of her nerve back later, but after this she's never *quite* as brash as she was in her first appearances.] The Doctor makes an attempt at "bonding" with her which is reminiscent of his relationship with Jo, though he doesn't take the same fatherly / mentor-like approach to her. This is the last time she really gets to scream.

The TARDIS When the Ship gets too close to the Exxilon City's energy-draining influence, it's incapable of taking off and the interior lights go out. [Since 'the power of a sun' supposedly fuels the TARDIS - see **What Makes TARDISes Work?** under 1.3, "The Edge of Destruction" - it's unthinkable that the City might have completely drained its energy reserves. If the console draws power from some nigh-inexhaustible source, then it seems likely that the City drains the energy only as it reaches the TARDIS systems.]

The TARDIS is supposedly on its way to Florana when it lands on the Exxilon planet, and the City appears to make it "crash". [Is the City capable of reaching into the vortex? As on the many occasions when we see the TARDIS hovering in space, the implication may be that the Ship briefly materialises in "real" space to get its bearings during the journey, and pops into existence too close to the Exxilon planet this time.] The TARDIS doors won't open when the Ship's powered down, but alternatively, a manual handcrank for the doors is kept in the console room alongside an oil lamp. In a nearby cabinet there's an electric torch. A red light flashes on the console when there's a 'mains' power failure, but the TARDIS has emergency power units *and* emergency storage cells. Oddly, there's still a hint of light in the console room even when the power goes out.

The Doctor describes the TARDIS as a living thing, and believes that its energy sources should never stop.

An Exxilon gets into the console room here, and menaces Sarah. [She leaves the Ship as soon as she's knocked it out, so it's entirely possible that the Exxilon wanders further into the TARDIS corridors and is still there even now. There's certainly no sign of it leaving.] There are sea-side clothes and items on board, though Sarah may have brought them specially for the trip to Florana.

The Non-Humans
• *Daleks.* They move by psychokinetic power, i.e. their brains fuel their casings, although their guns must have a different energy source as the City of the Exxilons can drain their weapons but not stop them moving. When the guns aren't functioning, it doesn't take the Daleks long to fit themselves with projectile weapons instead. One Dalek self-destructs out of shame when its prisoner escapes. [This sort of thing only happens once more, in 25.1, "Remembrance of the Daleks". It's

difficult to find any logic in this, unless the Dalek is unstable and considers itself a *serious* liability to the Dalek species. Perhaps Daleks become extraparanoid when their guns don't work properly. They visibly panic when they realise they can't back up any of their threats.]

The Daleks have a 'plague missile', perhaps suggesting that they started the plague which is currently ravaging the human colony worlds, though this is by no means clear. [Plague is a standard Dalek weapon; see 2.2, "The Dalek Invasion of Earth" and 10.4, "Planet of the Daleks". But they believe that one missile on Exxilon will make landing by humans impossible, which makes the plague sound a lot more severe and instantaneous than the one troubling the outer planets.]

Their plan is to blackmail the 'space powers' into acceding to their demands, which is unusually subtle for them. Dalek ships are, as ever, featureless silver vessels with simple geometric forms. The Doctor acknowledges Daleks to be brilliant technicians, calling them the most technically advanced life-form in the galaxy [i.e. at this point in time - because they *can't* be as sophisticated as extinct species like the Daemons - and certainly not including the Time Lords]. He also states that they have a 'scorched planet policy' [meaning, they destroy any resources they can't use to stop anybody else finding a use for them]. After a 7,000-volt electric shock, one Dalek has its non-conductive shielding burnt out but survives.

In this era, the Daleks recognise the Doctor on sight and - of course - use TARDIS-shaped targets when testing weapons. [They most probably know him from 10.3, "Frontier in Space".]

• *Exxilons.* Inhabitants of Exxilon, a world that's full of rocks and not much else, Exxilons are humanoid but with hairless skins and blank, oversized eyes [so they *look* like they all live in the dark]. Once a highly sophisticated civilisation, they explored space but came unstuck when they made their City a living, thinking thing, as the City had no need of them and drove out those it didn't destroy. They're now primitive savages who see the City as a shrine and sacrifice visitors to their gods. Though "heretics" in Exxilon's breakaway group retain their civilised ways and want a return to the days of science, members of the main faction just grunt and chant their way through life. Weirdly, the exiled Exxilons' skins look like glittery rock even though they seem to be dissenters rather than a sub-species. [A mineral-rich diet? Maybe they eat parrinium.]

• *The City.* Possibly one of the Seven-Hundred Wonders of the Universe [the Doctor says it 'must be' one of the Seven-Hundred Wonders, so it may just be a figure of speech], but it gets blown up here. Though the City of the Exxilons looks like any run-of-the-mill high-tech futuristic city with shiny white corridors, it's actually alive. The pulsing beacon at its highest point drains energy from any source in the area, while its "roots" underground have a habit of slinking through the subterranean tunnels, blowing things up on contact.

Anyone entering the City is exposed to a number of potentially lethal logic puzzles before they can reach the City's brain. The Doctor believes it has a reason for doing this, but he never explains what it is. [It clearly wants minds that are useful, possibly as servants. There's an ancient corpse sitting in the chair in its "control room", though the City seems to function perfectly well with no staff at all.] The City's control centre can generate zombie-like "antibodies", basically human / Exxilon types with a mean streak and half-formed features.

Planet Notes

• *Florana.* Following his sales pitch to Sarah [see the previous story], the Doctor now adds that Florana's water is effervescent, so you can't sink in it.

• *Venus.* The Doctor adds to the already-lengthy list of "Venusian" things in his repertoire by mentioning Venusian hopscotch. As their feet are so big, it must be murder.

History

• *Dating.* It's an era in which Earth has a well-established space-going military, and humanity knows about the Dalek threat. [It can't be before 2200, and the Empire-like nature of the humans - not to mention their old-style names - would indicate a time before 3000. Human concerns involve a plague that's sweeping all of space, not just domestic problems on the homeworld, suggesting an era after the wars and riots of "Frontier in Space". A date between 2600 and 2900 would be most likely. See **What's the Timeline of the Earth Empire?** under 10.3.] The father of one of the humans was killed in the 'last Dalek war'. [So there have been several Dalek wars, starting with the events of "Frontier in Space"? The Daleks in this story come across as opportunists, making the most of the space-plague rather than planning to

con-quer the u-ni-verse, which might mean that at this point all the great Dalek armies have been wiped out and they're struggling to become a major power again.]

The Marine Space Corps has been sent to Exxilon because the chemical parrinium is as common as salt there, whereas it's priceless on Earth. And parrinium is the only known way to cure / immunise against the space-plague. 10,000,000 people on the outer planets and colonies will die without it. The MSC people use sulphagen tablets as pain-killers, and Galloway mentions a new 'Z-47' spacecraft they've been planning. Hearteningly, English people in the future still say "leftenant" rather than "lootenant".

Carvings in the City of the Exxilons closely resemble the carvings of the Peruvian Incas, and the Doctor believes the Exxilons travelled to Earth to teach the Incas how to build their temples [c. 1000 BC]. Bellal claims that Exxilon had grown old before life began on other planets. [The way his people remember it, and probably not accurate.]

The Analysis

Where Does This Come From? In 1968, Erich von Daniken wrote *Chariots of the Gods*, a book which had made its way into almost every middle-class home in western Europe by the early '70s and become essential reading even for people who didn't believe a word of it. Von Daniken's argument was that aliens had visited all the "great" ancient civilisations, something he demonstrated by comparing wall-paintings and hieroglyphs with photos of space-suits from the NASA missions (as if space-suits had inspired human art, and not the other way around…). It changed popular culture, and provided science fiction with a whole new currency, effectively prepping the world for the "space-mythology" of the *Star Wars* boom just a few years later.

Von Daniken's ideas are so familiar now that they barely seem like ideas at all, but ancient civilisations weren't *always* linked with UFOs in the popular consciousness. After all, when *Doctor Who* had done its "Atlantis" story (9.5, "The Time Monster"), the Atlanteans' nemesis turned out to be a pseudo-mystical Greek God rather than an alien in a hi-tech spaceship. *Chariots of the Gods* tied SF and antiquity together once and for all, something which had been done before by writers like Immanuel Velikhovski (his "Worlds In Collision" theory - that all religion was the result of Venus being hurled across space when it broke off from the surface of Jupiter, causing the Red Spot and guiding Moses - was amazingly popular), but never so uncritically or so fashionably. Well, except maybe in Nazi Germany: see also 16.1, "The Ribos Operation".

"Death to the Daleks" features the series' first major expedition into Von Daniken's land, although you could argue that "The Daemons" (8.5) was at least a preliminary survey of the terrain. The City is, perhaps, the earliest filmed version of the *Chariots* idea not pitched as a documentary and "hosted" by a former *Star Trek* regular. The Incas were among the many civilisations supposedly inspired by the ancient space-travellers, and the logic-pictograms we see outside the Exxilon City are a close match for the real-world symbols which apparently demonstrate humanity's alien heritage. At least, according to *Chariots* and the many books that followed it (e.g. *Our Mysterious Spaceship Moon*, which "proves" that the moon is actually an enormous alien vessel steered into Earth orbit millions of years ago... no wonder the Silurians ran for cover).

No surprise, then, that the scenes set around the City walls stand out more than anything else in the story. The Space Corps nonsense is standard SF fare, but the City was Terry Nation's one shot at doing something *hip*, turning his old ruined-civilisation background (c.f. 1.2, "The Daleks") into a piece of popular anthropology. Whether *he* believed a word of it is another matter.

Young and / or non-British readers might also like to bear in mind that during the '70s, the UK was hit by power-cuts that blacked out whole swathes of the country. The opening scenes on the TARDIS, as everything powers down and goes dark, might... *might*... almost be considered a kind of satire. Many at the time thought the non-use of synthesisers was an energy-saving measure...

Things That Don't Make Sense Yet *again*, Terry Nation has difficulty understanding the scale of space. "Planet of the Daleks" assumes that 10,000 Daleks is a huge army in galactic terms, whereas here it's said that 10,000,000 people on the outer planets will die without parrinium. Is that all? So, the death-toll for a plague that must have spread across huge swathes of the galaxy is a figure not much more than the population of a decent-sized

city? [Possibly humans can cure most plague cases without exotic alien chemicals, but the parrinium is needed to cure those few plague victims who don't respond to the drugs. In other words, it's the only *guaranteed* cure rather than the only possible treatment.] And as for the idea that the Daleks can hold the whole galaxy to ransom with the lives of a relatively small number of people on the outer planets...

One of the "tests" inside the City involves the benevolent native Bellal triggering a loud sonic blast which makes him temporarily psychotic, but the Doctor - who has his back turned - doesn't notice anything happening until he turns round and sees the Exxilon pointing a gun at him. [The sonic blast only affects Exxilon senses?] Similarly, the Daleks bellow out their plan to betray the humans when they're about five feet away from the humans, and even the One They Call the Doctor doesn't notice (N.B. the Daleks whispered in the rushes of the story, but the director stepped in and stopped it).

From a narrative point of view, the tests to reach the City's heart are thoroughly pointless anyway; the Doctor triggers a nervous breakdown in its brain, but that becomes irrelevant as the Earth Marines blow up the beacon and allow everyone to escape. The breakdown may save the future of the Exxilon species, but it's not really connected to the rest of the plot, and Bellal doesn't even get the time-honoured epilogue speech about being able to build a better future for his people.

The Daleks believe that their plague missile will make it impossible for future human missions to land on, or collect parrinium from, Exxilon. Have they never heard of robots?

Critique Terry Nation once again misses the point of the programme and provides a dry, po-faced *Flash-Gordon*-style adventure serial with the Doctor as its all-purpose hero, in which the Space Corps personnel recite all the usual sci-fi lines while Sarah gets to scream like a generic companion. Here the Doctor has nothing to kick against except the City's blank walls, and he's even separated from the Daleks for most of the story, removing any possibility of dramatic flair.

As with "Planet of the Daleks", much of the plot seems to be stitched together out of pieces from previous Nation stories, starting with the calcified Exxilon in the first episode and culminating in a Dalek space-plague / blackmail attempt. Having the humans not automatically trust the Doctor, and indeed making a justifiable deal with the Daleks to achieve their mission at the expense of his life, is potentially interesting but frittered away after episode two. And as ever, the need to end episode one with a "Dalek cliffhanger" results in a lot of tedious Doctor-and-companion-explore-a-quarry scenes consuming much the story's first quarter, even though the following episodes are so muddled that some of the plot needed introducing a lot earlier on.

That this is business-as-usual is indicated even in the opening shot. A man runs for his life across a barren wilderness. Just as we recognise him as Terry Walsh, he gets an arrow in his guts and falls down a cliff, western-style. Even the Dalek guns make six-shooter noises, over the obvious sound of cap-guns in the studio.

Anything not familiar from "Planet of the Daleks" becomes so now, as Robert Holmes takes several ideas attempted here and re-uses them to patch holes in other scripts during his period as script editor. Tick them off as you go: the re-writes of "The Hand of Fear" episode four, "Pyramids of Mars" episode four, "Revenge of the Cybermen" episode three (in which the Doctor, Commander Stevenson and Lester planting a bomb, whereas here it's Galloway and Hamilton) and "The Masque of Mandragora" are all hinted at here.

The Facts

Written by Terry Nation. Directed by Michael Briant. Viewing figures: 8.1 million, 9.5 million, 10.5 million, 9.5 million.

Supporting Cast Duncan Lamont (Dan Galloway), John Abineri (Richard Railton), Neil Seiler (Commander Stewart), Julian Fox (Peter Hamilton), Joy Harrison (Jill Tarrant), Mostyn Evans (High Priest), Michael Wisher (Dalek Voices), Arnold Yarrow (Bellal).

Working Titles "The Exxilons".

Cliffhangers The Daleks roll out of their spaceship to face the humans, and open fire (although the tight close-up of a Dalek gun goes on for so long that it's fairly clear the weapons aren't working); in the subterranean tunnels, one of the City's snake-like "roots" rears up over the Doctor; and in what may be the least dramatic cliffhanger in Doctor Who history, the Doctor stops Bellal treading on a funny-coloured stretch of floor inside the Exxilon City.

The Lore

• Director Michael Briant had worked on some of the 1960s Dalek stories, and consciously attempted to evoke the same mood. To this end he had the Daleks' casings re-painted, and made their ship controls look Raymond Cusick-esque. He also used the "dolly" railway-style tracks used by cameras to propel the Daleks smoothly across the quarry location; you can, alas, see them quite plainly.

• By this stage, even Terry Nation was allegedly getting bored of the Daleks. Terrance Dicks suggested many of the plot ideas here before he bowed out and let Robert Holmes do the script-editing. It's worth noting that the original story outline described an "elixir" on Exxilon rather than a magic mineral (compare with Dicks' own script for 13.5, "The Brain of Morbius"). Holmes didn't like the Daleks at all, and although the legend that he invented the title of this story himself as a way of "expressing himself" is provably untrue, it *has* been suggested that he insisted on the name "parrinium" because it sounds so much like "perineum". And if that sort of rude word-play seems unlikely, just remember that this *is* Robert Holmes we're talking about (see 10.2, "Carnival of Monsters")...

• The stripes in Bellal's skin and the glowing symbols on the city walls were pioneering uses of front axial projection, involving the same tiny prisms used to make the reflective patches in Hi-Vis jackets and road-signs. The system reflects light exactly back along its axis, so a light mounted on the camera will make something glow very brightly without injuring the actors. It didn't quite work here. (See the glowing green skin infection in 10.5, "The Green Death", to find out how it should have looked.)

• Contrary to popular belief, the chanting of the Exxilons is *not* recycled from "The Underwater Menace" (4.4). One of the authors of this present volume has just spent ninety minutes with a cassette of "The Underwater Menace" in order to verify this. Some of the chanting even sounds as if it could have been supplied by Mostyn Evans, who plays the High Priest (and was Dai the Death in "The Green Death", one of the aforementioned glowing corpses).

11.4: "The Monster of Peladon"

(Serial YYY, Six Episodes, 23rd March - 27th April 1974.)

Which One is This? This year's story with "Monster" in the title turns out to be "The Curse of Peladon: Bigger, Longer and Uncut". More monsters, more extras, more improbable costumes, more Ice Warriors and more topical satire, sort of.

Firsts and Lasts First time the TARDIS is seen to return to a planet other than Earth (even the second trip to Skaro was done under Dalek-power).

Six Things to Notice About "The Monster of Peladon"...

1. The unashamed sequel to "The Curse of Peladon" (9.2), "Monster" returns to the sci-fi / medieval / glam-rock world of its predecessor but pulls out all the stops and aims at a full-blown "political" epic. This time there's a naïve young Queen who's having trouble with the commoners; a war against a rival galaxy; treachery and subterfuge from the Ice Warriors; and of course, the usual appearances by Royal Beasts and alien delegates. Once again, expensive-looking film-shoots are used to try to convince viewers that the scenes set in caverns and on mountain ledges are actually filmed on location instead of in a BBC studio.

2. Back on form after her screaming-and-asking-stupid-questions phase in "Death to the Daleks", here Sarah Jane Smith makes the most overt feminist stand of the series by lecturing Queen of Peladon about Women's Lib, apparently changing the course of the planet's history with the words 'there's nothing "only" about being a girl'. An inspiration for girl-adventurers everywhere, or a clumsy attempt at tackling hip social issues by a writer who doesn't bother including any female characters *except* for the companion and the lisping Queen (Alpha Centauri doesn't count)? You decide.

3. Fans of Terry Walsh - the series' stalwart stunt expert and Doctor-double - will enjoy the protracted fight sequence in episode four, which not only allows him to show off his moves but also lets us get a good look at his face when he's "doubling" for Jon Pertwee. He also plays the Guard Captain who's killed at least three times, and various other guards, so either the Pels have cracked cloning or they've got big families. Other things you shouldn't be able to see (but can) include the leg of the man inside the Aggedor costume, when the furry trousers come away from the furry boots during his death-scene.

4. However, the most immediately striking thing about "The Monster of Peladon" (and yes, again, it's easy to mock) is the fashion sense. Particularly the hair. While the nobles of Peladon get to wear the usual Tolkienesque flowing robes and exotic jewellery, the miners are supposed to have a more "working class" look, which involves them wearing enormous dyed afros as part of their uniform. At the time this was known as the "Dickie Davies" look, after the silver-streaked sportscaster; now it's "The Rachel". You can only assume that since the miners are supposed to be "burrowing folk", the costume department thought it'd be fitting for them to look like badgers.

5. In "The Curse of Peladon" some viewers had actually been surprised that a story set in space and written by Brian Hayles had featured the Ice Warriors. Yet in "Monster", not only were they the only thing from the previous story which hadn't turned up during the first couple of episodes, but Barry Letts had said three months earlier - in the *Radio Times* letters page - that they'd be back for this story. Anyone who hadn't read Letts' comment might also have picked up the hint from Frank Bellamy's postage-stamp-sized illustration for that episode (in those days everyone got the *Radio Times*, and it came out on the Tuesday before the episode), or heard it from someone at school. Nevertheless, the Ice Warriors' return was made a surprise cliffhanger.

6. Vega Nexos, a faun-like alien apparently from the planet Luvvie, is killed after three minutes of screen-time and never gets a proper send-off. Nonetheless, he's a hero to a generation thanks to the collectable cardboard stand-up figures given away with Weetabix breakfast cereal (see **Why Was There So Much Merchandising?**). Watching it now it's amazing that he wasn't in the series more, so fondly is he remembered.

The Continuity

The Doctor Deliberately goes back to Peladon to see how the planet's getting on, the first time he's seen to follow up "old cases". He's capable of going into complete sensory withdrawal when necessary, and obviously has experience of trisilicate. He claims there's nothing he likes more than a quiet life, but it's impossible to believe him.

• *Ethics.* When cornered, the Doctor has no compunction about using Eckersley's heat-ray to kill one of the Ice Warriors. He goes on to kill several others who are threatening the miners. [Initially he uses the device because it's the only chance of survival he and his friends have, although subsequent uses suggest that he's ready to fight military-style campaigns when he feels it's needed.]

• *Inventory.* The Doctor uses his useless pocket-watch [11.2, "Invasion of the Dinosaurs"] to induce 'light hypnosis' in Aggedor. He performs another distracting conjuring-trick with a coin from his pocket, so he's obviously never short of spare change.

The Supporting Cast

• *Sarah Jane Smith.* Much more independent here than during her last "adventure", and much less prone to rely on the Doctor, though she's no longer arguing with him every step of the way. She's certainly taking the "exploring alien planets" idea in her stride, so much so that she's ready to criticise the Doctor for landing in '*another* rotten, gloomy old tunnel'. She also claims that the Doctor has always told her 'where there's life, there's hope'. [Since we've never heard him say anything of the sort to her, it suggests that more time has passed between them than we know about. The reference to another rotten, gloomy old tunnel might imply unseen adventures since "Death to the Daleks", while the 'where there's life…' line foreshadows the Third Doctor's dying words in the next story. Did they ever get to Florana?] The Doctor decides to take her back to Earth at the end of the story, without her asking, perhaps demonstrating that he doesn't see her as a full-time companion. Yet.

The TARDIS The scanner's on the blink.

The Non-Humans

• *Ice Warriors.* Commander Azaxyr [again, not referred to as an "Ice Lord"] is in charge of the Federation troops sent to keep order on Peladon, so the Ice Warriors would seem to be the Federation's "UN peacekeepers". However, Azaxyr is actually loyal to a faction which wants a return to the Martians' military past.

Alpha Centauri suggests that only the Doctor calls the Martians "Ice Warriors", yet Azaxyr later refers to his troops that way, the only time this happens. They don't recognise the Doctor here. The standard Ice Warrior weapon is now a small hand-held rod which kills instantly [the "special effect" seems to suggest that it makes people implode] and can burn through metal. Warmth makes them dizzy and sluggish. They no longer refer to Mars as their home.

As in their first appearance, one of the Ice Warriors in Azaxyr's retinue has a differently-shaped helmet to the others [see 5.3, "The Ice Warriors"].

• *Alpha Centauri.* The same hexapod who was on Peladon fifty years previously, and there's no sign of ageing other than 'a little grey around the tentacles', so the species must be quite long-lived. He's now the Federation's ambassador on Peladon.

• *Vega Nexos.* The representative of the planet Vega is satyr-like, with furry legs and cloven hooves but a human top half, and no modesty as he prances around naked even in the company of the Queen. His slitty eyes just emphasise his animal-like appearance, and the claim that the people of Vega are experts in mining techniques underlines the fact that he's obviously supposed to be some kind of burrowing mole-person. "Nexos" would seem to be his name or title.

• *Aggedor.* The Royal Beast of Peladon is the same specimen the Doctor met last time, so it's another long-lived species. He makes a good tracking-animal. Aggedor dies here, and the implication is that he's the last of his kind.

Planet Notes

• *Peladon.* Fifty years after the Doctor's last visit, Peladon is established as a Federation member that's still regarded as primitive by the other planets. A single individual acting as both Chancellor and High Priest now advises Queen Thalira [odd that she doesn't call herself "Peladon", like her father]. The old King died when the Queen was young, and everyone on Peladon knows the story of the Doctor, while Chancellor Ortron - who meets his end here - took over the day Hepesh died [he must have been *very* young for a Chancellor, unless the Pels age well]. The monarch still has a big butch Champion. Women of non-noble rank are now allowed in the throne-room, though the miners aren't usually allowed in the citadel, which is over-

Why Was There So Much Merchandising?

No-one growing up after *Star Wars*, or in another country would bother to ask such a question.

Indeed, looking back at it now, the idea that a chocolate bar, a cereal packet freebie or two, some comic strips, a "Fluid Neutraliser", the Chad Valley "Give-A-Show Projector" (just don't ask), toy Daleks and the occasional 7" record is some kind of marketing bonanza seems absurd. Yet this misses a crucial point: the BBC didn't need the revenue to finance the programme. Nor was anybody at the Corporation making a big profit, which admittedly contradicts the way we now think about the word "Corporation".

The BBC started broadcasting television in 1936. Only Hitler's Germany had anything like it, and the Nazis used it for sport, DIY, home-making hints and trite documentaries about the lives of ordinary people (what an unthinkable waste of the medium). It wasn't until 1955 that the government permitted commercial television, that is, television with advertising breaks but no sponsorship of programmes. As a quid pro quo, the commercial network was allowed to keep all the revenue from advertising while the BBC kept all the revenue from the Television Licence, with which everything was financed from Benjamin Britten's commission to write *Peter Grimes* down to the cost of *Blue Peter* badges.

Doctor Who came out of the Drama Department's budget, along with all the Jane Austen adaptations, soap operas, one-off plays (at least four a week back then) and serials. Any revenue from selling any of these overseas, or making "I Heart *Dixon of Dock Green*" tea-towels, went into the overall drama budget and not to the individual programmes. BBC Enterprises maintained strict quality control.

Christmas 1964 was something of a surprise to British parents. Instead of nice, ordinary toys like jigsaws and teddies, kids wanted anything with either the Beatles or a Dalek on it. There'd been TV spin-off fads before, Davy Crockett hats and Robin Hood material, but the scale of that year's commerciality was unprecedented. Over the next ten years there'd be a steady stream of *Doctor Who* merchandising; other guidebooks can tell you all about the plastic-and-PVC artefacts of that era, and what they're worth on the open market these days, but that's not the point. To the kids, they were priceless.

This is what most people failed to realise then (except, of course, Gerry Anderson). Any programme which invites you into a world generates an excitement about "relics" from that world. These days they're collectable and you're supposed to need the set, but to a child in those days it was an emotional attachment, the prospect that it might all be real (you knew it wasn't, but only when anyone asked you). *Star Wars* is now remembered as being the grandfather-god of all merchandising, but the "breakthrough" of the *Star Wars* era was a range of collectibles that the under-sixteens could buy for themselves with pocket-money. In the days when you had to wait for your birthday before you got hold of the *War of the Daleks* board-game with the plastic moulded Emperor, things were more valuable. And by being all BBC-ish about it, the *Doctor Who* office maintained a level of craftsmanship and "good faith", so that the attitude of the programme carried on throughout. With founding script-editor David Whitaker ghost-writing much of the material in the early annuals and supervising the Dalek comic-strip, everything was aesthetically self-consistent, which is what children love most about fantasy.

While the BBC maintained rights over the series, the TARDIS, Bessie and so on, there were two big anomalies: the face of the lead actor, and Terry Nation's (contentious) claim over the Daleks. Nation and Pertwee cashed in big time. Any long-term fan will have his or her favourite crass example (a *Dalek Annual* in which Skaro has a "Hall of Fame" with statues of prominent Daleks... think about it), but what's interesting is the extent to which they still stuck within the BBC's overall guidelines. Reading the *Dalek Pocket-Book and Space Traveller's Guide* you can see that Nation was as big a fanboy as any of us, in love with the world he was making up even when it led to absurdities like the continent called "Darren" and the "infra-green" invisibility ray.

The tenth anniversary saw a small change in this. Barry Letts - for better or worse - managed the publicity for the series personally, and maintained close links with the staff at *Countdown*, a boys' paper with strips based on *Doctor Who*, *UFO*, *Planet of the Apes* and the like. The 1973 *Radio Times* anniversary special, which opened a can of Drashig-sized worms at the time (see **What Are These Stories Really Called?** under 3.2, "Mission to The Unknown"), allowed tantalising glimpses behind the scenes for the first time. Patrick Troughton had been dead against this, except for children who won competitions, while as producers Lambert and Wiles never even thought about it.

continued on page 167...

looked by Mount Megeshra. Peladon has ostensibly never dishonoured a treaty.

The miners, being commoners, are generally superstitious idiots who don't trust alien technology unless they can shoot someone with it. Still, the story ends with the workers and nobles forging better relations. It turns out that Peladon is rich in trisilicate. [A mineral which, in "The Curse of Peladon", was said to be found only on Mars. In "The Curse of Peladon" the Doctor blames the Ice Warriors for an attack on the other delegates simply because he finds traces of trisilicate in the area, so with hindsight the fact that the stuff is found all over Peladon makes him look rather silly.] Federation membership has benefited the upper classes, but not the miners. The Doctor can't decide whether the word for the people of Peladon is "Pels" or "Peladonians".

[Thalira looks plausibly like a child of King Peladon, but also unnervingly like Katy Manning. Fan-writers have picked up on this for stories about what Jo did after breaking up with Professor Jones…]

History

• *Dating*. 'About' fifty years after the Doctor's last visit [see 9.2, "The Curse of Peladon"; by now it's probably in the 3900s, and that's certainly the view taken by both the later New Adventures and Lance Parkin's *History of the Universe*].

The Federation is currently involved in a war against Galaxy Five, and desperately needs trisilicate for use in circuitry, heat-shields, inert micro-cell fibres and radionic crystals. Eckersley states that the Federation's whole technology is based on trisilicate, and that whoever has it will win the war. [The Federation must have known about Peladon's trisilicate before the planet joined, which may be why Peladon was given membership despite its rather backward society. If trisilicate is so vital then Mars must have been a major power in galactic politics until now, and the discovery of *another* source of the mineral might motivate Azaxyr's revolt. The New Adventures have suggested that Galaxy Five is a terrorist organisation rather than an actual *galaxy*, and though there's nothing to contradict that here, it's not the implication of either this story or 3.4, "The Daleks' Masterplan". Since Galaxy Five is threatening Earth again by 4000 AD, perhaps its assault on the Milky Way began with terrorist strikes rather than full-scale invasion fleets.]

Alpha Centauri claims that the Federation was the victim of a vicious and unprovoked attack, and that Galaxy Five refuses to talk, but it becomes anxious to negotiate a peace treaty after its plot on Peladon fails; Centauri baldly states that the war is over. Trisilicate is a transparent yellowish ore in its natural form, and the Federation uses sonic lances to mine it. Duralinium is this week's futuristic-sounding building substance, while the agents of Galaxy Five use a matter-projector and a directional heat-ray to fake the appearances of Aggedor's spirit.

Federation law usually forbids summary executions, and doesn't allow natives of 'primitive' planets to acquire sophisticated weapons [from other Federation worlds, although it's notable that Peladon is *described* as primitive despite its status as a member-planet]. Alpha Centauri sends for security troops, but the troops can't be recalled once they've been summoned, leaving their commander in charge of Peladon and able to declare martial law. Azaxyr's strong-arm tactics wouldn't be tolerated in time of peace.

The Analysis

Where Does This Come From? Initially, the Doctor's return to Peladon was intended to be a comment on imperialism, the way technologically-advanced outsiders get the rulers sucking up to them even though the local workers end up being exploited twice over. However, events outside the programme made a more topical aspect of the story important.

At the time of the crises mentioned under "The Green Death" (10.5), it had become almost an annual ritual for Britain's miners to go on strike in support of other afflicted unions. In early 1973 the miners themselves had grievances, and other unions supported them. The two big issues were safety in the job (as diagnoses of pneumoconiosis increased) and the National Coal Board's strategy to "rationalise" by closing pits. Two centuries of community and tradition were bound up in the oldest mines, and the intransigent government gave no replacement for the single-industry towns' *raison d'etre*. Barry Letts and Terrance Dicks realised that there was not only a dramatic opportunity, but almost a *duty*, to write about this. That it happened while they were filming the location-work for "The Green Death" must have added to the impact.

Why Was There So Much Merchandising?

...continued from page 165

Marvel UK launched *Doctor Who Weekly* in 1979, and even *then* it took a while for the magazine to get into the groove of regular behind-the-scenes material, with the early issues pretending that the Doctor himself was the editor and acting as if it were all "real". (Some readers actually complained when "making of" articles were finally published, on the grounds that it spoiled the illusion, which seems incredible when you consider that the publication eventually mutated into *Doctor Who Magazine*.) But by this time all the annoying post-*Star-Wars* US series with cute robots and children for "audience identification" had arrived, and they needed merchandising to pay the bills. Hence the cute robots and children.

So from the BBC's point of view, the exploitation of money-spinning rights was a means to an end, a way of preserving the bond with the audience. Don't forget, prior to 1970 *Doctor Who* was a brand image for oddness, not a series of individual adventures. Most of the public couldn't remember the plots but knew the sort of thing that might happen. The *Radio Times* illustrations, and the programme's aesthetic of "difference", all helped viewers participate in this. In the pre-video, pre-channel-zapping age, once you selected a channel you were there for the night, and Saturday nights belonged to BBC1. *Doctor Who* belonged to Saturday nights, so if you wanted to continue inhabiting the "place" it created then you needed your Target novelisations, Rolykin Daleks and "Masterplan Q" chocolate bars (or, if you're shameless, your underpants with Tom Baker on).

After the 1983 anniversary, the position changed again. It's been argued that this was the point when *Doctor Who* became something you bought, not something provided as a "public service" in which you opted to participate or not. Certainly the number of reunions, returns of old monsters and gimmicky collectibles increased geometrically. (This was the era of *Knit a TARDIS* and *The Doctor Who Cookbook*, though the latter has now attained a certain kitsch status for its sheer stupidity... also, it's not a bad cookbook).

To an extent, of course, this was simply a result of the length of time the programme had been on the air. The people making the series belonged to a generation that had known it all their lives, so it's not surprising that fetishism for the past became part of the programme. In an era when yuppies were surrounding themselves with executive toys in order to find some kind of second childhood,

the programme-makers did what they could to turn back time by revisiting the stories of the '60s - most blatantly in 22.1, "Attack of the Cybermen" - and producing more than enough toys of their own. As with his mentor Letts, producer John Nathan-Turner managed the merchandising at least as well as the programme, which was increasingly looking like "product" itself. When people wax nostalgic about spin-offery, they forget that Colin Baker spawned the largest number of spin-off items, not Pertwee or Hartnell.

However, most of these items were forgettable or unavailable in the high streets. By this stage the actual programme was an embarrassment in many quarters. It had been demographically reclassified, and become a "cult" instead of "one of the most successful family entertainment series ever made". It's worth mentioning that although the various generations of *Doctor Who* viewers are usually distinguished by "their" Doctor or "their" title sequence, you could - at a pinch - define someone's era by the *Doctor Who* board-game they remember most. (Board-games are bound to be telling, of course, since they ask for more overt involvement than action figures and are too expensive to be anything but extra-special Christmas presents).

When ratings were high, and the programme was full of "space" stories dominated by Tom Baker's performance, the Strawberry Fair company released - lo! - a generic "space" board-game with Baker's face all over it and no other *Doctor Who* connection at all. It was clearly designed for members of a mass audience who might have recognised the logo from TV and been taken in. Whereas the game released by Games Workshop in the early '80s, when the series knew it had a permanent fanbase and aimed itself at a more "obsessive" audience, was a more "obsessive" game pitched at all the *Dungeons and Dragons* players. (Games Workshop only acquired the rights to a handful of characters from the TV series, incidentally. In the days when we were too young to know about copyright, we honestly thought that the companion called "Mary Jane" was just a typo. Likewise, the game's equivalent of an Ice Warrior is a man made out of ice.)

The last *Doctor Who* board-game ever released, in the dying days of 1988, was an exercise in cult-nostalgia which shovelled in as many characters and concepts from the TV series as possible but obviously wasn't meant for the general public at all. Shockeye has an Inner Force of 80 and a Dodecahedron skill of 50, if you were wondering.

Whilst the miners' leader Joe Gormley had a deal of sympathy, his charismatic deputy Arthur Scargill saw this as a means to rid the country of a class-biased, money-obsessed Tory government. Whilst an older generation of miners remembered how things had been before the nationalisation of coal in 1945, Scargill's supporters - mainly younger miners - didn't think that knowing it used to be worse was the same as accepting the status quo. A winter of power-cuts was almost traditional in the Heath / Pertwee era (the dates coincide eerily), but taking into account the oil crisis after the Yom Kippur War and a general sense that the '60s were finally over, Christmas 1973 was an odd time.

Typical of *Doctor Who*, the view taken here is a reconciliatory one. There are agitators and pig-headed idiots on both sides, but ultimately progress is only made when the classes start talking to each other. It's therefore a much more "balanced" view of the strike than many people were offering at the time, though it's questionable whether anybody in Britain's mining communities would have thanked the programme for depicting the workers as easily-led halfwits who run screaming from their jobs when they think they've seen a ghost.

Ettis' insane rant about people "selling out" is particularly disturbing. Whereas "The Curse of Peladon" had shown that ghosts were 'solid, hairy fact', this story has the spirit of Aggedor representing what the British would call a "Drake's Drum", that part of folklore and tradition which is supposed to return to aid the nation in its darkest hour. While real-world politicians evoked the 'spirit of the Blitz' and national solidarity, so the Peladonian miners cling to the 'spirit of Aggedor'. Because they're worth it.

Things That Don't Make Sense Peladon obviously treats its miners much more fairly than we're led to believe, since the mines are fitted with a heating system that can be adjusted for comfort like a great big radiator. The Doctor's hearing is once again questionable, as several guards in clanking armour file into the temple of Aggedor behind him without him noticing. His martial arts skills must be failing him as well, as Ettis beats him in one-on-one combat, even though we've frequently seen the Doctor trounce combat-hardened opponents twice the man's size.

One of the characters in attendance at Thalira's

court is the Unexplained Woman in the Purple Frock, who looks like some kind of lady-in-waiting but vanishes without explanation in episode five. [Is she one of Azaxyr's hostages, or - just as plausibly - Eckersley's contact in the court? It's worth mentioning that the New Adventure *Legacy* gives her a name (Lianna), claims she's a hand-maiden and then has her speared to death.] Ortron took over as Chancellor immediately after Hepesh died. He must therefore have known the details of Hepesh's death. So why is he confused when the Doctor survives being thrown to Aggedor?

Critique Another sitting target for members of the post-'80s generation, who have trouble dealing with the simplistic politics, the apparent lack of a subtext and - most of all - the terrible hats. But as with "The Curse of Peladon", much of the criticism that's aimed at it is the criticism of a sixteen-year-old sneering at a twelve-year-old.

This is a fable, even a fairy-tale, not an attempt at "serious" science-fiction. Whereas stories like "Death to the Daleks" get things hopelessly wrong by giving *Doctor Who* all the worst aspects of a Saturday-morning adventure serial (so that even the Doctor himself becomes a generic hero in the *Buck Rogers* mould, more inclined to join the Space Marines than to deflate their ridiculous pomposity), Brian Hayles understood what *works* about old-fashioned SF adventure: the sheer joy of exploring peculiar worlds full of peculiar people in peculiar outfits.

"The Monster of Peladon" realises what the limitations of the series are, and crucially, it *knows* that it's aiming for "rollicking fantasy" rather than anything more literary or tough-edged. And there's no question that the story makes the most of what it's got. Whereas "Curse" felt rather hemmed-in by its low budget, here the writer and director make good use of both the six-part format and the ready-made sets, so that before long Peladon starts to feel like a complete world... even if it's one of those fairy-tale worlds where anyone can wander off to the throne-room to see the Queen whenever they feel like it.

This is the generous view of the story, of course. However, it needs to be said that opinion is divided between those who see "Monster" as being "The Curse of Peladon" done properly and those who see it as being "The Curse of Peladon" without the element of surprise.

The Facts

Written by Brian Hayles. Directed by Lennie Mayne. Viewing figures: 9.2 million, 6.8 million, 7.4 million, 7.2 million, 7.5 million, 8.1 million.

Supporting Cast Donald Gee (Eckersley), Nina Thomas (Thalira), Frank Gatliff (Ortron), Rex Robinson (Gebek), Ralph Watson (Ettis), Ysanne Churchman (Voice of Alpha Centauri), Stuart Fell (Body of Alpha Centauri), Gerald Taylor (Vega Nexos), Graeme Eton (Preba), Terry Walsh (Guard Captain), Nick Hobbs (Aggedor), Alan Bennion (Azaxyr), Sonny Caldinez (Sskel).

Cliffhangers The "spirit" of Aggedor appears before the Doctor and the Queen's Champion after they're sealed into one of the caverns of the mine; beneath the temple, the *real* Aggedor looms out of the darkness towards the Doctor and Sarah; the Doctor opens the door of the (supposedly deserted) refinery, and an Ice Warrior shambles out; in the cave overlooking the citadel, Ettis beats the Doctor in one-on-one combat, but the sonic lance self-destructs when Ettis tries to use it; the Ice Warriors burn their way through the door of the refinery where the Doctor and company are hiding.

The Lore

- Roy Evans, Bert the Funny-Little-Welshman from "The Green Death", plays a miner identified in the credits as "Miner" but in the script and most guidebooks as "Rima".
- Contrary to the (admittedly appealing) claim made in various other guidebooks and fanzines, the words mouthed by the Doctor when Aggedor appears at the end of episode one are 'what the *blazes* is it?', not 'what the bloody hell is it?'.

11.5: "Planet of the Spiders"

(Serial ZZZ, Six Episodes, 4th May - 8th June 1974.)

Which One is This? The end of an era, in more ways than just the obvious one. Giant spiders materialise inside mystic Buddhist symbols, then hurl themselves at people's backs. But when the Doctor comes face-to-face with a *really* giant spider, he's so badly-damaged that he has no choice but to go through "the change"…

Firsts and Lasts The last story of the Third Doctor's run (although Jon Pertwee will be back once more for 20.7, "The Five Doctors") also sees the end of the UNIT era as we know it. Though the next season opens with a half-hearted attempt to get the Fourth Doctor to work with the same old team, this is the last time the Doctor, the Brigadier, Sergeant Benton and Mike Yates all come together as a "family". In fact, the real Yates will never be seen again after this (he turns up in cameo as a phantom, again in "The Five Doctors"). Naturally, Pertwee gets his last few opportunities to shout 'hai!' before his departure. Total number of 'hai!'s in the Third Doctor's run: 73. Total number of other martial arts exclamations ('akira!', 'on y va!', etc): 7.

Needless to say, the final regeneration scene introduces Tom Baker as the new Doctor. Indeed, the word "regeneration" is used to describe the Doctor's transformation for the first time here. The Brigadier mentions UNIT's medical officer, Dr. Sullivan, who doesn't show himself but becomes a regular fixture in Season Twelve. The Doctor calls the Brigadier "Alistair" for the first time, and we finally get a hint of the man's private life.

And it may seem trivial, but it speaks volumes: this story sees the last use of oscilloscope traces to represent "science-ness" in the *Doctor Who* universe. From now on it's fake computer graphics.

Six Things to Notice About "Planet of the Spiders"…

1. These were the days when a change of Doctors wasn't taken *absolutely* for granted. In later years it was an accepted rule of the programme that when one actor left the series, the Doctor simply had to receive a major wound before he could turn into his replacement, but in the 1970s the series still felt there should be some deeper reason behind it.

As if to sum up everything we've seen over the previous five years, "Planet of the Spiders" is deliberately structured as a Buddhist parable. The Tibetan Master Cho-Je sets the rules in the first episode. ('A man must go inside, and face his fears and hopes, his hates and his loves, and watch them wither away… the old man must die, and the new man will discover to his inexpressible joy that he has never existed'.) The zen references to the world we know being 'the world of change' sound as if they're directed straight at the audience, and in his final episode the Third Doctor goes through the motions of a Tibetan-style "initiation", facing his greatest fear even though he knows it'll turn him into somebody else. (Compare this with 24.1, "Time and the Rani", in which the Doctor regenerates after unexpectedly getting a bump on the head. And see **When Was Regeneration Invented?**.)

2. Leaving aside Jon Pertwee's big goodbye, the main attractions here are the spiders located on Metebelis 3, another monster species specifically designed to give people the willies. Sadly, they're a little too rubbery for their own good - see **The Lore** for the reasons - and it's most noticeable whenever one of them launches itself through the air and lands on someone's back. Also worthy of mention is the noise the spiders make when they're displeased and upset, particularly in episode six, which makes them sound as if they're having an orgasm and tasting something unpleasant at the same time.

3. Jon Pertwee's well-known love of vehicles has dogged the series ever since "Spearhead from Space", but here - as a goodbye present - he gets to indulge himself to the full. The centrepiece of episode two is a *twelve-minute* chase, in which the Doctor and Lupton (the story's human villain) get to play with Bessie, the Whomobile, a gyroplane, a speedboat and a one-man hovercraft, not to mention the police car that gets dragged into things for comic relief. And only *after* all of this do Lupton's spider employers decide to teleport him off the planet, making the whole exercise a bit pointless.

The Whomobile even demonstrates the ability to fly halfway through the chase, a special effect that's achieved by using CSO to superimpose the vehicle on top of some aerial shots of an escaping gyroplane, which isn't terribly convincing for two reasons. One: the background is shot on film, and the foreground is shot on video. Two: the Whomobile is silver when we see it on the ground, but for the effects shots it seems to have been sprayed gold. (This is a result of the reflective metal being buffed down so that the blue of the blue screen, or more likely green in this case, doesn't make half the car vanish. You still wonder why they bothered.)

4. Amidst all this zen and motor-action come a host of little character moments which, fittingly enough, seem to sum up the whole UNIT era. Sergeant Benton starts explaining the principles of good coffee-making in the middle of an interplanetary crisis. The Brigadier tries to keep his stiff upper lip when confronted by a belly-dancer ('very fit, that girl… I must adapt some of those movements as exercises for the men'). And the Doctor begins the story as the know-it-all hero of the piece, but ultimately has the limelight stolen from him by his Tibetan master and realises he's had everything his own way for much too long.

5. The people of Metebelis 3, being simple village-folk oppressed by the giant spiders, all speak with west-country accents and - again, fittingly for the last story of this era - are the most '70s of all the '70s supporting casts. Perms, sideburns and *Jason King* moustaches abound, as do clothes that make them look as if they're about to start singing about the dawning of the Age of Aquarius; one of them is even played by quintessential '70s man and *New Avengers* star, Gareth Hunt. Meanwhile Neska, the generic maternal old woman of the village, gives one of the funniest overwrought-school-play performances of the series ('Sabor my husband my love why did you do it why why?') in wildly inappropriate shoes.

6. But what's *really* noticeable here is that "Planet of the Spiders" is one of the very few stories in which the Doctor achieves nothing, with the possible exception of personal enlightenment. He spends much of the plot trying to prevent the Great One getting hold of the blue crystal from Metebelis 3, but when she finally acquires it… she self-destructs, rendering most of the story completely unnecessary, as she *still* would have self-destructed (and thus liberated the planet) if the Doctor had never gone anywhere near the place. And perhaps that's intentional, since ultimately this *is* supposed to be a story about the Doctor confronting his worst fears in order to become a new (and better?) man. But you still have to feel sorry for the various members of the supporting cast who die needlessly thanks to the Doctor's intervention. Starting with the unfortunate Professor Clegg at the end of episode one.

The Continuity

The Doctor At UNIT HQ the Doctor has built the IRIS machine - the Image Reproducing Integrating System - as part of his experiments into human extra-sensory perception; psychometry, telepathy and clairvoyance are all covered by his 'particular field'. He brashly states that psychic powers lie dormant in most humans, but that psychokinesis is a rarely-developed faculty. [This is the first and only time he's seen performing non-TARDIS-related experiments on Earth, unexpected since he's now got a fully working Ship. Nor does he give a second thought to IRIS after this story. Is he starting to think of Earth as home, and just looking for excuses to stay? If so, then this doesn't survive his regeneration. It's not known how he finds out about the psychic Professor Clegg.]

The IRIS machine displays the thoughts of anyone attached to it on a video-screen. The blue crystal from Metebelis 3 kills Clegg, and the Doctor acknowledges that he's responsible. [It may help him accept what K'Anpo says, to wit…]

K'Anpo believes that the Doctor's greed for knowledge is his own personal demon. [The Master surmised as much, and the Doctor acknowledges that he's got a curiosity problem *again* just before he dies in 21.6, "The Caves of Androzani"]. His self-sacrifice almost comes across as a form of atonement for causing all this trouble. He feels fear when the Great One takes over his mind, and she states that he's not used to it [nor is he used to his enemies being mentally stronger than he is, which is probably what scares him]. When he goes to face the Great One in her cave, he does it even though he knows it'll kill him. Afterwards he insists that facing his fear was more important than just going on living.

The Doctor states that when a Time Lord's body wears out it "regenerates", which is why they live such a long time, the first time this is made explicit. The 'crystal rays' in the cave of the Great One devastate every cell in the Doctor's body, and he returns to UNIT HQ in the TARDIS after more than three weeks away. [At least from UNIT's point of view. The novel *Love and War* charmingly suggests that it actually takes the Third Doctor's body ten years to reach the point of regeneration, and that the Doctor lies helpless on the TARDIS floor for the entire time. Whether you believe this or not, there is the suggestion here that the Doctor has been suffering for some time before he gets back to Earth.]

He states that he got lost in the time vortex, and that the TARDIS brought him 'home'. The Doctor seems to be dead at first, and it's apparently only K'Anpo's presence which gives the cells a 'push' and forces the change. K'Anpo warns that he'll be a little erratic once he becomes a new man. The Third Doctor's last words: 'While there's life, there's…'

The Doctor doesn't recognise K'Anpo on sight, though the man seems familiar to him [see **Do Time Lords Always Meet In Sequence?** under 22.3, "The Mark of the Rani"].

• *Inventory.* Seen in close-up here, the sonic screwdriver has blatantly changed shape in the last year or so. [Yet Professor Clegg "senses" the events of 10.2, "Carnival of Monsters", when he holds it. So it must be the same device, at least in part, even if the Doctor's modified it.]

• *Background.* The Doctor knows the traditions of Tibet [see 5.2, "The Abominable Snowmen"] as well as a little of the Tibetan language. He claims to have been a friend of Harry Houdini, who taught him a thing or two about escapology. He states that Sergeant Benton makes the best cup of coffee in the word 'next to Mrs. Samuel Pepys'. [Odd, as she didn't actually like the stuff, although Pepys' diaries note her delight in this new thing called "tea" that's being imported. Deb, Pepys' mistress, apparently loved coffee. So maybe the Doctor's just being discreet.]

Here the Doctor reiterates that when he was young a hermit lived behind 'our house', and that he spent some of the finest hours of his life with the old man [q.v. 9.5, "The Time Monster"]. It was from the hermit that he first learned how to look into his own mind.

• *The Whomobile.* Yes, it flies. It's a nippy mover on land, capable of at least 90 mph.

The Supporting Cast

• *Sarah Jane Smith.* Writes articles for *Metropolitan* magazine, selling them to someone called Percy [as before, she still has a life on Earth and hasn't become the Doctor's full-time travelling companion]. The Doctor calls her his 'assistant' even outside the context of UNIT.

• *Jo Grant.* She's still in the Amazon, at her twenty-ninth native village, and she and Professor Jones haven't found their toadstool yet. She sends the blue crystal from Metebelis 3 back to England because the Indian porters say it's 'bad magic'.

• *UNIT.* UNIT's Medical Officer is called Sullivan [12.1, "Robot", etc]. Despite UNIT's status as a top-security establishment, Sarah is still allowed to hang around the HQ three weeks after the Doctor vanishes and she loses her "I'm his assistant" excuse.

A minor UNIT staff member has obviously been given the job of servicing the Whomobile. UNIT tea is apparently awful, unlike Benton's coffee. The HQ is around eighty miles from the

Buddhist retreat in Mortimer. [Mortimer is near Reading, Berkshire, so the HQ's location is plausibly Gloucestershire or Hereford and Worcester. See under 8.3, "The Claws of Axos". The garage seems to be the same one seen in "The Daemons" and "The Three Doctors".] The lab has a stuffed crocodile suspended from the ceiling.

• *The Brigadier.* Owns a watch that was given to him in a Brighton hotel by a young lady named Doris, eleven years ago [see 26.1, "Battlefield"]. The watch was a thank-you for something the Brigadier doesn't want to talk about. Here the Brigadier's at his most bluff and impatient. His response to the Doctor's regeneration: 'here we go again'.

• *Captain Yates.* After his fall from UNIT, he's getting his act together at a Buddhist retreat. He seems almost completely "cured" here [again suggesting that he was temporarily unbalanced during 11.2, "Invasion of the Dinosaurs"], and Sarah trusts him even though she was on the receiving end of his treachery. His 'compassion' protects him from the spiders' attacks, proving that he's ready to sacrifice himself out of principle, not just because it's his duty as a soldier. His last recorded words: a rather nelly 'ooh, I feel fine' after zen-power brings him back from the dead. He drives a nice red sporty number.

The TARDIS The co-ordinates for Metebelis 3 are still wired into the programmer [after 10.5, "The Green Death"]. When the Doctor goes there to find Sarah, the Ship lands in exactly the right location even though the Doctor has no idea where she might be, the Doctor noting that the Ship is 'no fool'. [The TARDIS might be able to home in on its "crew". On the other hand, this could well be the only inhabited area on the planet, and the TARDIS certainly seems to have a habit of landing in populated places.]

The TARDIS key is currently a medallion on a chain. Inside the Ship is a machine in an old leather satchel which makes a wobbly electronic noise when activated, and restores the Doctor after he's wounded by energy-bolts. The device also acts as a mineral analyser and a shield to the spider-energy. It gets left on Metebelis 3.

The Time Lords

• *K'Anpo Rimpoche.* The hermit who played such an important part in the Doctor's formative years [see 9.5, "The Time Monster"] now turns out to be the Abbot at the Buddhist retreat which Mike Yates is attending on Earth. [Pure coincidence, or is something mystical going on here? "Rimpoche" is a traditional title given to the Abbot of a monastery, but it's also used to describe a reincarnated lama, which seems apt.]

He goes by the Tibetan name of K'Anpo, and seems to know more about what's going on than anyone could possibly have told him. He can "see" the spider that's possessing Sarah, as can the Doctor after being told to 'see through my eyes'. [Telepathy, or more zen? Compare this to the Doctor's anecdote about the daisy in "The Time Monster".] The Doctor refers to him as a 'guru', and he says that the Doctor was 'always a little slow on the uptake'.

K'Anpo is a Time Lord, but states that 'the discipline they serve was not for me'. He knows of the Doctor borrowing a TARDIS, and regenerated before going to Tibet. The Doctor's comment - 'I had to get away, I hadn't your power' - indicates that K'Anpo left via mental, rather than mechanical, means. [This would also seem to indicate that K'Anpo left first, so has he been keeping track of the Doctor's career?]

Cho-Je, a spiritual guide at the centre, is also a Time Lord 'in a sense, but in another sense he doesn't exist'. He's a projection of K'Anpo's own self, something which even the Doctor doesn't immediately grasp; K'Anpo apparently knows everything Cho-Je witnesses. [Symbolically, he represents the "new man" in the Buddhist parable about the old man dying and being replaced.] K'Anpo seems to be able to sense his own death approaching, and when he dies Cho-Je appears out of nowhere to "merge" with his body, producing an individual who looks like Cho-Je but speaks of himself as K'Anpo.

The new K'Anpo can levitate and materialise out of thin air, surrounded by a glowing aura [hinting that he isn't really "there"]. He also seems to be the catalyst which triggers the Doctor's regeneration. [These things are all part of the 'power' the Doctor speaks of, they're not inevitable results of the regeneration. K'Anpo's move to Tibet is a relatively recent event in his life, yet his new body looks and sounds Tibetan, perhaps a sign that powerful Time Lords can influence their biological change to match their mental state. See also 18.7, "Logopolis".]

Cho-Je / K'Anpo is never heard of again, and the Doctor never expresses an interest in meeting

When was Regeneration Invented?

When William Hartnell left *Doctor Who* in 1966, one of the most bizarre (but nonetheless great) decisions in television history was made: to get a younger and significantly different actor to fill his role, and use the Doctor's alien biology as an excuse to make this sort of thing seem perfectly acceptable. According to received wisdom, this is how the concept of "regeneration" was born, the idea that Time Lords can change their bodies whenever they're badly damaged and thus ensure the series' longevity.

Received wisdom, however, is dubious at best.

We tend to forget, now, how the Hartnell / Troughton change was pitched to its original audience. In part four of "The Tenth Planet" and part one of "Power of the Daleks", there's no suggestion that it's normal for the Doctor to change his whole persona whenever he's injured. The word used in the script is *renewal*, and even that comes from an incredulous comment made by Ben, to which the apparent newcomer responds with another question. The Doctor isn't giving anything away at this stage, and his claim that the change is 'part of the TARDIS' hints that this isn't just some kind of biological super-power.

The implication, weird as it seems now, is clear: Patrick Troughton's Doctor is supposed to be an extension of William Hartnell's. Perhaps not simply a younger version, but at the very least they're aspects of the same identity, the Second Doctor drawing a parallel with a caterpillar turning into a butterfly.

And there *is* a kind of logic there. At heart the First Doctor is just as mischievous as the Second, but too old, tired and impatient to extol the virtues of anarchy in the way the Troughton version does (the original idea, according to then-script-editor Gerry Davis, was a "Jekyll and Hyde" transition). They're the same individual to a far greater extent than the Third and Fourth Doctors are, or the Fourth and Fifth, or the Fifth and Sixth, or the Sixth and Seventh. It should be remembered that *Doctor Who Monthly* - the only half-reliable source of *Doctor Who* information, until the mid-'80s boom in programme guides - believed as late as 1982 that the First and Second Doctors were supposed to be the same man. A "Matrix Data-Bank" column from that year informs its readers that they shouldn't confuse "regenerations" (e.g. Pertwee into Baker) with the "rejuvenation" of Hartnell into Troughton.

So if the writers and producers didn't invent the idea of "regeneration" in 1966, then when *did* they come up with it? In "The War Games", when the Second Doctor turns into the Third? Again, no. In "The War Games" the Doctor is utterly horrified by the idea of the Time Lords changing his face ('you can't just change what I look like!'). Though later fan-lore insists that the Time Lords "force" a regeneration on him, this *isn't* what the story says and it's obviously not what Terrance Dicks and Malcolm Hulke had in mind when they wrote it. As it's described in episode ten, the Doctor is undergoing some peculiar Time Lord surgery to alter his form as part of his punishment. It's certainly not a natural part of Time Lord life, and in "Spearhead from Space" the Third Doctor's personality seems to have several hold-overs from the Troughton days, as if he's been changed on the outside but hasn't been completely re-formatted on the inside. And throughout the Pertwee era, when the phrase "Time Lord" becomes common currency and the Doctor frequently discusses his people's politics with the Master, there's no mention of regeneration as a standard fitting of the species.

By the time the Third Doctor turns into the Fourth, the audience is used to the idea of a different actor taking over the Doctor's role… but *still* doesn't take it as read that the power to change is one of the Doctor's built-in abilities, and *still* requires the story to explain it. Even given that enough time has passed since "The War Games" for a new audience to come along, there's no assumption that parents will tell younger viewers 'oh, yes, this is what he does'.

In "Planet of the Spiders" it's stated for the very first time that regeneration (a new word!) is what happens when a Time Lord's body gets worn out, and it sounds suspiciously like an attempt to justify the events of "The Tenth Planet" and "The War Games" to viewers who are about to meet yet *another* version of the Doctor. It's a word that's hitherto been more commonly used in a religious context, to suggest spiritual re-awakening, which is what K'Anpo seems to have been through in order to astrally-project to UNIT HQ. It's noticeable that even here, the Doctor can't regenerate without turning the whole process into a life-changing ritual, and he seems to need K'Anpo's help - a 'push' - to make the final change.

Regeneration isn't really taken for granted until "The Deadly Assassin" (14.3), and even here there are anomalies, as if Robert Holmes is being cagey about formalising things. It's said that Time Lords can regenerate twelve times, the closest thing we've had to a "rule" so far, yet Runcible asks if the

continued on page 175...

up with his old mentor. [Does he stay on Earth? Does the retreat stay open, after meditation goes out of fashion?]

The Non-Humans

• *Spiders*. Normal-sized spiders came to Metebelis 3 with the human colonists, but grew in size and intelligence after being exposed to the blue crystals. The humans didn't find out until it was too late. The 'eight-legs' we see are cruel, arrogant and predatory without exception, and all are female, certainly those who make up the council under the queen spider Huath. [Is this a species that eats the males after mating? The prospect of a 'coronation' thrills the spiders, who make 'mmMMMmm' noises when it's proposed. The novelisation suggests that a deposed queen is eaten.]

When a spider jumps onto a human being's back, it vanishes but can still be "heard" by its carrier / victim, who gains the spider's power to kill, hurt or stun with bolts of blue [mental] energy. A level of clairvoyance is also part of the bargain, plus the ability to teleport objects over short distances. [People can quite comfortably sit in chairs while they've got spiders on their backs, so the spiders in some way join with their hosts' bodies instead of just turning invisible.] The spiders themselves have acute telepathic senses.

Buddhist-style rituals can be used to summon spiders to Earth from Metebelis 3, apparently in the future. The rites performed by Lupton and his friends can also make illusionary tractors appear on Britain's roads, which may or may not have something to do with the spiders' influence. A naturally-occurring mineral on Metebelis can block the spiders' power, and their energy bolts are less effective on compassionate or innocent minds [which may be why the Doctor isn't killed when he's hit by one].

At the heart of spider society lies the Great One, a spider vastly bigger and more powerful than the queen, at least sixty feet across and surrounded by a "web" of the planet's blue crystals which - she believes - should give her infinite mental power when completed. Even without it, her power is such that she can control the Doctor's actions.

The Great One's aim is to conquer the universe, though her followers just see Earth as being rightfully theirs. She insists she's searched all of time and space for the 'perfect' crystal taken by the Doctor. [Meaning that her mental powers are almost on a par with Time Lord technology. It's possible that Lupton's faux-Buddhist rituals are meaningless in themselves, and just act as a psychic focus for the spiders. The creatures *can* move between worlds and centuries on their own, but it uses up a lot of their mental power. The Great One must be aware of the Blinovitch Limitation Effect, or she would have taken the crystal from Metebelis 3 before the Doctor ran off with it.]

Ultimately, the completed web destroys the Great One rather than making her infinitely powerful. The other spiders may well be destroyed along with her.

['In another sense', as Cho-Je might have said, 'they don't exist'. This is a story which blurs the line between metaphor and stated fact. It's strongly hinted that the spiders are the "demons" produced by a clouded mind meditating for power rather than for the sake of meditation. This is the way Cho-Je sees it, and under the circumstances he's as trustworthy as the Doctor in these matters. The story of the spiders evolving as a result of the crystals doesn't bear close examination, and for once we're offered an alternative, that they're a result of Lupton and his friends projecting their "evil" out of conventional space and time. "Snakedance" (20.2) offers a pseudo-science figleaf for the same idea, again involving blue crystals. In this case we can accept either interpretation, depending on age, taste and what time of day it is.]

Planet Notes

• *Metebelis 3*. Here it's a very different world to the one the Doctor visited before ["The Green Death"], and this is evidently a later point in its history. It's no longer blue all over, the Doctor now claiming that it's called the blue planet because the moonlight's blue. [In "The Green Death" he claimed it had a blue sun, which it clearly doesn't, but it *was* a blue-lit night during his last brief visit.]

The planet is inhabited by humans, descendants of human colonists, who've been kept in a Medieval state by the giant spiders. The spiders now live in great artificial citadels while the humans live in shoddy villages. The 'eight-legs' have been known to wipe out whole communities of wayward humans, including Skorda, and there's a strict curfew. Both humans and spiders eat sheep, which were brought to the planet on the ship, although spiders prefer human meat;

When was Regeneration Invented?

...continued from page 173

Doctor's had a 'face-lift' as if that's more likely than a full bodily change. (In retrospect we might assume that Runcible-the-Fatuous is just being casual about regeneration, but that doesn't seem to be the way the scene's written.)

For obvious reasons, "The Invasion of Time" (15.6) has to assume the existence of regeneration as a given in order for Borusa to return without actor Angus Mackay. Leela is familiar with the idea because the Doctor's been so off-hand about it, dismissing the Rutans' lack of ability in this field. The idea has become a standard fixture even among casual viewers by the time we reach "Destiny of the Daleks" (17.1). By this point the change of actors is so familiar to the audience that producer Graham Williams and script editor Douglas Adams can be casual, even jokey, about the phenomenon. Romana apparently changes her form in much the same way that she might change her wardrobe.

Far from being a clever device invented in 1966, regeneration actually emerges as a way of tying together the various approaches taken by the programme's various production teams, and the idea only becomes "solid" once people have stopped questioning it. When Tom Baker's Doctor was scheduled to leave the series in 1981, young fans who'd never seen a regeneration accepted it without hesitation, because they'd read all about it in *DWM* and *The Making of Doctor Who*. But even here, the script is wary of taking too much for granted. When the Fourth Doctor becomes the Fifth in "Logopolis", writer Christopher H. Bidmead still feels he needs a "reason" to have the Doctor change. He creates the character of the Watcher, a deliberate echo of K'Anpo's intervention in the previous change-over story, to help the transfor-

mation go smoothly (but see 18.7 for more).

By the time of "The Caves of Androzani" and the Fifth Doctor's shift into the Sixth, the Doctor's constantly using the word "regeneration" to describe his ability to re-create himself, but as a writer Robert Holmes still doesn't want it to seem completely normal. The dying Fifth Doctor states that 'it feels different this time', and well it might. This is the first time it's happened unaided, the first time that one person - one *person*, remember, since the First and Second Doctors were basically the same man - has turned into another without outside assistance. The first time, in short, that the process runs the risk of being arbitrary (see also **Who Are All These Strange Men in Wigs?** under 13.5, "The Brain of Morbius").

And to be frank, the idea of a damaged Time Lord becoming a completely new person doesn't make a lot of sense. Why do they do things that way? Why don't they just regenerate into the *same* form, or at least a younger, fitter version of it? Why go through the inconvenience of taking on a new personality, and seemingly at random? Especially when you consider the static, conservative nature of Time Lord society. Biologically and neurologically, it's workable, but it's out of keeping with the culture we're shown. You could also argue that it's aesthetically awkward, but that's another debate.

The fact remains that the only "normal" regeneration for the Doctor, the only one pitched as a routine rebirth-of-an-injured-body, is the last and least convincing change of the entire BBC run: the moment at the start of "Time and the Rani" when the Sixth Doctor bangs his head on the TARDIS floor and becomes the Seventh, a metamorphosis so bland that it's accepted as a purely functional part of the programme. But it took twenty-three years to get that far.

---

their victims are stored in webbing.

In addition to its power to cure brainwashing and spider-possession, the blue crystal from Metebelis 3 alters the brain of the "backward" Tommy, turning him into a potential genius within hours. It causes indoor "wind" and earth tremors when Lupton's people are performing a spider-summoning ceremony, and kills the psychic Professor Clegg who's holding it at the time. The Doctor states that he went to Metebelis 3 deliberately to get the crystal, but he had no idea of its importance. The Great One describes it as the 'one last perfect crystal of power', necessary to complete the crystalline web which reproduces

the pattern of her brain. [It's bizarre that she knows there was once a perfect crystal on Metebelis 3, even though there are presumably none in her own time. It's also bizarre that the Doctor just stumbled across it on his last, hurried, visit. Did this "one crystal" actually *want* to be found, like the key artefact in *The Lord of the Rings*, ever-so-fashionable in the early '70s...?]

History

• *Dating*. [On Earth, it's probably early 1975 by now. See **What's the UNIT Timeline?** under 8.5, "The Daemons".] The parts of the story set on Metebelis 3 are harder to date, but the planet's people are human and have been there for centuries, so it must be well after 2100. The Doctor only describes this as 'the future'. [There's still some dispute about whether Metebelis is in the Acteon *group* or the Acteon *galaxy*. "Group" seems more likely - see 10.2, "Carnival of Monsters", for the reasons - but if it's "galaxy" then the Earth ship must have landed there a long way into the future, since humanity doesn't appear to have intergalactic travel even in 3000 AD.]

It's been 433 years since the human ship crashed in the mountains where the blue crystals are found, and it happened just after the ship came out of 'time-jump' with insufficient fuel. [Implying time-travel, so these humans are *very* advanced. No human beings anywhere else in the series are said to have reliable time-ships, not even tens of thousands of years from now.]

Here the Brigadier establishes that there was a period of 'months' between the Second Doctor's last appearance on Earth [6.3] and the Third Doctor's arrival [7.1]. The Buddhist retreat is near Mortimer according to the sign at the train station, but Sarah refers to 'Mummerset'. [N.B. Not a real county, but the way actors and critics describe the all-purpose "yokel" accent used in the kind of films, plays and TV shows where you can get ambushed by imaginary tractors. Mummers were strolling players, usually amateur, who put on Christmas plays in neighbouring villages. Somerset is a county where they don't really talk like that but Londoners think they do.]

The Analysis

Where Does This Come From? It's Buddhism's last stand, and the end-of-an-era feel goes much deeper than just the departure of the lead actor. Incoming producer Philip Hinchcliffe would take the programme in a much more abstract direction, tearing the Doctor away from Earth and away from his role as scientific zen-master to UNIT, so this is Barry Letts' and Robert Sloman's final opportunity to show us their vision of the "head trip" Doctor.

Or, to put it another way: Mike Yates says that 'everybody's going on about meditation of one sort or another', and this is the last time the series joins in until "Snakedance", nine years later. Pertwee pronounces the word "guru" as if it's a new, exotic, *foreign* thing to say, not a standard part of the western vocabulary, which tells you just how trendy all of this was supposed to be.

Even if you leave aside the pop-Buddhist, joss-stick-flavoured imagery - including a mystical mandala that looks more like the cover of a rock album than the kind of monster-summoning symbol we saw in "The Daemons" - the story's still 80% spiritual metaphor, as Cho-Je tells us right from the start. Meditation is a good thing, but when used by people with bad intentions it releases demons. (Lupton, the main villain for much of the story, is just bitter about losing his job and wants revenge on the world more than he wants "understanding".) K'Anpo rams the point home at the end of the story by talking about invisible spiders on people's backs as if *everyone's* got them, not just the possessed.

If the script goes out of its way to ensure that all the spiders represent cruelty, selfishness and power-lust, then that's nothing compared to the rhetoric of the Great One, who speaks for the raging ego and comes across as every Buddhist's / hippy's worst nightmare. She even talks of becoming 'power' itself rather than 'powerful', before insisting that the universe bows down before 'the great all-powerful me'.

Naturally, then, compassion and innocence are the things that can block the spiders' influence. Child-like Tommy isn't weighed down by the same self-obsession as the grown-ups, and Yates is capable of overcoming it through an attempted act of self-sacrifice. The message, spoken out loud, is 'you don't have to be dominated'. But this time the enemy's within, it's not a great big space-robot representing the forces of fascism.

And since his meddling has led to so much suffering, is that supposed to be karma at work in the Doctor's own act of self-destruction...? Could be. There's never been any indication that reincarnation exists in the *Doctor Who* universe (unless you count the similarly Buddhism-flavoured 19.3, "Kinda"), so regeneration's the closest you'll ever get. Whether the story provides a good "message" is another matter, since K'Anpo's words about the Doctor's greed for knowledge almost come across as a warning against asking too many questions, in direct contrast to the programme's apparent belief in science and scientific investigation. And why *do* all the evils of the universe have female voices?

This isn't what you'd call *pure* Buddhism, though. In the years since 1974 we've become more apt to separate "Eastern spirituality" from "psychic phenomena". Levitating Tibetan monks aside, few people now would assume that zen-power gives you the ability to move things with your mind. Here the rules are different. All mental powers are part of the same process, so the story opens with the Doctor performing experiments into psychic abilities, and this is supposed to lead naturally into the events at the Buddhist retreat. It's taken as read that the spiders' powers are psychic, or at least psychological. Experimenting with the psychic Professor Clegg, the Doctor even asks the man if he feels up to 'bending the odd fork', probably the most pop-topical moment of the story. From Buddhism to Israeli psychic Uri Gellar in one move, and what's striking - what's almost unthinkable, now - is that the programme-makers don't see the two things jarring at all. Mind-power is the order of the day. Spiritual, psychological or scientific, in '70s-speak it's all the same thing.

We said 80%. The remainder includes Arthurian parables (Buddhism and Arthurian myth *also* went together in those days), with the crystal cave suggesting the trap into which Nimue coerced Merlyn. It's worth noticing that the Queen uses the tricks associated with Morgan le Fay (see also 26.1 "Battlefield" and 16.3, "The Stones of Blood"), while Sarah is earlier accused of 'feminine wiles'. The Doctor's lab is equipped with the traditional crocodile of the Renaissance mage, as T. H. White used for *his* Merlyn. That the pure knight - in this case Tommy - gets the "grail" is in keeping with Barry Letts' comparison of the Doctor to Parcifal, so we're not imagining *all* of this.

Lupton's life-story, however, is almost from a different script. His corporate career, while usefully petty as a source for a cosmic threat, is the most adult and tangible thing in the entire Pertwee run. And of course, there was no way this era of the programme could end without a *Quatermass* reference. The IRIS scene, in particular the recording of Clegg's final thoughts, is a direct lift from *Quatermass and the Pit* with spiders replacing the grasshopper-Martians.

As an aside: the joke about Archimedes shouting 'I'm a streaker' isn't quite as crap as it might sound, given that "streaker" was a relatively new word at the time. (Which doesn't make it *funny*, but still...)

Things That Don't Make Sense   It's a day for inconsistencies. The Brigadier, once a crack shot even in a crisis (see 8.2, "The Mind of Evil") can't bring Lupton down with his revolver even though Lupton's moving at hobbling-speed and they're facing each other across an empty car park. Bessie, which once had the power to move at impossible speeds across Britain's countryside, is now demoted to being a "quite fast" car which struggles to match the Whomobile's 90 mph. The spiders possessing Lupton's friends can sense the vibrations of the crystal when they're in the same building, but the one "riding" Sarah can't sense it when she's in the same room. Likewise, Lupton's spider can't find the crystal in a box under the stairs even though she can home in on it when she's eighty miles away.

And pure, well-balanced minds are supposedly less prone to the spiders' attacks than others, yet a single blast from one of Lupton's crowd kills K'Anpo. Even if he's old and weak, surely his great wisdom and all-round niceness should give him more of a shield? It's odd, too, that Tommy somehow knows how to pronounce words like "symmetry" on first reading after the blue crystal balances his brain. But more annoyingly, when he becomes "intelligent" he has perfect BBC diction instead of talking in Mummerset. How are accent and intelligence so intimately connected? If he's copying the others, wouldn't he be more prone to copy them before his transformation than after?

Not so much a mistake as a loose end... the blue crystal causes a miniature earthquake and lethal poltergeist-like phenomena when Lupton's renegade Buddhists perform a summoning ritual eighty miles away, which is reasonable. But this is the *second* time they've performed the ritual, even if it's the first time the spider fully materialises. Since the blue crystal was still in the post and on its way to UNIT HQ at the time, are there several dead postmen at the local GPO office?

Critique   It's a game of two halves, really. Apart from *that* chase sequence, the Earth-based scenes are exceptional; interesting, moody and designed to leave the audience in no doubt that this is a modern-day fable, with good character parts all round and good character actors to fill them (you can never go wrong with actor Cyril Shaps). The regulars are putting in just that little bit more effort, allowing you to compare them directly with Season Seven. Nicholas Courtney in particular has to find new ways to do the same old schtick - saying 'good grief', shooting at people, being British in unlikely circumstances - and manages well. On its own, the first episode is one of the best of the entire Pertwee run, looking like nothing so much as a "final summary" of everything the programme had tried to do during Letts' regime as producer.

Tragically, the whole thing falls to pieces the moment the characters set foot on Metebelis 3. Much of Season Eleven has been running on empty, both in terms of plots (which were increasingly excuses to indulge Pertwee's mid-life crisis) and inventiveness of the concepts beyond 'do it again, bigger'. Even though everything since "The Time Monster" has been leading up to this point, it's perfunctory rather than climactic. Aside from the shot of daybreak, the "alien planet" scenes are low-budget telefantasy at its worst, from the irritating villagers to the cack-handed scenes inside the spider citadel. The Doctor's ultimate face-off against the Great One is let down by CSO effects that look *tired* rather than technically inept.

In the end it's a story which demands you ignore the overtly SF elements and try to concentrate on the "proper" drama, since you can't deny that the Third Doctor's death scene works exactly the way it's supposed to. And as in "The Time Monster", George Cormack is the one person who can make the Doctor's character look sheepish without even trying.

The Facts

Written by Robert Sloman. Directed by Barry Letts. Viewing figures: 10.1 million, 8.9 million, 8.8 million, 8.2 million, 9.2 million, 8.9 million.

Supporting Cast: Cyril Shaps (Professor Clegg), John Dearth (Lupton), Christopher Burgess (Barnes), Terence Lodge (Moss), Carl Forgione (Land), Andrew Staines (Keaver), Kevin Lindsay (Cho-je), John Kane (Tommy), Terry Walsh (Man with Boat), Kismet Delgado (Spider Voice), Gareth Hunt (Arak), Geoffrey Morris (Sabor), Jenny Laird (Neska), Joanna Munro (Rega), George Cormack (K'anpo).

Cliffhangers The "renegade" Buddhists perform their ritual in the cellar of the retreat, and one of the spiders appears in the middle of their man-

dala; after a protracted chase sequence, the Doctor finally catches up with Lupton on a speedboat, only to find that the man has vanished from the driver's seat; attempting to rescue Sarah on Metebelis 3, the Doctor is brought down by an energy-bolt from one of the spiders' guards, collapsing before he can crawl back into the TARDIS; in the spiders' larder, a web-bound Sarah is overjoyed to see the Doctor arrive, until she realises that he's being led in by the guards; Lupton's "gang" at the Buddhist retreat, all of them possessed by spiders, team up against Tommy and hit him with energy-bolts. (Strange, really, that the last cliffhanger of the Third Doctor's era doesn't involve the Doctor at all; note also that the scenes are in a different order during the recap in episode six.)

The Lore

• Robert Sloman submitted the storyline for "The Final Game", intended to be the last story of the Third Doctor's run, three months before Roger Delgado's fatal crash. Conceived as the final, climactic showdown between the Doctor and the Master, the initial idea was that the two Time Lords would be revealed as parts of the same persona, the Master as Id and the Doctor as Ego. (Sloman admits that he pinched this from *Forbidden Planet*. However, given the nature of "Planet of the Spiders", it's at least possible that this Doctor / Master relationship was going to be implied through metaphor rather than being explained scientifically.) At the end of the story, the Doctor and the Master would be caught up in some form of Reichenbach-Falls-style mutually-destructive act, during which the Master would finally see the error of his ways and sacrifice his life to save the Doctor and the universe. This would allow the sadder and wiser Doctor to literally begin a new life, and move him a significant step closer to spiritual awakening, although with a long way to go. Some of what Barry Letts had in mind is to be found in the flying reptile cavalry charge from the 1993 radio story "The Paradise of Death", especially the conversation about 'untying the knots in my mind'.

• Back in the real world, where "Planet of the Spiders" was made instead... Letts once again co-wrote this story, allowing Sloman sole credit.

• The life insurance for Roger Delgado was a shambles, since he died in an unlicensed taxi. His widow, Kismet Delgado, was left in dire financial straights. Pertwee and his wife Ingeborg helped out, while Letts did his part by arranging an Equity card so that she could play Huath the spider-queen.

• It was around the time of "The Green Death" that Pertwee's back problems began to affect his work, though with painkillers and trusses he persevered, as far as stunt-doubles would allow. Often he'd be in his dressing-room wearing hair-curlers and a "corset", leading to raised eyebrows. While filming at Marchant Barracks with the Wessex Regiment, a Sergeant walked in on him and yelled: 'Bloody Hell! Doctor Who's a pooftah!'

• After a directive from the BBC Drama heads, the animatronic spiders originally designed for the story were replaced with less "scary" ones. Nevertheless, "Boris" - the "walking" spider - became an emblematic effect. Legendary BBC spaceship-builder and monster-wrangler Mat Irvine appeared on many childrens' television programmes giving hints to young model-makers, and frequently displayed Boris, partly to reassure people that it was a model. There were still letters of complaint to the *Doctor Who* office from arachnophobes. Irvine himself, of course, was last seen as one of the judges on *Robot Wars*.

• A less successful effect involved the assault on the spider citadel. Even Letts admitted that the CSO wasn't up to snuff, and the scenes were cut. This made episode six under-run by about five minutes, hence the drastic reconfiguration of the cliffhanger at the start of the episode.

• And episode six wasn't the only one. The 'hai!' scene which ends episode three, and is protractedly reprised in the next instalment, was filmed for episode four. Episode three under-ran badly, and should have ended with Sarah's line 'sorry, Doctor'.

• The arachnophobes weren't the only ones with grievances. Angry Buddhists - if such a thing can be imagined - wrote letters of complaint to the *Radio Times* about all of this. Letts patiently explained everything, rather condescendingly, which is why this one story is regarded as "Buddhism 101".

• The Great One (note that name, and consider "Number One" in *The Prisoner*, another villain revealed as the hero's ego) speaks her death-scene almost entirely in Iambic Pentameter.

• The script stated that the Gompa - where Cho-Je and the boys let it all hang out - was located in North Wales, not in Mortimer, where the train station is. This would be consistent with all the other casual references to UNIT HQ being somewhere in the west of England.

• "Planet of the Spiders" and 12.1, "Robot" were filmed concurrently. Various hairstyle anomalies had to be ironed out, sometimes literally.

• Pertwee ended up buying nearly all the vehicles seen in episode two.

• John Levene ad-libbed the line about 'hairdressing'.

• The story was repeated in a one-episode format, three days after Christmas 1974, as a lead-in to "Robot" (12.1) which began the next day. God, it was exciting!

the end notes

1 **Enoch Powell:** Conservative politician, who infamously spoke out against the UK's rising black population in the '60s and predicted a bloody confrontation between the races. "We should've listened to Enoch" is one of the favourite sayings of lazy British racists.

2 **Oswald Mosley:** Charismatic leader of the British fascist movement, and during World War Two a focus for those who believed that Britain should be allied with the Nazis instead of fighting them. However, in the 1930s a fascist Britain under someone like Mosley seemed worryingly feasible even *without* a German invasion. A suave, dynamic sort of Nazi sympathiser, he was the model for many charming-but-evil masterminds in post-war British fiction and even had the right sort of black moustache for upper-class villainy.

3 **Sooty and Sweep:** British glove-puppets, who've now been appearing on UK television for three generations. Children's presenter Matthew Corbett, the man (literally) behind Sooty in the '70s and '80s, makes an unexpected appearance in "The Daemons" (8.5) as one of the Master's Satanists.

4 **Bruce Forsythe:** the best-known (and highest paid) British variety entertainer of the 1970s. H[i] series *The Generation Game* was at one point th[e] highest-rated thing on television, and was shown o[n] Saturday evenings right after *Doctor Who*. Nobod[y] raised in that era can remember one withou[t] remembering the other. It was all part of a weekl[y] ritual, the like of which younger generations brought up in a world where *everyone's* got a TV, an[d] there's no day of the week when the entire famil[y] watches it together - simply can't imagine.

5 **Catweazle:** Children's fantasy series of the earl[y] '70s, about a magician from the eleventh centur[y] who's transported to the twentieth and has difficult[y] drawing the line between "magic" and "science". It got far more in common with *Doctor Who* than *Sta[r] Trek* has. (Peter Butterworth - the Meddling Mon[k] from 2.9 "The Time Meddler" - was a member of th[e] regular cast, thus completing the "Time Meddler" / "Time Warrior" / *Catweazle* circuit.)

NTRODUCING THE ALL
introducing the all-new novel...
the all-new no

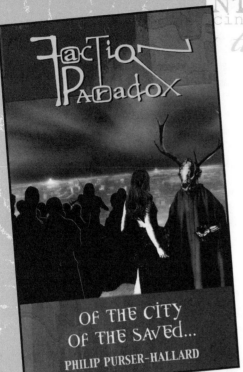

introducing the all-new novel...

ⅎacTioN Paradox

OF THE CITY
OF THE SAVED...

The young madwoman in the Tube carriage is recounting, in painstaking detail, the imminent future history of the City. Her cracked voice rises then descends to murmurs, as she delineates diverse catastrophes due in the coming weeks.

It would make grim listening if anyone were paying attention, but her fellow passengers are awkwardly, apologetically ignoring her. The Neolithic sculptor in designer furs; the family of burnished bronze/chrome cyborgs; the tall robed Bedouin and the red-beard Viking; the slim six-armed posthuman and her troglodytic lover—each of the other passengers gazes ahead, embarrassed, at the wormhole-vortex outside the carriage windows.

No-one ever listens to Kassandra, daughter of Troy.

The City is troubled, nonetheless. An unquiet breeze is rustling in its lanes and alleyways: whispering in innumerable ears, rippling the surface of a myriad lives. There is a sea-change coming, it whispers, dark clouds roiling in from your imaginary horizons. Something is abroad, something that does not belong alongside your safe afterlives with all their comforting and comfortable certainties. It has no form, but spreads among you like a fashion or a rumour. Call it an urban legend. Or simply call it change.

Most of the Citizens—the resurrected human populations of the vanished Universe itself—are ignorant of its passing as they go about their business, their parties and affairs and carnivals and works of art. Their recreated existences satisfy and thrill them—they pay no heed to hints that this great festival of resurrection might one day come to an end.

Some listen, though, and these remember the assault by the War-time powers three decades before. They recall uneasy rumours: that the powers have developed potent weapons, capable of harming or killing Citizens within the City's galaxy-wide bounds; that agents back in the (original) Universe have been recruiting entire human civilisations to act as their fifth column in the City. In tabloid headlines, T-shirt slogans, conspiracy forums and murmuring campaigns, these reckless imaginings are propagated.

Some voices in the vast Chamber of Residents, and even the City Council itself, call for active monitoring of the partially human 'collaterals', the aliens unworthily resurrected by mere virtue of miscegenous ancestries. Hard-liners urge the closure of the Uptime Gate into the Universe, even (surely suicidal) pre-emptive strikes against the Warring powers themselves.

At the secret Parliament established in the City by the resurrected members of Faction Paradox, discussion concerns itself with more arcane matters. A spate of dangerous omens has begun to sweep the City, a plague of ill portents spreading concern among the superstitious (among whom the Parliament's members are proud to count themselves). The enigmatic Godfather Avatar, whom few present have seen without his tricorn hat and heavy antlered bone-mask, catalogues them for the Mothers and the Fathers in a whisper like the death of leaves.

In Augustus District, a wizened haruspex slices open the belly of a pterodactyl imported from the Earth's Jurassic period, and spreads the scaly skin wide. He stares at its entrails in perplexity for some long moments, before crying out in hor-ror. His fellow augurs hustle him away, wide-eyed and babbling, then return to torch the pterosaur's bloody remains.

Experimenters in a lab at Clarendon University discover unexpectedly that the traces drawn by certain subatomic particles, when accelerated through a light-emitting substrate, have begun to spell out occult sigils in a depraved alphabet. The Head of Department closes down the project before it reaches its conclusion.

In Supplicity District a boy-child is born with a single head, arising from the cen-tre of his shoulders. His bicephalic parents gaze at him in fourfold dismay.

These events, though, are distractions. (Except for the deliberations of the Parliament, that is. To dismiss the Faction is never a wise idea.) Transitory moments, they are of ultimately no significance: at the most they represent the City's interrupted subroutines at nervous play. The events of true significance to the City — the seeds from which stories arise as emergent structures, signal out of noise — are to be found elsewhere.

For instance...

In a rundown residential-cum-business block in Paynesdown District, a man who is called Rick Kithred observes a stranger loitering in the back yard; while at the Ignotian family's opulent villa, the housekeeping software informs a youth named Urbanus that his great-grandfather wishes to see him.

Councillor Ved Mostyn of Wormward District wonders what to wear for his hot date tonight (he's thinking maybe manacles). Julian White Mammoth Tusk, a City-born Neanderthal, peers despondently into his bank account and wonders how to pay his detective agency bills.

Three academics face unique dilemmas. Large numbers of barbarians start migrations. A minotaur gets drunk with a hermaphrodite. A private eye named Tobin fingers the handle of her gun distractedly.

And—inevitably—into more than one of their lives will shortly stalk Godfather Avatar himself, of the Rump Parliament of Faction Paradox, on bony limbs.

Because even in the City of the Saved, nothing is ever quite *that* unpredictable.

OUT NOW. Retail Price: $14.95.

1309 Carrollton Ave #237
Metairie, LA 70005
info@madnorwegian.com

www.madnorwegian.com

introducing the all-new novel...

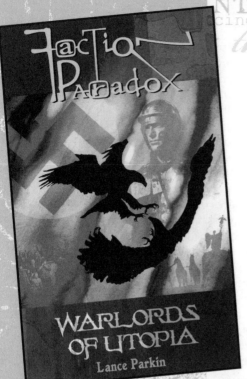

Faction Paradox
WARLORDS OF UTOPIA
Lance Parkin

Faction Paradox
WARLORDS OF UTOPIA

Adolf Hitler, the Gaol.

In the exact centre of the island was a tower. It was an ugly concrete stump four storeys high, a brutalist version of a medieval keep. There were tiny slits for windows. There wasn't a door. Around the tower, thorns and weeds had grown into a jungle. The tower held one prisoner.

Surrounding it was an electric fence. And the guards. Millions of strong men and women with the bodies they should have had, unmarked by armband or tattoo, allowed to grow up and grow old. Proud people, many with names like Goldberg, Cohen and Weinstein. Men and women who would never forgive. Men and women who lived in the vast, beautiful community that surrounded the tower, keeping him awake with their laughter, their music, the smell of their food, the sight of their clothes, the sound of their language and their prayers and the cries of their babies. They felt they had a duty to be here. They had always been free to leave, but few had.

On Resurrection Day itself, some had realised that as everyone who had ever lived was in the City, then *he* was here. It had taken longer to hunt him down. Few knew where he'd been found, how he'd been leading his life. Had he tried to disguise himself? Had he proclaimed his name and tried to rally supporters? It didn't matter. He had been brought here, his identity had been confirmed and he had been thrown in the tower that had been prepared for him.

Some of those living in sight of the tower had wondered if they were protecting him from the people of the City, not protecting the City from him. And it was true: the City - the glorious, colourful, polymorphous, diverse City, with uncounted races of people living side by side - was the ultimate negation of the prisoner's creed. The vast, vast majority people of the City didn't care who he was and couldn't comprehend his beliefs, let alone be swayed by his rhetoric. Individuals who'd killed, or wanted to kill, many more people than he had remained at liberty and found themselves powerless. Had imprisoning him marked out as special? Such things were argued about, but the prisoner remained in his tower.

Every day bought requests from individuals, organisations and national group-ings who had come up with some way to harm him within the protocols of the City. There were also representations from his supporters, or from civil liberties groups, concerned that his imprisonment was vigilante justice or that no attempt was being made to rehabilitate him. There were historians and psychologists and journalists who wanted to interview him. There were those that just wanted to gawp at or prod the man they'd heard so much about. All of them were turned away.

One man had come here in person. An old Roman, in light armour.

The clerk, a pretty girl with dark hair and eyes, greeted him.

'Your name?'

'Marcus Americanius Scriptor.'

While she dialled up his records and waited for them to appear on her screen, she asked: 'He's after your time. You're a historian?'

'I was,' the old man said. 'May I see him?'

'The prisoner isn't allowed visitors, or to communicate with the outside world. He is allowed to read, but not to write. Oh, that's odd. Your record isn't coming up.'

'It wouldn't.' The Roman didn't elaborate.

He looked out over the city to the tower. The young woman was struck by how solemn his face was. Most people who came all the way out here were sightseers, sensation seekers. Even some of the gaolers treated the prisoner with levity. Mocking him, belittling him.

'Don't you ever want to let him loose?' he asked, finally. 'Let him wander the streets, let his words be drowned out. On another world he was an indifferent, anonymous painter.'

'It sounds like you know that for certain,' she said, before checking herself. 'To answer the question: no. He stays here.'

'I met him,' the Roman told her. 'On a number of occasions.'

She frowned.

'A long story,' he told her. 'I suppose I'm concerned that you torture yourselves by having that monster in your midst.'

The woman had heard many people say such a thing.

'Not a monster. A human being.'

'But the only human being you've locked away for all eternity.'

'The wardens have ruled that he will be freed,' she told him.

Americanius Scriptor seemed surprised. 'When?'

'First he must serve his sentence, then he will be released.'

'When?' he asked again.

'In six million lifetimes,' she told him.

Marcus Americanius Scriptor smiled.

'I'll be waiting for him,' he told her. He turned and headed back to the docks.

Release Date: November 2004. **Retail Price:** $17.95

1309 Carrollton Ave #237
Metairie, LA 70005
info@madnorwegian.com

www.madnorwegian.com

the book that started it all...

Faction Paradox

The Book of the WAR

A novel in alphabetical order. Before the *Faction Paradox* book series, there was the War: the terminal face-off between two rival powers and two rival kinds of history, with only the renegades, ritualists and subterfugers of Faction Paradox to stand between them and pick the wreckage clean.

Marking the first five decades of the conflict, *The Book of the War* is an A to Z of a self-contained continuum and a complete guide to the Spiral Politic, from the beginning of recordable time to the fall of humanity. Part story, part history and part puzzle-box, this is a chronicle of protocol and paranoia in a War where the historians win as many battles as the soldiers and the greatest victory of all is to hold on to your own past.

Assembled by Lawrence Miles (*Dead Romance*), with illustrations by Jim Calafiore (*Exiles, Aquaman*), *The Book of the War* is a stand-alone work which dissects, defines and pre-wraps the *Faction Paradox* universe, and explains just how things ended up starting this way...

Available now.
Format: Trade PB, 256 pgs.
MSRP: $17.95
Also available as a hardback edition, signed by Miles and Calafiore and strictly limited to 300 copies, from our website. **MSRP:** $34.95

www.faction-paradox.com

1309 Carrollton Ave #237
Metairie, LA 70005
info@madnorwegian.com

mad norwegian press

I, Who 3: The Unauthorized Guide to *Doctor Who* Novels and Audios... $21.95

Prime Targets: The Unauthorized Guide to *Transformers, Beast Wars* and *Beast Machines*... $19.95

Dusted: The Ultimate Unauthorized Guide to Buffy the Vampire Slayer, by Lawrence Miles, Lars Pearson & Christa Dickson...$19.95

Redeemed: The Unauthorized Guide to Angel... $19.95 (upcoming)

Dead Romance by Lawrence Miles, contains rare back-up stories... $14.95

ALSO AVAILABLE NOW...
- *I, Who vols. 1 to 3: The Unauthorized Guide to Doctor Who Novels and Audios* by Lars Pearson...$19.95 [vols. 1-2], $21.95 [vol. 3]
- *Faction Paradox: This Town Will Never Let Us Go,* by Lawrence Miles...$14.95 [softcover], $34.95 [signed, limited hardcover]

COMING SOON...
- **A History of the Universe [Revised]:** The Unauthorized Guide to the Doctor Who Universe by Lance Parkin, $24.95
- *Faction Paradox: Warring States* by Mags L Halliday, $17.95

www.madnorwegian.com

ABOUT TIME

1975-1979

SEASONS 12 TO 17

Coming Soon... In *About Time 4*, Lawrence and Tat delve headlong into *Doctor Who* Seasons 12 to 17, the main bulk of the Tom Baker era, exploring the show's "gothic" phase (under producer Philip Hinchcliffe) and its aftermath (under producer Graham Williams).

Essays in this volume include: "Where (and When) is Gallifrey?", "Why Couldn't the BBC Just Have Spent More Money?", "Why Does Earth Keep Getting Invaded?" and *"War of the Daleks:* Should Anyone Believe a Word of It?"

Also Coming Soon...
About Time 5 (Seasons 18-21, out in 2004)

About Time 6 (Seasons 22-26 and the TV Movie, out in 2005)

About Time 1 (Seasons 1-3, out in 2005)

About Time 2 (Seasons 4-6, out in 2005)

MSRP: $19.95 (*About Time 4*); $14.95 (all other volumes)

www.madnorwegian.com

1309 Carrollton Ave #237
Metairie, LA 70005
info@madnorwegian.com

mad norwegian press

1-866-DW-AMERICA
(Toll Free!)

doctorwho@deadparrotdiscs.com

All the finest imported and domestic Doctor Who collectibles...
Fans serving fans since 1989!

Doctor Who...

- BBC
- BBV
- Big Finish
- Cornerstone
- Dapol
- Panini
- Product Enterprise
- Stamp Centre
- Virgin
- Telos
- ...and more!

...and MUCH more!

- British Telly &
  Cult TV
- Sci-fi, Fantasy &
  Horror
- Anime
- Music & Movies
- AS SEEN ON TV

www.deadparrotdiscs.com

FREE GIFT WITH EVERY ORDER!

▲ *(Dare we say... it's about time!)*

The Comic Guru Presents!

www.thecomicguru.co.uk

One of the UK's leading Doctor Who retailers!

DOCTOR WHO

Faction Paradox!
Short Trips!
Merchandise!
Audio Adventures!
Models & Collectibles!
Novels & Novellas!
Comics!

We ship worldwide, too!

Tel/Fax: +44 (0)29 20 229119

OPEN THE DOOR TO
A NEW DIMENSION

www.galaxy4.co.uk

who made all this ?

Lawrence Miles is the author of… hold on… yeah, *eight* novels now, the most recent of them being the first volume in the ongoing *Faction Paradox* series, *This Town Will Never Let Us Go*. After co-writing *Dusted* - a guide to *Buffy the Vampire Slayer*, also published by Mad Norwegian - he suddenly found that he'd been cured, and didn't want to see another episode of *Buffy* ever again. So once *About Time* is finished, he's planning on constructing a great ceremonial pyre and burning the complete collection of *Doctor Who* videos and CDs that's taken him nearly twenty years to assemble. Favourite story in this book: "Carnival of Monsters". Least favourite: "Planet of the Daleks".

Recovering academic **Tat Wood** is the person most compilers of previous guidebooks went to for advice and cultural context. Despite having written for *Film Review, TV Zone, Starburst, SFX, Dreamwatch, Doctor Who Magazine, X-pose* and just about every major fanzine going, he has a rich, full and complex life. Currently lecturing and tutoring, he is busy mentoring mature students from across the Commonwealth and the new Europe whilst attempting to break into mainstream "literary" fiction. Tragically, this is interrupted by people wanting to get the lyrics to half-forgotten 1960s TV themes ringing him rather than bothering with the Internet (because he's quicker). Although culturally adept and well-rounded, he has lived in Ilford for the last ten years. Favourite story in this book: "Carnival of Monsters". Least favourite: "The Monster of Peladon".

Mad Norwegian Press

Publisher/Series Editor
Lars Pearson

Copy Editor
Fritze CM Roberts

Interior/Cover Design
Christa Dickson

Cover Art
Steve Johnson

Associate Editors
Marc Eby
Dave Gartner
Val Sowell
Joshua Wilson

Technical Support
Michael O'Nele
Robert Moriarity

1309 Carrollton Ave #237
Metairie, LA 70005
info@madnorwegian.com
www.madnorwegian.com